Workbook

Progress in

SADLIER-OXFORD

Mathematics

$\frac{1}{5}$

Catherine D. LeTourneau

with
Elinor R. Ford

Sadlier-Oxford
A Division of William H. Sadlier, Inc.
www.sadlier-oxford.com

Contributing Illustrators: Liz Conrad, Gary Johnson, Dan Sharp

Contents

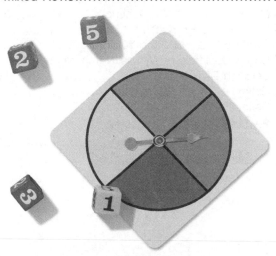

C Denotes Common Core lesson.

C Denotes Common Core lesson.

C Denotes Common Core lesson.

Additional Common Core Contents

Place Value to Billions

Name _____

Date _____

	Billions			Millions			Thousands			Ones		
hundreds	tens	ones	hundreds	tens	ones	hundreds	tens	ones	hundreds	tens	ones
		8,	5	0	6,	7	3	4,	0	2	0

Standard Form:
8,506,734,020

Word Name: eight billion,
five hundred six million,
seven hundred thirty-four thousand,
twenty

Write the place of the underlined digit. Then write its value.

1. 6̲71,248,101 _____
   _____

2. 4̲,725,921,001 _____
   _____

3. 50,97̲8,206,978 _____
   _____

4. 72,360,5̲21,000 _____
   _____

5. 141,624̲,805,093 _____
   _____

6. 85̲0,139,122,952 _____
   _____

Write the number in standard form.

7. four hundred three million,
   seventy one thousand, two hundred
   _____

8. nine billion, seven million, six hundred two
   _____

9. eighty-six billion, twelve thousand,
   four hundred sixty
   _____

10. one hundred ten billion,
    three hundred thousand
    _____

11. four hundred billion, six
    _____

12. twenty-four million
    _____

13. 180 million
    _____

14. 925 billion
    _____

Write the word name for each number. Use short word names when you can.

15. 13,481,309,526 _____
    _____

16. 750,000,000,000 _____

17. 191,000,000 _____

C Use with Lessons 1-1 and 1-2, pages 30–33 in the Student Book.
C Then go to Lesson 1-3, pages 34–35 in the Student Book.

1

Expanded Form

Name _____

Date _____

Standard Form	Expanded Form

$4{,}260{,}048 = (4 \times 1{,}000{,}000) + (2 \times 100{,}000) + (6 \times 10{,}000) + (4 \times 10) + (8 \times 1)$
$\phantom{4{,}260{,}048} = 4{,}000{,}000 + 200{,}000 + 60{,}000 + 40 + 8$

Complete the expanded form of each number.

1. $2894 = ($ _____ $\times 1{,}000) + (8 \times$ _____ $) + ($ _____ $\times 10) + ($ _____ $\times 1)$

2. $36{,}805 = (3 \times$ _____ $) + (6 \times$ _____ $) + ($ _____ $\times 100) + ($ _____ $\times 1)$

3. $6{,}497{,}000 = ($ _____ $\times 1{,}000{,}000) + (4 \times$ _____ $) + (9 \times$ _____ $) + (7 \times$ _____ $)$

4. $83{,}750{,}446 = ($ _____ $\times$ _____ $) + ($ _____ $\times$ _____ $) + ($ _____ $\times 100{,}000) +$

   $(5 \times$ _____ $) + ($ _____ $\times$ _____ $) + (4 \times$ _____ $) + ($ _____ $\times$ _____ $)$

5. $120{,}004{,}962 = ($ _____ $\times$ _____ $) + (2 \times$ _____ $) + ($ _____ $\times$ _____ $) +$

   $($ _____ $\times 100) + (6 \times$ _____ $) + ($ _____ $\times$ _____ $)$

Write each in standard form.

6. $70{,}000 + 40 =$ _____   7. $3000 + 80 + 2 =$ _____

8. $600{,}000 + 500 + 10 + 6 =$ _____

9. $2{,}000{,}000{,}000 + 90{,}000{,}000 + 1{,}000{,}000 + 700{,}000 =$ _____

10. $5{,}000{,}000{,}000 + 200{,}000{,}000 + 90{,}000{,}000 + 10{,}000 + 400 + 8 =$ _____

Write in expanded form.

11. 786,300 _____

12. 1,022,004 _____

13. 329,400,090 _____

14. 4,005,678,910 _____

Write a, b, c, or d to answer questions 15–17.

a. 732,045   **b.** 372,405   **c.** 327,540   **d.** 723,504

15. In which number does the 7 show how many one thousands? _____

16. Which numbers show 3 hundred thousands? _____

17. Which numbers show the same number of hundreds? _____

Problem Solving

18. Recently, the population of London was 7,421,209. Write this number in expanded form.

   _____

2

Thousandths

$\frac{8}{1000} = 0.008$	$\frac{162}{1000} = 0.162$
Standard Form: 0.008	**Standard Form:** 0.162
Word Name: eight thousandths	**Word Name:** one hundred sixty-two thousandths

Write as a decimal.

1. $\frac{6}{1000}$ _____

2. $\frac{78}{1000}$ _____

3. $\frac{407}{1000}$ _____

4. $\frac{50}{1000}$ _____

Write the value of the underlined digit.

5. 0.$\underline{6}$13 _____

6. 0.2$\underline{5}$7 _____

7. 0.0$\underline{9}$1 _____

8. 0.20$\underline{6}$ _____

Write the decimal in standard form.

9. thirty-two thousandths _____

10. one thousandth _____

11. nine thousandths _____

12. two hundred nine thousandths _____

13. six hundred twelve thousandths _____

14. fifty thousandths _____

Write the word name for each decimal.

15. 0.941 _____

16. 0.007 _____

17. 0.086 _____

18. 0.301 _____

19. 0.040 _____

20. 0.800 _____

Problem Solving

21. A metal rod is six hundred twenty-five thousandths of a meter long. Write this length as a decimal in standard form.

_____

Use with Lesson 1-4, pages 36–37 in the Student Book.
Then go to Lesson 1-4A, pages 177–178 in this Workbook.

3

Decimals Greater Than One

Name _____

Date _____

Ones	Tenths	Hundredths	Thousandths
5.	3	7	4

Standard Form: 5.374

Word Name: five and three hundred seventy-four thousandths

Write the place of the underlined digit. Then write its value.

1. 4.8̲32 _____

2. 61.672̲ _____

3. 106.24̲5 _____

4. 15̲.133 _____

5. 2̲28.7 _____

6. 9̲4.01 _____

Write each number in standard form.

7. seventy-nine and four hundred thirty-one thousandths _____

8. two hundred three and six tenths _____

9. five and eighty-eight hundredths _____

10. nine hundred ninety-nine and four thousandths _____

11. three and fifty-two thousandths _____

Write the word name for each number.

12. 16.72 _____

13. 4.285 _____

14. 210.009 _____

15. 58.007 _____

16. 116.8 _____

17. 34.34 _____

18. 8.031 _____

Problem Solving

19. Natalie walked a mile in 19.086 minutes.
Write the word name for her time. _____

20. Ben's time for the one-mile walk was seventeen
and five hundred two thousandths minutes.
Write Ben's time in standard form. _____

Use with Lesson 1-5, pages 38–39 in the Student Book.
Then go to Lesson 1-6, pages 40–41 in the Student Book.

Compare and Order Numbers

Name _____

Date _____

Order from least to greatest: 3581, 3851, 3158, 3285

Align by place value.	**Compare the digits in each place, starting at the left.**
3581	
3851	$3 = 3$
3158	$1 < 2,\ 2 < 5,\ 5 < 8$
3285	

The order from least to greatest: **3158, 3285, 3581, 3851**

To compare and order decimals, use the same rules for comparing and ordering whole numbers.

Compare. Write <, =, or >.

1. 347,693 _____ 347,764

2. 5,178,240 _____ 50,100,299

3. 675,167 _____ 675,157

4. 0.45 _____ 4.5

5. 0.02 _____ 0.020

6. 5.842 _____ 0.584

7. 8,621,905 _____ 8,621,935

8. 937,435,010 _____ 937,350,119

9. 6,054,835,199 _____ 654,835,199

10. 24,009,075 _____ 24,090,750

Write in order from least to greatest.

11. 92,248; 93,248; 93,148; 94,000 _____

12. 612,038; 621,038; 622,037; 612,037 _____

13. 7,835,620; 7,835,590; 7,825,780; 783,590 _____

14. 38; 0.38; 3.8

15. 0.01; 0.1; 0.001

_____

_____

16. 2.213; 2.243; 2.231

17. 0.67; 0.668; 0.68

_____

_____

Write in order from greatest to least.

18. 326,500; 326,050; 326,005; 326,505 _____

19. 11,450; 111,450; 111,540; 1,145,000 _____

20. 6,974,000; 6,447,000; 6,947,000; 699,999 _____

21. 3.58; 0.358; 35.8

22. 9.70; 9.07; 90.7

_____

_____

23. 1.063; 1.633; 1.033

24. 21.240; 21.426; 21.264

_____

_____

C Use with Lesson 1-6, pages 40–41 in the Student Book.
C Then go to Lesson 1-7, pages 42–43 in the Student Book.

Rounding Numbers

Name _____

Date _____

Round to the place of the underlined digit.

54,906 ⟶ 55,000   3.516 ⟶ 3.5

652,163 ⟶ 700,000   71.571 ⟶ 72

8,403,177 ⟶ 8,400,000 $864.12 ⟶ $900.00

Round each number to the place of the underlined digit.

1. 291,564 _____
2. 678,519 _____
3. 845,009 _____
4. 372,509,387 _____
5. 954,618,085 _____

Round each to the greatest place.

6. 737,121 _____
7. 507,892 _____
8. 495,382 _____
9. 254,068 _____
10. 24,491,630 _____
11. 85,037,124 _____

Round each to the nearest *whole number, tenth,* and *hundredth.*

12. 5.419 _____
13. 8.566 _____
14. 67.935 _____
15. 22.193 _____
16. 84.177 _____
17. 39.528 _____
18. 128.726 _____
19. 434.582 _____
20. 275.509 _____

Round each to the nearest *ten cents, dollar, ten dollars,* and *hundred dollars.*

21. $815.76 _____
22. $352.68 _____
23. $549.53 _____
24. $922.58 _____
25. $406.39 _____
26. $634.82 _____

Use with Lesson 1-7, pages 42–43 in the Student Book.
Then go to Lesson 1-8, pages 44–45 in the Student Book.

Addition Properties/ Subtraction Rules

Name _____

Date _____

Commutative Property	Identity Property	Associative Property
$7 + 6 = 13$	$5 + 0 = 5$	$(3 + 4) + 8 = 15$
$6 + 7 = 13$	$0 + 5 = 5$	$3 + (4 + 8) = 15$
$5 + 4 = 9$ ← Inverse	$4 - 4 = 0$	
$9 - 4 = 5$ ← Operations	$4 - 0 = 4$	

Find the missing number. Name the property of addition that is used.

1. $9 + 3 =$ ___ $+ 9$ _____ **2.** $7 = 7 +$ ___ _____

3. $4 =$ ___ $+ 4$ _____ **4.** $8 +$ ___ $= 5 + 8$ _____

5. $7 + (6 + 3) = (7 + 6) +$ ___ _____

6. $(5 +$ ___$) + 3 = 5 + (4 +$ ___$)$ _____

Add. Use properties of addition to find shortcuts.

7.
$$\begin{array}{r} 1 \\ 3 \\ 7 \\ + 5 \\ \hline \end{array}$$
8.
$$\begin{array}{r} 4 \\ 1 \\ 6 \\ + 3 \\ \hline \end{array}$$
9.
$$\begin{array}{r} 9 \\ 2 \\ 1 \\ + 6 \\ \hline \end{array}$$
10.
$$\begin{array}{r} 0 \\ 8 \\ 2 \\ + 9 \\ \hline \end{array}$$
11.
$$\begin{array}{r} 6 \\ 7 \\ 4 \\ + 0 \\ \hline \end{array}$$
12.
$$\begin{array}{r} 3 \\ 5 \\ 2 \\ + 5 \\ \hline \end{array}$$

13. $4 + 7 + 6 + 3 =$ _____ **14.** $1 + 5 + 6 + 7 =$ _____ **15.** $0 + 5 + 7 + 2 =$ _____

16. $1 + 8 + 1 + 9 =$ _____ **17.** $2 + 3 + 4 + 5 =$ _____ **18.** $1 + 0 + 9 + 5 =$ ___

Complete the related fact.

19. $2 + 6 = 8$ **20.** $9 - 5 = 4$ **21.** $9 + 7 = 16$

$8 - 6 =$ ___ $4 +$ ___ $= 9$ $16 -$ ___ $= 9$

22. $1 - 1 = 0$ **23.** $16 - 9 = 7$ **24.** $7 + 4 = 11$

$0 + 1 =$ ___ ___ $+ 9 = 16$ ___ $- 4 = 7$

Find the missing addend.

25. $8 +$ ___ $= 17$ **26.** ___ $+ 9 = 11$ **27.** $7 +$ ___ $= 13$

28. $6 +$ ___ $= 14$ **29.** ___ $+ 0 = 4$ **30.** ___ $+ 9 = 10$

31. ___ $+ 8 = 8$ **32.** $5 +$ ___ $= 13$ **33.** $2 +$ ___ $= 9$

Use with Lesson 1-8, pages 44–45 in the Student Book.
Then go to Lesson 1-9, pages 46–47 in the Student Book.

Estimate Sums and Differences

Name _____

Date _____

Front-End Estimation		Rounding	
5263 ⎫ about 1000		5263 ⟶ 5300	
2886 ⎭		2886 ⟶ 2900	
694 ⎫ about 1000		694 ⟶ 700	
+ 7243 ⎭		+ 7243 ⟶ + 7200	
rough estimate: **14,000**		16,100	
adjusted estimate:			
14,000 + 1000 + 1000 = 16,000			

Estimate the sum. Use front-end estimation. Then use rounding.

1.	7463	2.	4903	3.	1634	4.	4316
	7529		3746		271		4010
	+ 3984		+ 888		+ 1115		+ 2757

5.	9925	6.	8052	7.	$418.75	8.	$343.90
	8395		9894		69.46		69.25
	+ 4093		+ 2584		+ 293.68		+ 211.03

9. 6327 + 4896 + 2929 = _____

10. $281.17 + $91.87 + $329.67 = _____

11. $468.20 + $205.11 + $191.62 = _____

12. $570.10 + $101.01 + $75.50 = _____

Estimate the difference. Use front-end estimation. Then use rounding.

13.	8578	14.	$99.93	15.	9415	16.	$81.99
	− 7231		− 4.41		− 373		− 32.75

17.	5992	18.	9450	19.	$323.41	20.	6150
	− 4069		− 6846		− 13.19		− 3891

21. 8792 − 7128 = _____   22. $63.17 − $14.92 = _____

Problem Solving

23. On a business trip a salesperson drove 372 miles the first day, 338 miles the second day, and 178 miles the third day. Estimate her total mileage.

_____

Use with Lesson 1-9, pages 46–47 in the Student Book.
Then go to Lesson 1-10, pages 48–49 in the Student Book.

Addition: Three or More Addends

Add: 3476 + 409 + 1824 = _?_
Use rounding to estimate.

3476	⟶	3500
409	⟶	400
+ 1824	⟶	+ 1800
		about 5700

Add.

```
  1 1 1
  3476
   409
+ 1824
  5709
```

Use rounding to estimate. Then add.

1.
```
  96
  87
+ 51
```

2.
```
  94
  36
+ 62
```

3.
```
  76
  25
+ 59
```

4.
```
  533
  106
+ 999
```

5.
```
  695
  980
+ 243
```

6.
```
  100
  103
+ 798
```

7.
```
  676
   15
+ 575
```

8.
```
  284
   45
+ 295
```

9.
```
  382
  300
+ 948
```

10.
```
  7852
  3789
+ 2896
```

11.
```
  7852
  6317
+ 6276
```

12.
```
  4284
   979
+ 5610
```

13.
```
  6944
  9137
+ 8348
```

14.
```
   102
  1516
+ 3774
```

15.
```
  1881
  9795
+ 8721
```

16.
```
  $1.40
   6.07
+  8.63
```

17.
```
  $81.44
   70.90
+  52.64
```

18.
```
  $74.53
   41.40
+  39.39
```

19.
```
  $24.38
   97.90
+  46.09
```

20.
```
  $39.02
   36.49
+  48.98
```

21.
```
   22
  543
  916
+ 430
```

22.
```
  677
  502
  513
+ 462
```

23.
```
  2438
  9790
   609
+ 3902
```

24.
```
  $35.34
   40.48
   26.97
+   5.55
```

25.
```
  $21.59
   97.24
   10.03
+  45.45
```

Align and add.

26. 468 + 298 + 622 = _____

27. 3019 + 7747 + 140 + 7607 = _____

28. 67 + 263 + 279 = _____

29. 8626 + 7904 + 3735 + 9619 = _____

30. 695 + 980 + 243 = _____

31. 7055 + 5334 + 5795 + 2895 = _____

32. 829 + 24 + 589 = _____

33. 8144 + 7090 + 453 + 4140 = _____

34. 86 + 910 + 226 = _____

35. 8714 + 562 + 9495 + 3640 = _____

Use with Lesson 1-10, pages 48–49 in the Student Book.
Then go to Lesson 1-11, pages 50–51 in the Student Book.

9

Subtraction with Zeros

Name _____

Date _____

Subtract: 8000 − 6493

To subtract when the minuend has zeros, first use front-end digits to estimate, then regroup as many times as necessary *before* you start to subtract.

Estimate.	Regroup and Subtract.
8000	8̸0̸0̸0̸
− 6000	− 6 4 9 3
2000	1 5 0 7

Estimate using front-end digits. Then find the difference.

1.   600
   − 253

2.   800
   − 172

3.   500
   − 329

4.   400
   − 214

5.   900
   − 678

6.   200
   − 84

7.   500
   − 314

8.   300
   − 158

9. $7.00
   − 2.98

10. $6.00
   − 4.34

11.   7000
   − 6193

12.   4000
   − 2864

13.   9000
   − 5877

14.   5000
   − 1891

15.   8000
   − 4375

16.   1006
   − 729

17.   3004
   − 1949

18.   2001
   − 1863

19.   6008
   − 3855

20.   8005
   − 4466

Find the missing minuend.

21. [   ]
   − 271
    319

22. [   ]
   − 749
    466

23. [   ]
   − 3642
    4358

24. [   ]
   − 4195
    2805

25. [   ]
   − 2037
    5166

Align and subtract.

26. 8000 − 7638 = _____

27. $60.03 − $27.95 = _____

28. 2070 − 999 = _____

29. $80.00 − $16.27 = _____

30. 7004 − 1928 = _____

31. $50.20 − $7.68 = _____

Problem Solving

32. Shaya saved $50.00. She bought a jacket that cost $27.39. Did she have enough money left to buy a skirt for $23.99? _____

Use with Lesson 1-11, pages 50–51 in the Student Book.
Then go to Lesson 1-12, pages 52–53 in the Student Book.

Larger Sums and Differences

Name _____

Date _____

<table>
<tr><td colspan="2">Add: 696,285 + 401,604 + 16,297 = <u>?</u></td><td colspan="2">Subtract: $1860.13 − $1085.01 = <u>?</u></td></tr>
<tr><td>Estimate by rounding.</td><td>Add.</td><td>Estimate by rounding.</td><td>Subtract.</td></tr>
</table>

Estimate by rounding.   Add.

$$
\begin{array}{rcl}
 & & \overset{1\,1\,1\ \ 1\,2}{} \\
696,285 & \longrightarrow\ 700,000 & 696,285 \\
401,604 & \longrightarrow\ 400,000 & 401,609 \\
+\ 16,297 & \longrightarrow +\ 20,000 & +\ 16,297 \\
& \text{about}\ \ 1,120,000 & \overline{1,114,191}
\end{array}
$$

Estimate by rounding.   Subtract.

$$
\begin{array}{rcl}
 & & \overset{15}{\ \ 7\,\cancel{8}\,10} \\
\$1860.13 & \longrightarrow\ \$2000.00 & \$1\cancel{8}\cancel{6}\cancel{0}.13 \\
-\ 1085.01 & \longrightarrow -\ 1000.00 & -\ 1085.01 \\
& \text{about}\ \ \$1000.00 & \overline{\$\ \ 775.12}
\end{array}
$$

Use rounding to estimate. Then add or subtract.

1.	95,127 54,202 + 61,806	**2.**	49,437 97,296 + 34,622	**3.**	21,779 37,899 + 79,391	**4.**	64,595 34,783 + 24,518
5.	39,584 − 28,150	**6.**	50,337 − 13,873	**7.**	51,725 − 26,536	**8.**	70,443 − 18,540
9.	$862.61 + 790.48	**10.**	$373.53 + 961.95	**11.**	$871.44 + 456.23	**12.**	$545.01 + 419.70
13.	42,845 − 4,197	**14.**	56,104 − 38,963	**15.**	91,371 − 76,278	**16.**	57,794 − 34,063
17.	$155.66 − 73.85	**18.**	$257.26 − 161.75	**19.**	$542.07 − 84.72	**20.**	$911.19 − 723.67
21.	70,544 53,342 + 57,951	**22.**	28,956 30,194 + 77,474	**23.**	123,082 954,157 + 797,297	**24.**	$1692.64 7127.30 + 2324.96

Align. Then add or subtract.

25. 518,015 + 757,029 = _____

26. 278,279 − 44,647 = _____

27. 784,488 + 50,262 = _____

28. 162,821 − 105,277 = _____

Use with Lesson 1-12, pages 52–53 in the Student Book.
Then go to Lesson 1-13, pages 54–55 in the Student Book.

11

Roman Numerals

Name _____

Date _____

I	**II**	**III**	**IV**	**V**	**VI**	**VII**	**VIII**	**IX**	**X**
1	2	3	4	5	6	7	8	9	10
V	**X**	**XV**	**XX**	**XXV**	**XXX**	**XXXV**	**XL**	**XLV**	**L**
5	10	15	20	25	30	35	40	45	50
X	**XX**	**XXX**	**XL**	**L**	**LX**	**LXX**	**LXXX**	**XC**	**C**
10	20	30	40	50	60	70	80	90	100
C	**CC**	**CCC**	**CD**	**D**	**DC**	**DCC**	**DCCC**	**CM**	**M**
100	200	300	400	500	600	700	800	900	1000

Complete each to write the Roman numeral in standard form.

1. MCLXXV = 1000 + _____ + 50 + _____ + _____ + 5 = _____

2. CMXLIX = (1000 − _____) + (_____ − 10) + (_____ − _____) = _____

3. CDXXXIV = (_____ − 100) + (_____ + _____ + _____) + (_____ − _____) = _____

Write the Roman numeral in standard form.

4. MCDXL _____
5. CDIII _____
6. XCIV _____

7. CMVI _____
8. MCMXLVII _____
9. MMXX _____

10. CMXC _____
11. CMXLV _____
12. DCCXX _____

13. CCLXIV _____
14. XLIX _____
15. LXVIII _____

Write each as a Roman numeral.

16. 54 _____
17. 1985 _____
18. 3009 _____

19. 480 _____
20. 1507 _____
21. 2645 _____

22. 1535 _____
23. 729 _____
24. 1006 _____

25. 665 _____
26. 333 _____
27. 147 _____

Write the date each state was admitted into the Union as a Roman numeral.

28. Delaware – 1787
29. Idaho – 1890
30. Alaska – 1959

_____   _____   _____

Problem Solving

31. The year the United States Constitution was ratified is written
    in Roman numerals as MDCCLXXXIX. What is the standard
    number for this year? _____

12

Problem-Solving Strategy: Guess and Test

Name _____

Date _____

Read ▸ **Plan** ▸ **Solve** ▸ **Check**

Kerry has $15 less than Kevin. Together they have $45. How much money does each person have?

	Guess 1	Guess 2	Guess 3
Kevin	$40	$20	$30
Kerry	$25	$5	$15
Sum	$65	$25	$45

Guess an amount of money for Kevin. Subtract $15 to find the amount for Kerry. Check to see whether the sum is $45.

Kevin has $30. Kerry has $15.

1. Michelle and Michael collect baseball cards. Michael has 5 more cards than Michelle. Together they have 27 cards. How many cards does each have?

   _____

2. There are 12 red and blue pencils on a desk. There are twice as many red pencils as blue pencils. How many red pencils are on the desk?

   _____

3. Elena is 6 years younger than her brother Geraldo. The sum of their ages is 30. How old is Elena?

   _____

4. Doug paid $22 for two books. One book cost $5 more than the other. How much did each book cost?

   _____

5. Jeremy and Hanna collect coins. Jeremy has 7 fewer coins than Hanna. If together they have 83 coins, how many does Hanna have?

   _____

6. Linda received 75¢ in change, all nickels and dimes. There are 11 coins. How many nickels and how many dimes did she receive?

   _____

7. Jamie wants to get a fox, a goose, and a bag of grain safely across a river in a boat. He can take only 1 of the 3 in his boat at one time. If left alone together, the goose would eat the grain and the fox would eat the goose. How many trips will Jamie need to make?

   _____

8. An animal trainer wants to move 2 lions and a chimpanzee to another training area. He can transport only one animal at a time. He cannot leave the chimpanzee alone with either lion. How many trips will he have to make?

   _____

Use with Lesson 1-14, pages 56–57 in the Student Book.
Then go to Lesson 1-15, pages 58–59 in the Student Book.

13

Problem-Solving Application: Mixed Review

Solve each problem and explain the method you used. If needed, do all your work on a separate sheet of paper.

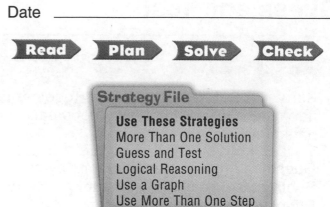

Strategy File

Use These Strategies
More Than One Solution
Guess and Test
Logical Reasoning
Use a Graph
Use More Than One Step

1. Anne, Kim, and Nancy have pets. One has a kitten, one has a puppy, and one has a gerbil. Kim has the gerbil. Nancy is a cousin of the person with the kitten. Who has the puppy?

   _____

2. The quotient of a 2-digit even number divided by a 1-digit number is a whole number greater than 4 and less than 6. What are all the possible numbers?

   _____

3. The difference between a number and 2 times the number is 7. The number is greater than 0. What is the number?

   _____

4. Rose spent $36 on two shirts. One shirt cost twice as much as the other. What was the cost of each shirt?

   _____

5. Benny has 53¢ in change. He has 8 coins. He has only 1 dime. What combination of coins does Benny have?

   _____

6. This year Julio's class consists of 9 people with blond hair, 14 people with brown hair, and 5 people with red hair. Last year, Julio had 26 people in his class. How many more or less people are in Julio's class this year than last year?

   _____

7. Zena buys 8 pieces of fruit. She buys fewer cantaloupes than apples and more apples than pears. She buys 3 pears. How many cantaloupes and how many apples did she buy?

   _____

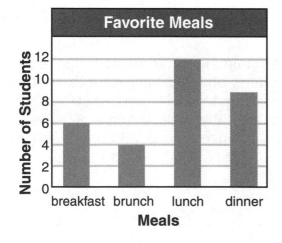

Use the graph at the left to solve.

8. How many students were polled in all?

   _____

9. How many more students prefer lunch than dinner?

   _____

Use with Lesson 1-15, pages 58–59 in the Student Book.

Factors and Products; Properties of Multiplication

Name _____

Date _____

Commutative Property	$5 \times 7 = 7 \times 5 = 35$
Associative Property	$(2 \times 7) \times 3 = 2 \times (7 \times 3) = 42$
Identity Property	$9 \times 1 = 1 \times 9 = 9$
Zero Property	$3 \times 0 = 0 \times 3 = 0$
Distributive Property	$5 \times (4 + 3) = (5 \times 4) + (5 \times 3) = 35$

Write as a multiplication sentence.

1. $2 + 2 + 2$ _____

2. $5 + 5 + 5$ _____

3. $1 + 1 + 1 + 1$ _____

4. $9 + 9 + 9 + 9 + 9$ _____

5. 7 _____

6. $8 + 8 + 8 + 8$ _____

Name the property of multiplication used.

7. $9 \times 7 = 7 \times 9$ _____

8. $1 \times 0 = 0$ _____

9. $2 \times (6 \times 3) = (2 \times 6) \times 3$ _____

10. $2 \times (5 + 2) = (2 \times 5) + (2 \times 2)$ _____

11. $3 \times 1 = 3$ _____

12. $0 \times 6 = 0$ _____

Find the missing number.

13. ___ $\times 3 = 3 \times 5$

14. $2 \times (7 + 8) = (2 \times$ ___$) + (2 \times 8)$

15. $8 \times$ ___ $= 0$

16. $8 \times 5 =$ ___ $\times 8$

17. $7 \times$ ___ $= 7$

18. $6 \times (7 \times 8) = (6 \times$ ___$) \times 8$

19. ___ $\times 4 = 4$

20. $3 \times (1 + 5) = ($___ $\times 1) + (3 \times 5)$

21.
$$\begin{array}{r} 9 \\ \times\underline{} \\ 36 \end{array}$$

22.
$$\begin{array}{r} 2 \\ \times\underline{} \\ 2 \end{array}$$

23.
$$\begin{array}{r} 5 \\ \times\underline{} \\ 45 \end{array}$$

24.
$$\begin{array}{r} 3 \\ \times\underline{} \\ 24 \end{array}$$

25.
$$\begin{array}{r} \\ \times\,8 \\ \hline 16 \end{array}$$

26.
$$\begin{array}{r} 4 \\ \times\underline{} \\ 28 \end{array}$$

Problem Solving

27. The product is 72. One factor is 9. What is the other factor? _____

28. There are 5 black keys in each octave on a piano. How many black keys are there on a 6-octave piano? _____

29. In a classroom there are 7 rows of desks with 4 desks in each row. How many desks are there in the classroom? _____

Use with Lessons 2-1 and 2-2, pages 66–69 in the Student Book.
Then go to Lesson 2-3, pages 70–71 in the Student Book.

15

Mental Math: Special Factors

Name _____

Date _____

Look for patterns when you multiply with 10 and with multiples of 10.

$10 \times 1 = 10$ $50 \times 4 = 200$

$10 \times 2 = 20$ $50 \times 5 = 250$

$10 \times 3 = 30$ $50 \times 6 = 300$

$10 \times 4 = 40$ $50 \times 7 = 350$

$$\begin{array}{r} 9 \\ \times\ 20 \\ \hline 180 \end{array}$$ one zero

$$\begin{array}{r} 80 \\ \times\ 5 \\ \hline 400 \end{array}$$ one zero

Find the products.

1. $10 \times 5 =$ _____

$10 \times 6 =$ _____

$10 \times 7 =$ _____

2. $2 \times 30 =$ _____

$2 \times 40 =$ _____

$2 \times 50 =$ _____

3. $30 \times 6 =$ _____

$30 \times 7 =$ _____

$30 \times 8 =$ _____

4. $3 \times 60 =$ _____

$4 \times 60 =$ _____

$5 \times 60 =$ _____

5. $50 \times 7 =$ _____

$50 \times 8 =$ _____

$50 \times 9 =$ _____

6. $7 \times 70 =$ _____

$7 \times 80 =$ _____

$7 \times 90 =$ _____

Multiply.

7. $\begin{array}{r} 60 \\ \times\ 2 \\ \hline \end{array}$

8. $\begin{array}{r} 80 \\ \times\ 6 \\ \hline \end{array}$

9. $\begin{array}{r} 70 \\ \times\ 5 \\ \hline \end{array}$

10. $\begin{array}{r} 3 \\ \times\ 50 \\ \hline \end{array}$

11. $\begin{array}{r} 9 \\ \times\ 30 \\ \hline \end{array}$

12. $\begin{array}{r} 8 \\ \times\ 40 \\ \hline \end{array}$

13. $\begin{array}{r} 10 \\ \times\ 9 \\ \hline \end{array}$

14. $\begin{array}{r} 90 \\ \times\ 4 \\ \hline \end{array}$

15. $\begin{array}{r} 20 \\ \times\ 7 \\ \hline \end{array}$

16. $\begin{array}{r} 6 \\ \times\ 60 \\ \hline \end{array}$

17. $\begin{array}{r} 7 \\ \times\ 80 \\ \hline \end{array}$

18. $\begin{array}{r} 9 \\ \times\ 70 \\ \hline \end{array}$

19. $3 \times 50 =$ _____

20. $20 \times 6 =$ _____

21. $40 \times 5 =$ _____

22. $70 \times 6 =$ _____

23. $9 \times 40 =$ _____

24. $8 \times 60 =$ _____

Problem Solving

25. Raynell opened 2 crates of oranges. Each crate contained 10 bags of oranges. There were 6 oranges in each bag. How many oranges were in the crates?

_____

26. Lisa placed 10 cards each in 5 rows. How many cards were there?

_____

Ⓒ Use with Lesson 2-3, pages 70–71 in the Student Book.
Ⓒ Then go to Lesson 2-4, pages 72–73 in the Student Book.

Patterns in Multiplication

Name _____

Date _____

Look for patterns when you multiply with 100,
1000, or their multiplies.

$$5 \times 6 = 30$$
$$50 \times 6 = 300$$
$$500 \times 6 = 3000$$
$$5000 \times 6 = 30,000$$

$$50 \times 60 = 3000$$
$$500 \times 60 = 30,000$$
$$5000 \times 60 = 300,000$$

$$\begin{array}{r} 600 \\ \times\ 7 \\ \hline 4200 \end{array}$$ 2 zeros

$$\begin{array}{r} 70 \\ \times\ 3000 \\ \hline 210,000 \end{array}$$ 4 zeros

Multiply.

1. $60 \times 20 =$ _____
$600 \times 20 =$ _____
$6000 \times 20 =$ _____

2. $50 \times 5 =$ _____
$500 \times 5 =$ _____
$5000 \times 5 =$ _____

3. $80 \times 40 =$ _____
$800 \times 40 =$ _____
$8000 \times 40 =$ _____

4. $70 \times 6 =$ _____
$700 \times 6 =$ _____
$7000 \times 6 =$ _____

5. $50 \times 70 =$ _____
$500 \times 70 =$ _____
$5000 \times 70 =$ _____

6. $30 \times 90 =$ _____
$300 \times 90 =$ _____
$3000 \times 90 =$ _____

7. $10 \times 10 =$ _____
$100 \times 10 =$ _____
$1000 \times 10 =$ _____

8. $20 \times 60 =$ _____
$200 \times 60 =$ _____
$2000 \times 60 =$ _____

9. $80 \times 80 =$ _____
$800 \times 80 =$ _____
$8000 \times 80 =$ _____

10. $\begin{array}{r} 6 \\ \times\ 300 \\ \hline \end{array}$

11. $\begin{array}{r} 8 \\ \times\ 200 \\ \hline \end{array}$

12. $\begin{array}{r} 7 \\ \times\ 5000 \\ \hline \end{array}$

13. $\begin{array}{r} 5 \\ \times\ 6000 \\ \hline \end{array}$

14. $\begin{array}{r} 4 \\ \times\ 9000 \\ \hline \end{array}$

15. $\begin{array}{r} 10 \\ \times\ 800 \\ \hline \end{array}$

16. $\begin{array}{r} 20 \\ \times\ 500 \\ \hline \end{array}$

17. $\begin{array}{r} 30 \\ \times\ 4000 \\ \hline \end{array}$

18. $\begin{array}{r} 90 \\ \times\ 2000 \\ \hline \end{array}$

19. $\begin{array}{r} 80 \\ \times\ 5000 \\ \hline \end{array}$

20. $600 \times 6 =$ _____

21. $300 \times 90 =$ _____

22. $800 \times 30 =$ _____

23. $7 \times 5000 =$ _____

24. $30 \times 3000 =$ _____

25. $50 \times 4000 =$ _____

26. $1000 \times 50 =$ _____

27. $9 \times 7000 =$ _____

28. $7000 \times 20 =$ _____

Problem Solving

29. If 8000 shoppers buy 6 pieces
of fruit each, how many pieces of
fruit do they buy in all? _____

Use with Lesson 2-4, pages 72–73 in the Student Book.
Then go to Lesson 2-5, pages 74–75 in the Student Book.

17

Estimate Products

Name _____

Date _____

To estimate the product of two numbers:
- Round each factor to its greatest place.
- Multiply.

$$217 \longrightarrow 200$$
$$\times\ 89 \longrightarrow \times\ 90$$
$$\text{about } 18{,}000$$

To estimate a series of addends of near the same value, multiply the number of addends by the number they "cluster" around.

$$\$71.23\ +\ \$72.91\ +\ \$68.15\ +\ \$69.50$$
$$\downarrow \qquad\quad \downarrow \qquad\quad \downarrow \qquad\quad \downarrow$$
$$\$70 \qquad \$70 \qquad \$70 \qquad \$70$$
$$\hookrightarrow 4 \times \$70 = \$280 \longleftarrow \boxed{\text{estimated sum}}$$

Round to estimate each product.

1. 44 × 27	**2.** 87 × 75	**3.** 27 × 67	**4.** 79 × 29	**5.** 23 × 48
6. 525 × 34	**7.** 223 × 58	**8.** 363 × 87	**9.** 478 × 19	**10.** 684 × 74
11. 613 × 438	**12.** 161 × 780	**13.** 202 × 195	**14.** 793 × 547	**15.** 463 × 211
16. $8.75 × 4	**17.** $95.17 × 13	**18.** $59.07 × 52	**19.** $89.49 × 821	**20.** $17.24 × 108

Estimate the sum. Use clustering.

21. 39 + 42 + 40 + 38 + 43 + 41 = _____

22. 78 + 81 + 79 = _____

23. 192 + 197 + 201 + 212 + 225 = _____

24. $202.25 + $189.05 + $199.60 + $211.81 = _____

25. $47.98 + $54.01 + $49.99 + $51.51 = _____

Problem Solving

26. A certain bicycle costs $199.95. About how much would 75 of these bicycles cost? _____

27. An average chicken weighs 7 pounds. The average cost per pound is $1.09. About how much would 200 chickens cost? _____

28. Sneakers are on sale for $49.99 per pair. About how much would 50 pairs cost? _____

Zeros in the Multiplicand

Name _____

Date _____

Multiply: 6 × 4507 = _?_

Multiply ones. Regroup.
Multiply tens. Add.

$$
\begin{array}{r}
^{4}\ \ \ \\
450\mathbf{7} \\
\times \quad \mathbf{6} \\
\hline
\mathbf{42}
\end{array}
$$

6 × 7 ones =
4 tens 2 ones
6 × 0 tens = 0 tens
0 tens + 4 tens = 4 tens

Multiply hundreds. Regroup.
Multiply thousands. Add.

$$
\begin{array}{r}
^{3\ 4}\ \ \ \\
\mathbf{45}07 \\
\times \quad \ 6 \\
\hline
\mathbf{27{,}0}42
\end{array}
$$

6 × 5 hundreds = 30 hundreds
= 3 thousands 0 hundreds
6 × 4 thousands = 24 thousands
24 thousands + 3 thousands =
27 thousands

Use rounding to estimate. Then multiply.

1. $\begin{array}{r} 5608 \\ \times \quad 4 \\ \hline \end{array}$
2. $\begin{array}{r} 6309 \\ \times \quad 9 \\ \hline \end{array}$
3. $\begin{array}{r} 1705 \\ \times \quad 7 \\ \hline \end{array}$
4. $\begin{array}{r} 8043 \\ \times \quad 4 \\ \hline \end{array}$
5. $\begin{array}{r} 4061 \\ \times \quad 8 \\ \hline \end{array}$

6. $\begin{array}{r} 5075 \\ \times \quad 5 \\ \hline \end{array}$
7. $\begin{array}{r} 2099 \\ \times \quad 6 \\ \hline \end{array}$
8. $\begin{array}{r} 9408 \\ \times \quad 2 \\ \hline \end{array}$
9. $\begin{array}{r} 6705 \\ \times \quad 3 \\ \hline \end{array}$
10. $\begin{array}{r} 8904 \\ \times \quad 7 \\ \hline \end{array}$

11. $\begin{array}{r} 47{,}008 \\ \times \quad 5 \\ \hline \end{array}$
12. $\begin{array}{r} 92{,}605 \\ \times \quad 6 \\ \hline \end{array}$
13. $\begin{array}{r} 44{,}031 \\ \times \quad 8 \\ \hline \end{array}$
14. $\begin{array}{r} 20{,}603 \\ \times \quad 9 \\ \hline \end{array}$
15. $\begin{array}{r} 50{,}987 \\ \times \quad 2 \\ \hline \end{array}$

16. $\begin{array}{r} 40{,}090 \\ \times \quad 3 \\ \hline \end{array}$
17. $\begin{array}{r} 30{,}008 \\ \times \quad 6 \\ \hline \end{array}$
18. $\begin{array}{r} 10{,}800 \\ \times \quad 4 \\ \hline \end{array}$
19. $\begin{array}{r} 35{,}007 \\ \times \quad 7 \\ \hline \end{array}$
20. $\begin{array}{r} 70{,}006 \\ \times \quad 8 \\ \hline \end{array}$

Find the product. You may use the distributive property.

21. 5 × 3087 = _____
22. 2 × 9708 = _____

23. 6 × 40,504 = _____
24. 9 × 10,056 = _____

25. 4 × 71,002 = _____
26. 3 × 90,085 = _____

27. 9 × 173,000 = _____
28. 7 × 804,310 = _____

Problem Solving

29. Each of the 4 sides of a building was
faced with 25,080 bricks. How many
bricks were used to face all the sides
of the building?

_____

Use with Lesson 2-6, pages 76–77 in the Student Book.
Then go to Lesson 2-7, pages 78–79 in the Student Book.

19

Multiply Two Digits

Name _____

Date _____

To multiply by two digits:	23	346	4721
• Multiply by the ones.	×13	× 54	× 76
• Multiply by the tens.	69	1384	28326
• Add the partial products.	+23	+1730	+33047
	299	18,684	358,796

Use rounding to estimate. Then multiply.

1. 10
    × 78

2. 45
    × 45

3. 59
    × 83

4. 16
    × 61

5. 20
    × 95

6. 454
    × 35

7. 149
    × 52

8. 928
    × 53

9. 89
    × 75

10. 401
     × 46

11. 645
     × 34

12. 104
     × 18

13. 77
     × 23

14. 959
     × 84

15. 494
     × 97

16. 9967
     × 33

17. 4952
     × 41

18. 6952
     × 17

19. 4229
     × 64

20. 8316
     × 23

Find the product.

21. 54 × 814 = _____

22. 70 × 427 = _____

23. 61 × 2277 = _____

24. 28 × 4898 = _____

25. 80 × 6985 = _____

26. 98 × 2232 = _____

Problem Solving

27. Growing Gardens had 18 daylily plants. Each
    plant produced 875 flowers. How many flowers
    did the plants produce?

    _____

Use with Lesson 2-7, pages 78–79 in the Student Book.
Then go to Lesson 2-8, pages 80–81 in the Student Book.

Multiply Three Digits

Name _____

Date _____

To multiply by three digits:
- Multiply by the ones.
- Multiply by the tens.
- Multiply by the hundreds.
- Add the partial products.

$$
\begin{array}{r}
721 \\
\times\ 184 \\
\hline
2884 \\
5768 \\
+721 \\
\hline
132{,}664
\end{array}
\qquad
\begin{array}{r}
2753 \\
\times\ 239 \\
\hline
24777 \\
8259 \\
+5506 \\
\hline
657{,}967
\end{array}
$$

Use rounding to estimate. Then multiply.

1. $\begin{array}{r} 218 \\ \times\ 446 \\ \hline \end{array}$
2. $\begin{array}{r} 236 \\ \times\ 878 \\ \hline \end{array}$
3. $\begin{array}{r} 610 \\ \times\ 374 \\ \hline \end{array}$
4. $\begin{array}{r} 397 \\ \times\ 526 \\ \hline \end{array}$
5. $\begin{array}{r} 270 \\ \times\ 581 \\ \hline \end{array}$

6. $\begin{array}{r} 868 \\ \times\ 259 \\ \hline \end{array}$
7. $\begin{array}{r} 259 \\ \times\ 178 \\ \hline \end{array}$
8. $\begin{array}{r} 585 \\ \times\ 931 \\ \hline \end{array}$
9. $\begin{array}{r} 438 \\ \times\ 759 \\ \hline \end{array}$
10. $\begin{array}{r} 245 \\ \times\ 378 \\ \hline \end{array}$

11. $\begin{array}{r} 312 \\ \times\ 798 \\ \hline \end{array}$
12. $\begin{array}{r} 151 \\ \times\ 592 \\ \hline \end{array}$
13. $\begin{array}{r} 956 \\ \times\ 243 \\ \hline \end{array}$
14. $\begin{array}{r} 939 \\ \times\ 114 \\ \hline \end{array}$
15. $\begin{array}{r} 984 \\ \times\ 632 \\ \hline \end{array}$

Find the product.

16. $9795 \times 872 =$ _____

17. $5815 \times 729 =$ _____

18. $1450 \times 259 =$ _____

19. $5044 \times 183 =$ _____

Problem Solving

20. A farmer planted 249 rows of cabbages. There were 267 cabbages in each row. How many cabbages did he plant? _____

21. In one month, Jane picked 623 baskets of cherries. If each basket held 382 cherries, how many cherries did she pick? _____

Use with Lesson 2-8, pages 80–81 in the Student Book.
Then go to Lesson 2-9, pages 82–83 in the Student Book.

21

Zeros in the Multiplier

Name _____

Date _____

When multiplying with zeros in the multiplier:
- You may omit the partial products of the zeros.
- Remember to align the other partial products correctly under the multiplier place.

	Long Way	Short Way
	8241	8241
	× 607	× 607
	57687	57687
	0000	+49446
	+49446	5,002,287
	5,002,287	

Use rounding to estimate. Then multiply.

1. 580
  × 605

2. 268
  × 508

3. 406
  × 950

4. 763
  × 580

5. 651
  × 807

6. 807
  × 309

7. 598
  × 902

8. 128
  × 650

9. 412
  × 510

10. 733
  × 450

11. 3326
  × 450

12. 5551
  × 803

13. 5639
  × 203

14. 2492
  × 807

15. 6181
  × 306

16. 3119
  × 240

17. 8225
  × 209

18. 5899
  × 602

19. 4216
  × 504

20. 26311
  × 390

Find the product.

21. 200 × 785 = _____

22. 300 × 254 = _____

23. 602 × 3476 = _____

24. 940 × 1769 = _____

25. 510 × 7776 = _____

26. 707 × 9753 = _____

Problem Solving

27. A stadium has 200 rows of 225 seats. How many seats are in the stadium? _____

22

Multiplication with Money

Name _____

Date _____

To multiply an amount of money:
- Multiply as usual.
- Write a decimal point in the product two places from the right.
- Write the dollar sign in the product.

$$\begin{array}{r} \$.59 \\ \times\ 31 \\ \hline 59 \\ +177 \\ \hline \$18.29 \end{array}$$

$$\begin{array}{r} \$7.87 \\ \times\ 264 \\ \hline 3148 \\ 4722 \\ +1574 \\ \hline \$2077.68 \end{array}$$

Multiply.

1. $\begin{array}{r} \$0.09 \\ \times\ \ \ 3 \\ \hline \end{array}$
2. $\begin{array}{r} \$1.02 \\ \times\ \ \ 4 \\ \hline \end{array}$
3. $\begin{array}{r} \$2.22 \\ \times\ \ \ 5 \\ \hline \end{array}$
4. $\begin{array}{r} \$6.12 \\ \times\ \ \ 9 \\ \hline \end{array}$
5. $\begin{array}{r} \$4.95 \\ \times\ \ \ 2 \\ \hline \end{array}$

6. $\begin{array}{r} \$1.47 \\ \times\ \ 28 \\ \hline \end{array}$
7. $\begin{array}{r} \$0.36 \\ \times\ \ 39 \\ \hline \end{array}$
8. $\begin{array}{r} \$7.92 \\ \times\ \ 16 \\ \hline \end{array}$
9. $\begin{array}{r} \$0.82 \\ \times\ \ 54 \\ \hline \end{array}$
10. $\begin{array}{r} \$1.66 \\ \times\ \ 87 \\ \hline \end{array}$

11. $\begin{array}{r} \$8.36 \\ \times\ \ 23 \\ \hline \end{array}$
12. $\begin{array}{r} \$4.92 \\ \times\ \ 79 \\ \hline \end{array}$
13. $\begin{array}{r} \$6.30 \\ \times\ \ 43 \\ \hline \end{array}$
14. $\begin{array}{r} \$0.83 \\ \times\ \ 98 \\ \hline \end{array}$
15. $\begin{array}{r} \$7.80 \\ \times\ \ 55 \\ \hline \end{array}$

16. $\begin{array}{r} \$17.56 \\ \times\ \ \ 70 \\ \hline \end{array}$
17. $\begin{array}{r} \$29.81 \\ \times\ \ \ 33 \\ \hline \end{array}$
18. $\begin{array}{r} \$65.29 \\ \times\ \ 107 \\ \hline \end{array}$
19. $\begin{array}{r} \$30.13 \\ \times\ \ \ 60 \\ \hline \end{array}$
20. $\begin{array}{r} \$40.04 \\ \times\ \ 598 \\ \hline \end{array}$

Find the product.

21. $39 \times \$8.47 =$ _____
22. $68 \times \$4.19 =$ _____
23. $460 \times \$2.77 =$ _____
24. $395 \times \$5.68 =$ _____
25. $810 \times \$29.72 =$ _____
26. $210 \times \$43.02 =$ _____

Problem Solving

27. How much would 75 gallons of gasoline cost if the price is $1.29 per gallon?

_____

Use with Lesson 2-10, pages 84–85 in the Student Book.
Then go to Lesson 2-11, pages 86–87 in the Student Book.

23

Problem-Solving Strategy: Use More Than One Step

Name _____

Date _____

Read ▶ **Plan** ▶ **Solve** ▶ **Check**

Taylor has three spools of thread. One of the spools is 18 inches long. Another is one foot long. Another is two feet long. What is the total length of Taylor's spools of thread?

18 in. + 1ft + 2 ft = ___?___
2 × 12 in. = 24 in.
18 in. + 12 in. + 24 in. = 54 in.

Hint:
1 ft = 12 in.

The total length is 54 in.

Solve. Do your work on a separate sheet of paper.

1. Zack pitches for his baseball team twice a week. He throws an average of 78 pitches a game. How many pitches did he throw in three weeks?

_____

2. Olivia gets her hair cut every other month. If she spends $25 on each hair cut, how much will Olivia spend in 2 years?

_____

3. Katie baked three dozen cupcakes for her school bake sale. She charged a quarter for each cupcake. If Katie sold all of the cupcakes, how much money did she make?

_____

4. Ella has three flowerbeds. Each has four rows of flowers in it. If there are 24 flowers in each row, how many flowers are there in all?

_____

5. Jose runs at an average rate of 6 miles per hour. He runs every day for 30 minutes. How many miles does Jose run a week?

_____

6. Ryan earns $7.50 an hour doing yard work. If he works 12 hours a week during an 11 week summer break, how much money will Ryan earn in all?

_____

7. Mrs. Ing walks 8 blocks from her house to her store. If she walks to and from work, and her store is closed on Sunday, how many blocks does she walk in a week?

_____

8. It takes Alan 40 minutes to do his math homework. If it takes twice as long to do his other homework as it takes to do his math, how long will it take Alan to finish all his homework?

_____

24

Problem-Solving Application: Mixed Review

Name _____

Date _____

Solve each problem and explain the method you used. If needed, do all your work on a separate sheet of paper.

Read ▸ Plan ▸ Solve ▸ Check

Strategy File

Use These Strategies
Guess and Test
Logical Reasoning
More Than One Solution
Use More Than One Step

1. Chan, Bruce, and Armando ride their bicycles to school. One bicycle is red, one is blue, and one is green. Chan does not ride a red bicycle, and Armando does not ride a red or blue bicycle. What color bicycle does each person ride?

   _____

2. The sum of a number added to itself is less than 15 and greater than 10. What are all the possible numbers?

   _____

3. Sam and Krista cleaned the house for a total of 270 minutes. Sam cleaned twice as long as Krista. How long did Krista clean?

   _____

4. Jennifer was born in the month whose name has the fewest letters. The date is an odd number. The sum of the digits is 2. When is Jennifer's birthday?

   _____

5. Chan ran for half a minute at 3 yd per second. Carrie ran for 25 seconds at 10 ft per second. Who ran farther?

   _____

6. A 2-digit even number is divided by 5. The quotient is a 1-digit even number. What are all the 2-digit numbers that fit this description?

   _____

7. Sanjay made pancakes for his family. If he and his 2 brothers want 4 each, and his mother and father each want half as many as Sanjay, how many pancakes did Sanjay need to make?

   _____

8. Sarah shares a folder with Emma. If there are 37 documents total and Sarah has 11 less than Emma, how many documents does each have in the folder?

   _____

9. Danny breaks a window in his house that costs $130. If he makes $6.50 an hour at his job where he works 4 hours a day, how many days will he have to work to pay for the window?

   _____

Understanding Division

Name _____

Date _____

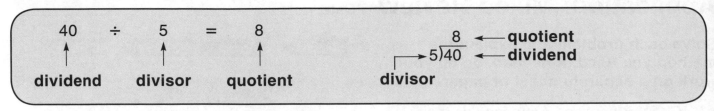

Complete.

1. $4 \times 5 = 20$

   $20 \div 5 =$ ___

   $20 \div 4 =$ ___

2. $7 \times 6 = 42$

   ___ $\div 7 = 6$

   ___ $\div 6 = 7$

3. $9 \times 6 = 54$

   $54 \div$ ___ $= 9$

   $54 \div$ ___ $= 6$

4. $8 \times 9 = 72$

   $72 \div 8 =$ ___

   $72 \div 9 =$ ___

Write all the related facts using the given numbers.

5. 4, 6, 24

   ___ ◯ ___ = ___

   ___ ◯ ___ = ___

   ___ ◯ ___ = ___

   ___ ◯ ___ = ___

6. 7, 7, 49

   ___ ◯ ___ = ___

   ___ ◯ ___ = ___

7. 5, 3, 15

   ___ ◯ ___ = ___

   ___ ◯ ___ = ___

   ___ ◯ ___ = ___

   ___ ◯ ___ = ___

8. 4, 9, 36

   ___ ◯ ___ = ___

   ___ ◯ ___ = ___

   ___ ◯ ___ = ___

   ___ ◯ ___ = ___

9. 7, 9, 63

   ___ ◯ ___ = ___

   ___ ◯ ___ = ___

   ___ ◯ ___ = ___

   ___ ◯ ___ = ___

10. 6, 5, 30

    ___ ◯ ___ = ___

    ___ ◯ ___ = ___

    ___ ◯ ___ = ___

    ___ ◯ ___ = ___

11. 3, 8, 24

    ___ ◯ ___ = ___

    ___ ◯ ___ = ___

    ___ ◯ ___ = ___

    ___ ◯ ___ = ___

12. 2, 6, 12

    ___ ◯ ___ = ___

    ___ ◯ ___ = ___

    ___ ◯ ___ = ___

    ___ ◯ ___ = ___

Complete each division. Find the value of n.

13. $1\overline{)65}$ with n above $n =$ ___

14. $98\overline{)0}$ with n above $n =$ ___

15. $10\overline{)10}$ with n above $n =$ ___

16. $1\overline{)100}$ with n above $n =$ ___

17. $20\overline{)n}$ with 0 above $n =$ ___

18. $1\overline{)n}$ with 6 above $n =$ ___

19. $n\overline{)12}$ with 1 above $n =$ ___

20. $n\overline{)19}$ with 19 above $n =$ ___

21. $n\overline{)20}$ with 5 above $n =$ ___

22. $6\overline{)36}$ with n above $n =$ ___

23. $n\overline{)48}$ with 8 above $n =$ ___

24. $4\overline{)n}$ with 4 above $n =$ ___

25. $n\overline{)28}$ with 7 above $n =$ ___

26. $3\overline{)12}$ with n above $n =$ ___

27. $n\overline{)32}$ with 8 above $n =$ ___

Use with Lesson 3-1, pages 96–97 in the Student Book.
Then go to Lesson 3-2, pages 98–99 in the Student Book.

Division Patterns

Name _____

Date _____

Use division facts and patterns with zero to divide with multiples of 10, 100, or 1000.

6 ÷ 6 = 1		40 ÷ 8 = 5
60 ÷ 6 = 10		400 ÷ 80 = 5
600 ÷ 6 = 100		4000 ÷ 80 = 50
6000 ÷ 6 = 1000		40,000 ÷ 80 = 500
60,000 ÷ 6 = 10,000		400,000 ÷ 80 = 5000

Find the quotient. Look for a pattern.

1. 36 ÷ 9 = _____ **2.** 28 ÷ 7 = _____ **3.** 54 ÷ 9 = _____

360 ÷ 9 = _____   280 ÷ 70 = _____   540 ÷ 90 = _____

3600 ÷ 9 = _____   2800 ÷ 700 = _____   5400 ÷ 90 = _____

36,000 ÷ 9 = _____   28,000 ÷ 7000 = _____   54,000 ÷ 90 = _____

360,000 ÷ 9 = _____   280,000 ÷ 70,000 = _____   540,000 ÷ 90 = _____

Divide.

4. $6\overline{)360}$ **5.** $8\overline{)720}$ **6.** $7\overline{)6300}$ **7.** $2\overline{)1800}$

8. $30\overline{)270}$ **9.** $40\overline{)280}$ **10.** $50\overline{)2500}$ **11.** $60\overline{)4200}$

12. $70\overline{)49,000}$ **13.** $80\overline{)16,000}$ **14.** $90\overline{)270,000}$ **15.** $20\overline{)400,000}$

Use basic facts and patterns to find the value of n.

16. 400 ÷ 8 = n **17.** 90 ÷ 3 = n **18.** 480 ÷ 6 = n

n = _____ n = _____ n = _____

19. 3500 ÷ n = 50   **20.** 1200 ÷ n = 60   **21.** 4900 ÷ n = 70

n = _____ n = _____ n = _____

22. 54,000 ÷ 90 = n **23.** 63,000 ÷ n = 700   **24.** 640,000 ÷ 8000 = n

n = _____ n = _____ n = _____

Compare. Write <, =, or >.

25. 16,000 ÷ 8 _____ 8000 ÷ 4   **26.** 1600 ÷ 2 _____ 1200 ÷ 4

27. 70,000 ÷ 10 _____ 70,000 ÷ 7   **28.** 2700 ÷ 3 _____ 3200 ÷ 4

C Use with Lesson 3-2, pages 98–99 in the Student Book.
C Then go to Lesson 3-3, pages 100–101 in the Student Book.

27

Three-Digit Quotients

Name _____

Date _____

Division Steps	Divide: 497 ÷ 3	Check.

Division Steps
- Decide where to begin the quotient.
- Estimate.
- Divide.
- Multiply.
- Subtract and compare.
- Bring down.
- Repeat the steps as necessary.
- Check.

Divide: 497 ÷ 3

```
    165 R2
3)497
  -3↓
   19
  -18↓
    17
   -15
     2
```

Check.

```
  165
×   3
  495
+   2
  497
```

Divide and check.

1. 7)782   **2.** 5)850   **3.** 6)672   **4.** 8)981

5. 4)3816   **6.** 7)6958   **7.** 3)1814   **8.** 5)3927

9. 908 ÷ 2 = _____   **10.** 856 ÷ 5 = _____   **11.** 313 ÷ 9 = _____

12. 4893 ÷ 3 = _____   **13.** 920 ÷ 7 = _____   **14.** 782 ÷ 6 = _____

Problem Solving

15. There are 975 cans at a factory. How many 6-packs can be made? How many cans will be left over?

16. Three friends equally share a bag of 813 pennies. How many pennies does each friend get?

_____   _____

Use with Lesson 3-3, pages 100–101 in the Student Book.
Then go to Lesson 3-4, pages 102–103 in the Student Book.

Larger Quotients

Name _____

Date _____

Divide: 93,857 ÷ 4

Repeat the division steps until the division is completed.

```
         2 3 4 6 4  R1
    4) 9 3,8 5 7
      - 8
        1 3
      - 1 2
          1 8
        - 1 6
            2 5
          - 2 4
              1 7
            - 1 6
                1
```

Check.

```
  23,464
×      4
  93,856
+      1
  93,857
```

Divide and check.

1. 3)78,260

2. 5)85,794

3. 6)96,726

4. 8)98,744

5. 6)43,487

6. 2)31,543

7. 4)28,529

8. 9)61,134

9. 5)141,585

10. 7)232,486

11. 8)522,872

12. 9)515,056

Problem Solving

13. Plants Plus has 21,073 tulip bulbs. If 5 bulbs are planted in each pot, how many pots are needed? How many bulbs are left over?

14. An automobile factory made 8500 cars. The same number of cars were sent to 4 cities. How many cars were sent to each city?

_____   _____

Use with Lesson 3-4, pages 102–103 in the Student Book.
Then go to Lesson 3-5, pages 104–105 in the Student Book.

29

Zeros in the Quotient

Name _____

Date _____

$5015 \div 5 = \underline{\ ?\ }$

Not enough hundreds or tens. Write 0s in the quotient.

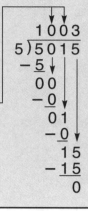

```
      1003
   5)5015
    - 5↓
      00
     - 0↓
       01
      - 0↓
        15
      - 15
         0
```

Check.
```
   1003
 ×    5
   5015
```

Divide and check.

1. $7\overline{)742}$

2. $6\overline{)612}$

3. $6\overline{)3047}$

4. $8\overline{)8720}$

5. $8\overline{)3254}$

6. $7\overline{)5643}$

7. $6\overline{)3664}$

8. $9\overline{)8910}$

9. $5\overline{)25,456}$

10. $7\overline{)56,756}$

11. $4\overline{)28,377}$

12. $8\overline{)73,674}$

Problem Solving

13. A farm has 2525 hens separated equally in 5 henhouses. How many hens are in each henhouse?

_____

14. An apple grower packs 816 select apples equally into 8 cases for shipment. How many apples will be in each case?

_____

☾ Use with Lesson 3-5, pages 104–105 in the Student Book.
☾ Then go to Lesson 3-6, pages 106–107 in the Student Book.

Short Division

Name _____

Date _____

$714 \div 3 = \underline{\;?\;}$

| $2 \times 3 = 6$ $\quad$ $7 - 6 = 1$ | $3 \times 3 = 9$ $\quad$ $11 - 9 = 2$ | $8 \times 3 = 24$ $\quad$ $24 - 24 = 0$ |

$$\overset{2}{3)\overline{7^{1}14}} \qquad \overset{23}{3)\overline{7^{1}1^{2}4}} \qquad \overset{238}{3)\overline{7^{1}1^{2}4}}$$

Use short division to divide. Then check.

1. $4)\overline{928}$
2. $6)\overline{150}$
3. $2)\overline{172}$
4. $5)\overline{75}$

5. $8)\overline{906}$
6. $7)\overline{2187}$
7. $3)\overline{843}$
8. $9)\overline{7668}$

9. $6)\overline{4637}$
10. $5)\overline{3317}$
11. $4)\overline{1937}$
12. $8)\overline{6103}$

Use short division to find the quotient.

13. $5)\overline{325}$
14. $7)\overline{1830}$
15. $4)\overline{2576}$
16. $9)\overline{2905}$

17. $3)\overline{256}$
18. $6)\overline{478}$
19. $2)\overline{1350}$
20. $8)\overline{3539}$

21. $5)\overline{42,387}$
22. $7)\overline{434,714}$
23. $3)\overline{25,016}$
24. $9)\overline{302,485}$

25. $8)\overline{25,696}$
26. $6)\overline{308,850}$
27. $4)\overline{38,148}$
28. $5)\overline{393,455}$

Problem Solving Use short division.

29. The total attendance at a 5-day fair was 631,760. If the attendance each day was the same, how many people visited the fair each day?

_____

C Use with Lesson 3-6, pages 101–102 in the Student Book.
Then go to Lessons 3-7 and 3-8, pages 108–111 in the Student Book.

31

Explore Divisibility;
Divisibility and Mental Math

Name _____

Date _____

A number is divisible by:

2 if its ones digit is divisible by 2. **5** if its ones digit is 0 or 5. **10** if its ones digit is 0. **3** if the sum of its digits is divisible by 3.

9 if the sum of its digits is divisible by 9. **6** if it is divisible by both 2 and 3. **4** if its tens and ones digits form a number that is divisible by 4.

Write the numbers each is divisible by.

1. 30 _____

2. 48 _____

3. 252 _____

4. 453 _____

5. 404 _____

6. 625 _____

7. 1740 _____

8. 294 _____

9. 2367 _____

10. 3180 _____

11. 1830 _____

12. 3732 _____

13. 1455 _____

14. 9300 _____

15. 24,528 _____

16. 45,330 _____

17. 120,603 _____

18. 345,680 _____

Problem Solving

19. A high school band of 100 musicians went on a trip to New York. They are staying in 3 hotels. Are the same number of musicians staying in each hotel?

_____

20. A hotel manager needed to seat 250 guests at a wedding party. Can he seat them in groups of 5 or 10?

_____

21. The manager has 122 flower arrangements. She wants to use all the arrangements and put the same number in each room. Should she put 2, 3, or 4 arrangements in each room?

_____

Use with Lessons 3-7 and 3-8, pages 108–111 in the Student Book.
Then go to Lesson 3-9, pages 112–113 in the Student Book.

Estimation:
Compatible Numbers

Name _____

Date _____

Estimate:	Use compatible numbers:	Think:
3689 ÷ 7 $\longrightarrow$	3500 ÷ 7 $\longrightarrow$	3500 ÷ 7 = 500 So 3689 ÷ 7 is about 500.
41,345 ÷ 83 $\longrightarrow$	40,000 ÷ 80 $\longrightarrow$	40,000 ÷ 80 = 500 So 41,345 ÷ 83 is about 500.

Estimate each quotient. Use compatible numbers.

1. 459 ÷ 9

2. 373 ÷ 4

3. 5892 ÷ 8

4. 2367 ÷ 7

_____

5. 921 ÷ 24

6. 350 ÷ 23

7. 375 ÷ 82

8. 425 ÷ 58

_____

9. 325 ÷ 14

10. 827 ÷ 43

11. 888 ÷ 45

12. 894 ÷ 29

_____

13. 1825 ÷ 32

14. 3157 ÷ 44

15. 1455 ÷ 53

16. 2740 ÷ 84

_____

Estimate to compare. Write <, =, or >.

17. 16,098 ÷ 42 ____ 20,924 ÷ 29

18. 9205 ÷ 33 ____ 8789 ÷ 27

19. 46,701 ÷ 91 ____ 48,763 ÷ 68

20. 24,869 ÷ 53 ____ 23,904 ÷ 78

Problem Solving

21. 5816 passengers were carried by an airplane in a 23-day period. About the same number were carried each day. Estimate the number of passengers carried each day.

_____

22. In 32 hours, 83,697 cars crossed a bridge. About the same number crossed each hour. About how many cars crossed each hour?

_____

23. Marvin has 3508 stamps shared equally among 14 albums. About how many stamps are in each album?

_____

24. A store has 993 books. About how many shelves are needed if each shelf holds 19 books?

_____

Use with Lesson 3-9, pages 112–113 in the Student Book.
Then go to Lesson 3-9A, pages 179–180 in this Workbook.

33

Teens as Divisors

12,416 ÷ 17 = __?__

Divide the hundreds.	Divide the tens.	Divide the ones.	Check.
$\times$ 8	73	730 R6	730
17)12,416	17)12,416	17)12,416	$\times$ 17
136	−119↓	−119↓	5110
7	51	51	730
17)12,416	−51	−51↓	12,410
−119	0	06	+ 6
5		− 0	12,416
Too large. Try 7.		6	

Find the quotient and the remainder. Then check.

1. 11)321

2. 13)435

3. 15)582

4. 17)6294

5. 19)7943

6. 12)8376

7. 14)92,462

8. 16)28,619

9. 18)47,829

10. 11)58,294

11. 15)183,247

12. 19)175,492

Problem Solving

13. A bank received 116,714 key chains to give to customers. Each of the 14 tellers received the same number of key chains. At most, how many did each teller receive? How many chains were left over? _____

34

Two-Digit Divisors

Divide: 2239 ÷ 43

Divide the tens.

$$\begin{array}{r} \times\ 6 \\ \ \downarrow \\ 43\overline{)2239} \\ 258 \end{array}$$

Too large. Try 5.

$$\begin{array}{r} 5 \\ 43\overline{)2239} \\ -215 \\ \hline 8 \end{array}$$

Divide the ones.

$$\begin{array}{r} 52\ \text{R}3 \\ 43\overline{)2239} \\ -215\downarrow \\ \hline 89 \\ -86 \\ \hline 3 \end{array}$$

Check.

$$\begin{array}{r} 52 \\ \times\ 43 \\ \hline 156 \\ 208 \\ \hline 2236 \\ +\ \ \ 3 \\ \hline 2239 \end{array}$$

Divide and check.

1. $31\overline{)69}$

2. $82\overline{)167}$

3. $46\overline{)184}$

4. $17\overline{)360}$

5. $73\overline{)4526}$

6. $75\overline{)3718}$

7. $54\overline{)2870}$

8. $91\overline{)6643}$

9. $27\overline{)5807}$

10. $22\overline{)4500}$

11. $38\overline{)4294}$

12. $64\overline{)3399}$

Problem Solving

13. A bird called the purple martin can eat 2400 mosquitos in 40 minutes. At that rate, how many can it eat per minute? _____

14. At a picnic, 52 people ate 416 shrimp. Each person ate the same number of shrimp. How many shrimp did each person eat? _____

15. Rachel took 188 pictures on her vacation. If each section of her photo album holds 24 pictures, how many sections could she fill? _____

C Use with Lesson 3-11, pages 116–117 in the Student Book.
Then go to Lesson 3-12, pages 118–119 in the Student Book.

Divide Larger Numbers

Name _____

Date _____

Divide: 109,345 ÷ 23

Repeat the division steps until the division is completed.

$$\begin{array}{r} \times \quad 4 \\ 23\overline{)109,345} \\ -92 \\ \hline 17 \end{array}$$

Divide.

$$\begin{array}{r} 4754 \text{ R3} \\ 23\overline{)109,345} \\ -92 \\ \hline 173 \\ -161 \\ \hline 124 \\ -115 \\ \hline 95 \\ -92 \\ \hline 3 \end{array}$$

Check.

$$\begin{array}{r} 4754 \\ \times \quad 23 \\ \hline 14262 \\ 9508 \\ \hline 109,342 \\ + \quad\quad 3 \\ \hline 109,345 \end{array}$$

Divide and check.

1. $14\overline{)54,692}$

2. $18\overline{)51,704}$

3. $19\overline{)17,784}$

4. $21\overline{)13,798}$

5. $36\overline{)33,120}$

6. $47\overline{)40,908}$

7. $42\overline{)10,083}$

8. $56\overline{)134,417}$

9. $93\overline{)985,826}$

10. $33\overline{)178,829}$

11. $81\overline{)31,579}$

Use with Lesson 3-12, pages 118–119 in the Student Book.
Then go to Lesson 3-13, pages 120–121 in the Student Book.

Divide Money

Divide: $1193.36 ÷ 14

To divide money:

• Place the dollar sign and the decimal point in the quotient.

• Divide as usual.

```
     $        .
14)$1193.36
```

```
     $   85.24
14)$1193.36
  −112
    73
   −70
    33
   −28
    56
   −56
     0
```

Divide and check.

1. 23)$17.25

2. 48)$41.28

3. 72)$136.08

4. 31)$17.98

5. 17)$15.13

6. 53)$35.51

7. 68)$621.52

8. 46)$162.84

9. 11)$94.93

10. 28)$26.32

11. 39)$1677.39

12. 17)$3485.34

Problem Solving

13. The combined savings from the summer jobs of 6 students was $825.78. How much did each student save if they all saved the same amount? _____

14. The cost of 14 identical sets of dishes is $1203.30. Find the cost of one set. _____

⊙ Use with Lesson 3-13, pages 120–121 in the Student Book.
⊙ Then go to Lesson 3-14, pages 122–123 in the Student Book.

Order of Operations

Compute: $(80 \div 2) - 2 \times (3 \times 5)$

• Do the operations within parentheses first.

• Multiply or divide from left to right.

• Add or subtract from left to right.

$(80 \div 2) - 2 \times (3 \times 5)$

$40 \quad - \quad 2 \times 15$

$40 \quad - \quad 30$

$40 \quad - \quad 30 \quad = 10$

Use the order of operations to compute.

1. $5 - 8 \div 2 + 7$ _____

2. $20 \div 4 + 3 \times 6$ _____

3. $(8 \times 7) + (56 \div 8)$ _____

4. $(42 - 12) \div (7 + 3)$ _____

5. $30 + 18 \div 3 - 12$ _____

6. $24 - 9 \div 3 \times 5$ _____

7. $2 + 6 \times 10 \div 30 + 7$ _____

8. $19 + 63 \div 9 \times 3 - 13$ _____

9. $59 - 35 \div 7 \times 4 + 53$ _____

10. $50 - 12 \div 3 \times 2$ _____

11. $20 \div 4 - 4 + (81 \div 9)$ _____

12. $25 - 6 \times 4 + (23 - 3) - 4$ _____

13. $(42 - 6) + 5 - 3 + (8 \times 3)$ _____

14. $3 + (37 - 1) \div 9 + (18 + 3)$ _____

15. $(5 \times 9) \div 5 + (8 \div 8)$ _____

16. $(64 \div 8) - 5 + (33 \times 3)$ _____

17. $(35 - 10) \div (4 + 1)$ _____

18. $20 + 6 \div (4 - 2)$ _____

19. $(6 \times 9) + (63 \div 7)$ _____

20. $32 \div 8 + 4 + (6 \times 0)$ _____

21. $(42 + 10) \div (4 \div 2)$ _____

22. $(55 - 15) \div (5 \times 2)$ _____

23. $(8 \times 8) + (9 \times 1)$ _____

24. $35 \div 7 + 5 - (7 \times 1)$ _____

Use with Lesson 3-14, pages 122–123 in the Student Book.
Then go to Lesson 3-14A, pages 183–184 in this Workbook.

Problem-Solving Strategy:
Make a Table/Find a Pattern

Name _____

Date _____

> **Read** ⟩ **Plan** ⟩ **Solve** ⟩ **Check** ⟩
>
> Wheels and Deals sells bicycles and tricycles. On their showroom floor there are 4 times as many bicycles as tricycles. There is a total of 33 wheels on all of the cycles. How many of each kind of cycle are there?
>
> | Tricycles | 1 | 2 | 3 |
> |---|---|---|---|
> | Bicycles | 4 | 8 | 12 |
> | Tricycle Wheels | 3 | 6 | 9 |
> | Bicycle Wheels | 8 | 16 | 24 |
> | Total Wheels | 11 | 22 | 33 |
>
> Make a table to find different combinations.
>
> There are 3 tricycles and 12 bicycles.

Solve. Do your work on a separate sheet of paper.

1. There are 5 more crows than cows in a farmer's field. There is a total of 52 legs on all of the animals. How many crows and how many cows are in the field?

2. Hannah has the same number of nickels as Heather has dimes. Together, the coins are worth $1.65. How many coins does each girl have?

3. Bao and Calvin use 6 lemons to make every 4 quarts of lemonade. They want to make 12 quarts of lemonade. How many lemons do they need?

4. Dexter has 36 pets. He has 3 times as many fish as mice and half as many cats as mice. How many of each pet does Dexter have?

5. The temperature in Tampa was 55°F at 5 A.M. It rose 7° every hour for the next 2 hours and then rose 8° every hour for 3 hours after that. It then remained constant until 3 P.M. What was the temperature at noon?

6. Becky's dad gives her money each time she washes the car. The first time he gave her $1.00. Each time after, he gave her $1.00 more than the time before. How much money will Becky have when she has washed the car 14 times?

7. Vonda has 3 more quarters than she has dimes in her pocket. She has no other coins. The total value of her coins is $1.80. How many quarters and how many dimes does Vonda have?

8. The temperature in Lakeview was 45°F at 7 A.M. It rose 5° each hour until noon. It remained steady for 3 hours. Then it fell 3° each hour until 8 P.M. What was the temperature in Lakeview at 8 P.M.?

Use with Lesson 3-15, pages 124–125 in the Student Book.
Then go to Lesson 3-16, pages 126–127 in the Student Book.

Problem-Solving Application: Mixed Review

Name _____

Date _____

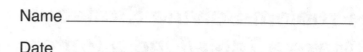
Read ⟩ Plan ⟩ Solve ⟩ Check

Solve each problem and explain the method you used. If needed, do all your work on a separate sheet of paper.

Strategy File

Use These Strategies
Make a Table/Find a Pattern
Interpret the Remainder
Use a Graph
More Than One Solution
Guess and Test
Logical Reasoning
Use More Than One Step

1. Peter, Sally, and Gina order sandwiches. They order a chicken salad, a tuna fish, and a cheese sandwich. Gina does not like tuna fish. Sally does not like chicken salad or tuna fish. What sandwich does each person order?

   _____

2. The sum of a 2-digit number and a 1-digit number is less than 100 and greater than 98. Name all the possible combinations.

   _____

3. Alicia has 25 days she can use for vacation. She wants to take some 7-day trips. How many 7-day trips can Alicia take?

   _____

4. The temperature at 10 A.M. was 78F°. It rose 5° each hour until noon, and rose 3° per hour for 2 more hours after that. Then it fell 2° per hour for 4 hours. What was the temperature at 5 P.M.?

   _____

5. Papi sold candles at the fair. She sold $169.74 on Friday, $235.95 on Saturday, and $219.21 on Sunday. What were her average sales per day?

   _____

6. Kate has 87¢. She has 10 coins. What coins does she have?

   _____

7. Gia is 4 years younger than her sister Joy. The sum of their ages is 74. How old is Joy?

   _____

Use the graph at the left to solve.

8. There are 31 days in July. About how many tourists did Carleton average per day in July?

   _____

9. There are 13 weeks in the summer. About how many tourists did Carleton average per week that summer?

   _____

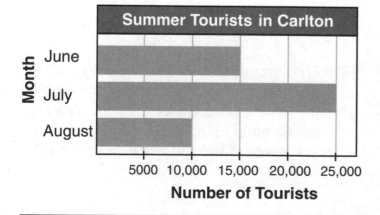

Summer Tourists in Carlton

Month: June, July, August

5000 10,000 15,000 20,000 25,000
Number of Tourists

Explore Factors, Primes, and Composites

Name _____

Date _____

> **Factors** are numbers that are multiplied to find a product.
> Factors of 40: 1, 2, 4, 5, 8, 10, 20, 40
>
> $$1 \times 40 = 40$$
> $$2 \times 20 = 40$$
> $$4 \times 10 = 40$$
> $$5 \times 8 = 40$$
>
> **A prime number** is greater than 1 and has exactly 2 factors, itself and 1.
>
> **A composite number** is greater than 1 and has more than 2 factors.

List all the factors of each number.

1. 3 _____

2. 8 _____

3. 12 _____

4. 17 _____

5. 25 _____

6. 43 _____

7. 44 _____

8. 18 _____

9. 62 _____

10. 28 _____

11. 67 _____

12. 71 _____

13. 70 _____

14. 77 _____

List all the prime numbers in exercises 1–14.

15. _____

**Complete each factor tree to find the prime factorization of each.
Use exponents when appropriate.**

16. 54
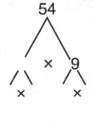
_____

17. 56
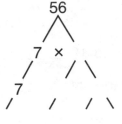
_____

18. 90
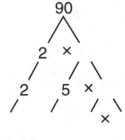
_____

19. 72

_____

20. 99

_____

21. 81

_____

Use with Lessons 4-1 and 4-2, pages 134–137 in the Student Book.
Then go to Lesson 4-3, pages 138–139 in the Student Book.

41

Greatest Common Factor

Name _____

Date _____

> Greatest Common Factor of 6 and 15: ?
>   Factors of 6: **1**, 2, **3**, 6
>   Factors of 15: **1**, **3**, 5, 15
>   Common factors of 6 and 15: **1, 3**
> Greatest Common Factor (GCF): **3**

List the factors, common factors, and GCF of each pair of numbers.

	Number	Factors	Common Factors	GCF
1.	8			
	10			
2.	12			
	20			
3.	6			
	27			
4.	15			
	40			

List the common factors of each set of numbers. Then circle the GCF.

5. 9 and 12 _____

6. 27 and 18 _____

7. 10 and 20 _____

8. 14 and 12 _____

9. 36 and 20 _____

10. 42 and 56 _____

11. 8 and 16 _____

12. 30 and 18 _____

13. 11 and 33 _____

14. 13 and 24 _____

15. 6 and 24 _____

16. 5 and 10 _____

Find the GCF of each set of numbers.

17. 16 and 20 _____

18. 8 and 24 _____

19. 8 and 28 _____

20. 14 and 21 _____

21. 9 and 27 _____

22. 24 and 40 _____

23. 12 and 10 _____

24. 22 and 33 _____

25. 24 and 36 _____

26. What is the GCF of 13, 11, 24?

27. What is the GCF of 8, 12, 20?

_____   _____

42

Use with Lesson 4-3, pages 138–139 in the Student Book.

Then go to Lesson 4-4, pages 140–141 in the Student Book.

Copyright © by William H. Sadlier, Inc. All rights reserved.

Fraction Sense

Name _____

Date _____

Closer to 0	**Closer to $\frac{1}{2}$**	**Closer to 1**
Numerator is much less than denominator.	Numerator doubled is about equal to denominator.	Numerator is about equal to denominator.
$\frac{2}{20}$ $\frac{1}{6}$	$\frac{3}{7}$ $\frac{5}{9}$	$\frac{7}{8}$ $\frac{10}{12}$

Write whether each fraction is *closer to 0, closer to $\frac{1}{2}$, or closer to 1.*

1. $\frac{3}{8}$ _____   2. $\frac{7}{12}$ _____   3. $\frac{1}{3}$ _____   4. $\frac{2}{9}$ _____   5. $\frac{6}{7}$ _____   6. $\frac{3}{5}$ _____

7. $\frac{2}{12}$ _____   8. $\frac{8}{15}$ _____   9. $\frac{17}{20}$ _____   10. $\frac{9}{10}$ _____   11. $\frac{5}{11}$ _____   12. $\frac{3}{13}$ _____

13. $\frac{77}{100}$ _____   14. $\frac{4}{25}$ _____   15. $\frac{27}{50}$ _____   16. $\frac{19}{100}$ _____   17. $\frac{15}{18}$ _____   18. $\frac{13}{50}$ _____

Estimate each fraction using compatible numbers.

19. $\frac{6}{21}$ _____   20. $\frac{11}{32}$ _____   21. $\frac{19}{39}$ _____   22. $\frac{29}{32}$ _____   23. $\frac{43}{81}$ _____   24. $\frac{10}{99}$ _____

Complete each to find the equivalent fraction.

25. $\frac{1 \times 4}{2 \times 4} = $ _____   26. $\frac{6 \div 2}{8 \div 2} = $ _____   27. $\frac{2 \times 3}{3 \times 3} = $ _____

28. $\frac{1}{4} = \frac{}{8}$ 29. $\frac{8}{12} = \frac{}{3}$ 30. $\frac{3}{4} = \frac{}{20}$ 31. $\frac{10}{12} = \frac{}{6}$

32. $\frac{12}{24} = \frac{1}{}$ 33. $\frac{15}{25} = \frac{3}{}$ 34. $\frac{3}{4} = \frac{18}{}$ 35. $\frac{4}{5} = \frac{32}{}$

36. $\frac{7}{50} = \frac{14}{}$ 37. $\frac{21}{99} = \frac{}{33}$ 38. $\frac{18}{72} = \frac{2}{}$ 39. $\frac{1}{8} = \frac{}{96}$

Write three equivalent fractions for each.

40. $\frac{8}{10}$ _____

41. $\frac{9}{12}$ _____

42. $\frac{10}{25}$ _____

43. $\frac{6}{8}$ _____

44. $\frac{3}{5}$ _____

45. $\frac{1}{10}$ _____

Use with Lesson 4-4, pages 140–141 in the Student Book.
Then go to Lesson 4-5, pages 142–143 in the Student Book.

Fractions in Lowest Terms

Name _____

Date _____

Write as a fraction in lowest terms: $\frac{16}{18}$

Divide the numerator and the denominator by their GCF.

Factors of 16: **1, 2,** 4, 8, 16

Factors of 18: **1, 2,** 3, 6, 9, 18

Common Factors: **1, 2**

Greatest Common Factor: **2**

$\frac{16 \div 2}{18 \div 2} = \frac{8}{9}$ ⟵ **lowest terms** or **simplest terms**

Is each fraction in lowest terms? Write *Yes* or *No*

1. $\frac{2}{10}$ _____
2. $\frac{8}{12}$ _____
3. $\frac{3}{10}$ _____
4. $\frac{7}{35}$ _____
5. $\frac{11}{33}$ _____

6. $\frac{5}{8}$ _____
7. $\frac{4}{18}$ _____
8. $\frac{6}{25}$ _____
9. $\frac{4}{9}$ _____
10. $\frac{6}{12}$ _____

11. $\frac{14}{26}$ _____
12. $\frac{18}{45}$ _____
13. $\frac{32}{44}$ _____
14. $\frac{18}{63}$ _____
15. $\frac{15}{23}$ _____

Name the GCF of the numerator and the denominator.

16. $\frac{3}{9}$ _____
17. $\frac{6}{12}$ _____
18. $\frac{14}{24}$ _____
19. $\frac{10}{15}$ _____
20. $\frac{24}{36}$ _____

21. $\frac{18}{45}$ _____
22. $\frac{19}{38}$ _____
23. $\frac{2}{16}$ _____
24. $\frac{7}{49}$ _____
25. $\frac{36}{42}$ _____

Write each fraction in simplest form.

26. $\frac{10}{25}$ _____
27. $\frac{8}{12}$ _____
28. $\frac{6}{16}$ _____
29. $\frac{9}{36}$ _____
30. $\frac{30}{50}$ _____

31. $\frac{14}{35}$ _____
32. $\frac{12}{16}$ _____
33. $\frac{2}{6}$ _____
34. $\frac{16}{18}$ _____
35. $\frac{2}{10}$ _____

36. $\frac{8}{40}$ _____
37. $\frac{3}{9}$ _____
38. $\frac{20}{60}$ _____
39. $\frac{6}{22}$ _____
40. $\frac{20}{24}$ _____

41. $\frac{9}{15}$ _____
42. $\frac{15}{20}$ _____
43. $\frac{10}{12}$ _____
44. $\frac{24}{32}$ _____
45. $\frac{21}{35}$ _____

46. $\frac{18}{36}$ _____
47. $\frac{27}{45}$ _____
48. $\frac{10}{25}$ _____
49. $\frac{54}{63}$ _____
50. $\frac{6}{30}$ _____

Problem Solving Write each answer in lowest terms.

51. There are 6 boys and 8 girls in a singing group. What fractional part of the group is girls? _____

52. Four of 12 people chose milk. What fractional part of the group chose other drinks? _____

53. Jake had 15 sports cards. Five of the cards show baseball players. What fractional part of the cards show baseball players? _____

Use with Lesson 4-5, pages 142–143 in the Student Book.
Then go to Lesson 4-6, pages 144–145 in the Student Book.

Fractions in Greater Terms

Name _____

Date _____

Rename a fraction as an equivalent fraction in greater terms by multiplying the numerator and denominator by the *same number*.

$$\frac{3}{5} = \frac{3 \times 3}{5 \times 3} = \frac{9}{15} \qquad \text{or} \qquad \frac{3}{5} = \frac{3 \times 6}{5 \times 6} = \frac{18}{30}$$

Greater-Terms Fractions

Write the letter of the equivalent fraction in greater terms.

1. $\frac{1}{3}$ _____   a. $\frac{5}{12}$ b. $\frac{3}{6}$ c. $\frac{4}{10}$ d. $\frac{5}{15}$ e. $\frac{9}{24}$

2. $\frac{2}{5}$ _____   a. $\frac{8}{40}$ b. $\frac{5}{10}$ c. $\frac{8}{20}$ d. $\frac{6}{16}$ e. $\frac{9}{45}$

3. $\frac{7}{8}$ _____   a. $\frac{15}{16}$ b. $\frac{28}{30}$ c. $\frac{35}{45}$ d. $\frac{48}{56}$ e. $\frac{56}{64}$

4. $\frac{1}{4}$ _____   a. $\frac{5}{21}$ b. $\frac{8}{32}$ c. $\frac{6}{30}$ d. $\frac{2}{4}$ e. $\frac{3}{20}$

5. $\frac{2}{9}$ _____   a. $\frac{14}{64}$ b. $\frac{8}{36}$ c. $\frac{8}{18}$ d. $\frac{12}{45}$ e. $\frac{16}{80}$

6. $\frac{1}{6}$ _____   a. $\frac{2}{18}$ b. $\frac{6}{30}$ c. $\frac{18}{48}$ d. $\frac{9}{54}$ e. $\frac{6}{35}$

Write the missing term.

7. $\frac{3}{4} = \frac{9}{}$ 8. $\frac{2}{3} = \frac{}{27}$ 9. $\frac{1}{5} = \frac{}{10}$ 10. $\frac{7}{8} = \frac{}{48}$ 11. $\frac{2}{9} = \frac{}{18}$

12. $\frac{4}{7} = \frac{}{35}$ 13. $\frac{1}{3} = \frac{6}{}$ 14. $\frac{2}{9} = \frac{}{36}$ 15. $\frac{3}{8} = \frac{}{24}$ 16. $\frac{1}{2} = \frac{5}{}$

17. $\frac{3}{7} = \frac{}{21}$ 18. $\frac{5}{6} = \frac{}{24}$ 19. $\frac{2}{3} = \frac{6}{}$ 20. $\frac{1}{6} = \frac{4}{}$ 21. $\frac{4}{9} = \frac{}{45}$

Write the equivalent fractions.

22. $\frac{3}{4} = \frac{}{16}$ 23. $\frac{1}{8} = \frac{3}{}$ 24. $\frac{2}{5} = \frac{}{15}$ 25. $\frac{9}{10} = \frac{27}{}$ 26. $\frac{5}{12} = \frac{15}{}$

27. $\frac{2}{7} = \frac{4}{} = \frac{}{28} = \frac{}{42} = \frac{14}{} = \frac{18}{}$ 28. $\frac{4}{9} = \frac{8}{} = \frac{16}{} = \frac{}{54} = \frac{32}{} = \frac{36}{}$

29. $\frac{1}{5} = \frac{}{15} = \frac{5}{} = \frac{}{35} = \frac{}{45} = \frac{11}{}$ 30. $\frac{3}{11} = \frac{}{22} = \frac{}{33} = \frac{12}{} = \frac{}{55} = \frac{21}{}$

Problem Solving

31. Suzy's class used $\frac{5}{8}$ of the cafeteria trays for their science display. There are 72 trays in all. Write a fraction in greater terms that shows how many trays were used. _____

Use with Lesson 4-6, pages 144–145 in the Student Book.
Then go to Lesson 4-7, pages 146–147 in the Student Book.

Multiples: LCM and LCD

Name _____

Date _____

> Multiples of 4: 0, 4, 8, **12**, 16, 20, **24**, 28, . . .
> Multiples of 6: 0, 6, **12**, 18, **24**, 30, 36, 42, . . .
> Nonzero common multiples of 4 and 6: **12, 24,** . . .
> Least Common Multiple (LCM) of 4 and 6: **12**
> Least Common Denominator (LCD) of $\frac{1}{4}$ and $\frac{1}{6}$: **12**

List the first ten nonzero multiples of each.

1. 9 _____

2. 7 _____

3. 5 _____

4. 8 _____

List the first four common multiples of each set of numbers.

5. 2, 4 _____ **6.** 2, 3 _____

7. 3, 5 _____ **8.** 4, 3 _____

9. 6, 8 _____ **10.** 5, 10 _____

11. 2, 3, 4 _____ **12.** 4, 6, 8 _____

Write the least common multiple (LCM) of each set of numbers.

13. 4 and 10 —— **14.** 3 and 5 —— **15.** 6 and 8 —— **16.** 6 and 12 ——

17. 7 and 8 —— **18.** 5 and 8 —— **19.** 2 and 6 —— **20.** 4 and 5 ——

21. 4 and 16 —— **22.** 4 and 12 —— **23.** 6 and 10 —— **24.** 4 and 8 ——

25. 2 and 4 —— **26.** 5 and 7 —— **27.** 7 and 9 —— **28.** 3 and 7 ——

29. 3, 4, and 6 —— **30.** 2, 5, and 8 —— **31.** 6, 12, and 24 ——

32. 5, 4, and 10 —— **33.** 4, 8, and 12 —— **34.** 7, 6, and 21 ——

35. 3, 6, and 9 —— **36.** 5, 10, and 15 —— **37.** 2, 6, and 10 ——

Write the least common denominator (LCD) of each set of fractions.

38. $\frac{2}{8}$ and $\frac{3}{12}$ —— **39.** $\frac{1}{3}$ and $\frac{4}{5}$ —— **40.** $\frac{5}{16}$ and $\frac{1}{4}$ —— **41.** $\frac{2}{9}$ and $\frac{3}{4}$ ——

42. $\frac{5}{6}$ and $\frac{1}{8}$ —— **43.** $\frac{3}{8}$ and $\frac{11}{16}$ —— **44.** $\frac{2}{3}$ and $\frac{5}{6}$ —— **45.** $\frac{1}{4}$ and $\frac{1}{3}$ ——

46. $\frac{1}{2}, \frac{3}{4}$, and $\frac{4}{5}$ —— **47.** $\frac{6}{7}, \frac{4}{6}$, and $\frac{2}{3}$ —— **48.** $\frac{3}{4}, \frac{1}{2}$, and $\frac{1}{6}$ ——

Use with Lesson 4-7, pages 146–147 in the Student Book.
Then go to Lessons 4-8 and 4-9, pages 148–151 in the Student Book.

Mixed Numbers; Fractions Greater Than or Equal to One

Name _____

Date _____

Read: three and two thirds

Write: $3\frac{2}{3}$

Rename $\frac{28}{8}$ as a whole number or a mixed number in simplest form.

$$\frac{28}{8} = 8\overline{)28}^{\;3\;R4} = 3\frac{4}{8} = 3\frac{1}{2}$$

Write a mixed number that represents the shaded part.

1. _____

2. _____

Write as a mixed number.

3. five and three tenths _____

4. three and seven twelfths _____

5. eight and one fifth _____

6. two and nine elevenths _____

7. ten and six sevenths _____

8. fifteen and two thirds _____

Round each mixed number to the nearest whole number.

9. $7\frac{9}{10}$ _____ 10. $4\frac{3}{4}$ _____ 11. $6\frac{1}{2}$ _____ 12. $8\frac{1}{3}$ _____ 13. $9\frac{3}{8}$ _____

Write a numerator to give each a value equal to 1.

14. $\dfrac{}{18}$ 15. $\dfrac{}{20}$ 16. $\dfrac{}{12}$ 17. $\dfrac{}{21}$ 18. $\dfrac{}{17}$ 19. $\dfrac{}{19}$ 20. $\dfrac{}{16}$

Write a numerator to give each a value greater than 1.

21. $\dfrac{}{3}$ 22. $\dfrac{}{5}$ 23. $\dfrac{}{6}$ 24. $\dfrac{}{12}$ 25. $\dfrac{}{9}$ 26. $\dfrac{}{15}$ 27. $\dfrac{}{20}$

Write each as a whole number or a mixed number in simplest form.

28. $\frac{17}{5}$ = ____

29. $\frac{20}{5}$ = ____

30. $\frac{11}{6}$ = ____

31. $\frac{20}{5}$ = ____

32. $\frac{14}{3}$ = ____

33. $\frac{54}{6}$ = ____

34. $\frac{16}{3}$ = ____

35. $\frac{36}{4}$ = ____

36. $\frac{37}{7}$ = ____

37. $\frac{7}{4}$ = ____

Tell which whole number each fraction is closer to.

38. $\frac{14}{5}$ = ____

39. $\frac{19}{3}$ = ____

40. $\frac{62}{7}$ = ____

41. $\frac{94}{8}$ = ____

42. $\frac{83}{9}$ = ____

Use with Lessons 4-8 and 4-9, pages 148–151 in the Student Book.
Then go to Lesson 4-10, pages 152–153 in the Student Book.

Compare and Order Fractions

Name _____

Date _____

Compare: $\frac{2}{5}$ _?_ $\frac{1}{3}$

LCD: 15

$\frac{2 \times 3}{5 \times 3} = \frac{6}{15}$ $\frac{1 \times 5}{3 \times 5} = \frac{5}{15}$

$6 > 5 \longrightarrow \frac{6}{15} > \frac{5}{15}$

So $\frac{2}{5} > \frac{1}{3}$.

Order from least to greatest: $\frac{4}{5}$, $\frac{1}{4}$, $\frac{3}{10}$

LCD: 20

$\frac{4}{5} = \frac{16}{20}$; $\frac{1}{4} = \frac{5}{20}$; $\frac{3}{10} = \frac{6}{20}$

$5 < 6 < 16 \longrightarrow \frac{5}{20} < \frac{6}{20} < \frac{16}{20}$

Least to greatest: $\frac{1}{4}$, $\frac{3}{10}$, $\frac{4}{5}$

Compare. Write <, =, or >.

1. $\frac{3}{10}$ __>__ $\frac{5}{20}$ 2. $\frac{4}{32}$ __<__ $\frac{7}{35}$ 3. $\frac{7}{12}$ __>__ $\frac{7}{24}$ 4. $\frac{1}{9}$ __<__ $\frac{1}{8}$

5. $\frac{2}{6}$ __<__ $\frac{3}{8}$ 6. $\frac{4}{7}$ __<__ $\frac{2}{3}$ 7. $\frac{5}{10}$ __=__ $\frac{1}{2}$ 8. $\frac{6}{8}$ __=__ $\frac{3}{4}$

9. $\frac{3}{8}$ __<__ $\frac{2}{5}$ 10. $\frac{7}{10}$ __>__ $\frac{2}{3}$ 11. $\frac{2}{3}$ __>__ $\frac{1}{4}$ 12. $\frac{8}{20}$ __=__ $\frac{2}{5}$

13. $\frac{6}{6}$ __=__ $\frac{40}{40}$ 14. $\frac{12}{8}$ __<__ $1\frac{2}{3}$ 15. $\frac{23}{21}$ ____ $\frac{7}{7}$ 16. $\frac{29}{8}$ ____ $3\frac{3}{4}$ $\frac{6}{8}$

17. $\frac{15}{12}$ __=__ $\frac{20}{16}$ 18. $2\frac{1}{5}$ __<__ $2\frac{3}{10}$ 19. $4\frac{3}{8}$ __>__ 4 20. 2 ____ $\frac{12}{7}$

Write in order from least to greatest.

21. $\frac{3}{8}$, $\frac{1}{7}$, $\frac{1}{2}$ _____   22. $\frac{2}{3}$, $\frac{1}{3}$, $\frac{7}{10}$ _____

23. $3\frac{5}{8}$, $3\frac{1}{2}$, $3\frac{3}{8}$ _____   24. $12\frac{1}{8}$, $12\frac{3}{10}$, $12\frac{1}{4}$ _____

25. $\frac{2}{3}$, $\frac{3}{4}$, $\frac{1}{6}$ _____   26. $2\frac{7}{8}$, $2\frac{1}{2}$, $2\frac{1}{3}$ _____

Write in order from greatest to least.

27. $\frac{1}{3}$, $\frac{1}{5}$, $\frac{4}{15}$ _____   28. $\frac{1}{8}$, $\frac{9}{16}$, $\frac{1}{4}$ _____

29. $\frac{1}{12}$, $\frac{3}{4}$, $\frac{3}{12}$ _____   30. $\frac{7}{4}$, $1\frac{1}{3}$, $1\frac{4}{9}$ _____

31. $\frac{1}{4}$, $\frac{1}{5}$, $\frac{3}{10}$ _____   32. $5\frac{5}{6}$, $5\frac{3}{4}$, $5\frac{11}{12}$ _____

Problem Solving

33. Adele and Morris took turns driving their car across the country. Adele drove $\frac{2}{3}$ of the way, and Morris drove $\frac{4}{12}$ of the way. Who drove less? _____

Use with Lesson 4-10, pages 152–153 in the Student Book.
Then go to Lesson 4-11, pages 154–155 in the Student Book.

Problem-Solving Strategy: Make an Organized List

Name _____

Date _____

Amos, Beth, Carl, and Dawn want to ride on the Ferris wheel. There is one empty car and only 2 people can ride in a car. In how many different ways can 2 friends ride in the empty car?

Amos	⟷	Beth
Amos	⟷	Carl
Amos	⟷	Dawn
Beth	⟷	Carl
Beth	⟷	Dawn
Carl	⟷	Dawn

Make an organized list of the possible pairs. Count the number of pairs.

There are 6 ways that 2 friends can ride in the empty car.

Solve. Do your work on a separate sheet of paper.

1. Nico, Paul, and Mary line up single file. How many different ways can they line up?

2. Hidori, Cherie, Ellis, and Morgan are running a race. In how many different ways might they finish the race?

3. You have nickels, dimes, and quarters to make a call that costs 75¢. How many different combinations of coins can you use to pay for the call?

4. Natasha has a red sweater and a white sweater. She can wear them with a blue skirt, yellow skirt, or black skirt. How many different outfits can she make?

5. You are at a party where crackers and cheese spreads are among the refreshments. You can choose any one of 4 kinds of spreads and put on it any one of 3 kinds of crackers. How many different choices do you have?

6. Julio, Barry, Lianne, Carl, Dennis, and Elena visit the amusement park. They want to ride on the bumper cars. Each car can hold two people. How many different ways can the friends ride together in a car?

7. Oscar, Max, Norma, Pasha, and Hank want to ride horses. There are 4 horses—Spanky, Rita, Buttercup, and Ebony. In how many different ways can the horses be assigned if Max and Oscar only ride on Spanky?

8. A building has 2 front doors, 2 doors on the left side, 2 back doors, and 2 doors on the right side. How many different ways can you enter and leave the building if you enter through a front door and then leave through any of the other doors?

Use with Lesson 4-11, pages 154–155 in the Student Book.
Then go to Lesson 4-12, pages 156–157 in the Student Book.

49

Problem-Solving Application: Mixed Review

Name _____

Date _____

Solve each problem and explain the method you used. If needed, do all your work on a separate sheet of paper.

Read ▸ Plan ▸ Solve ▸ Check

Strategy File

Use These Strategies
More Than One Solution
Use a Graph
Use More Than One Step
Logical Reasoning
Make an Organized List

1. Suki has 2 rings: one silver, one gold. She has 3 bracelets: one beaded, one leather, and one platinum. If Suki only wears one of each at a time, how many different ways can Suki accessorize?

   _____

2. The product of a 2-digit number and a 1-digit number other than 1 is greater than 20 and less than 25. What are all the possible combinations of numbers?

   _____

3. Robert has 5 coins that are worth 37¢ in all. Only 1 coin is a quarter. What are the other coins?

   _____

4. Bill spent $\frac{8}{10}$ hours reading. Carol spent $\frac{10}{8}$ hours reading. Sandy spent $1\frac{1}{5}$ hours reading. Who read for the greatest amount of time? How long did they read altogether?

   _____

5. Sara, Dirk and Dusty went for a walk. One walked $2\frac{1}{6}$ miles, one walked $\frac{9}{4}$ miles, and the other walked $\frac{25}{12}$ miles. If Sara walked the least and Dirk walked the most, how far did Dusty walk?

   _____

6. There are 27 trophies in the school display case. 12 are for swimming. What fraction of the trophies, in lowest terms, are not for swimming?

   _____

7. There are equivalent fractions for $\frac{1}{4}$ with a numerator between 3 and 6. What are the fractions?

   _____

Use the graph at the left to solve.

8. What fraction of Sal's class walks to school? Express your answer in lowest terms.

   _____

9. What fraction of Sal's class takes the bus to school? Express your answer in lowest terms and greater terms.

   _____

Sal's Class—Ways to Get to School

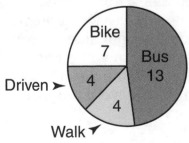

Bike 7
Bus 13
Driven 4
Walk 4

Use with Lesson 4-12, pages 156–157 in the Student Book.

Fraction Sums

Name _____

Date _____

$\frac{4}{9} + \frac{2}{9} = \frac{4+2}{9}$

$= \frac{6}{9} = \frac{2}{3}$ ← simplest form

Rename with like denominators. Then add.

$\frac{1}{8} = \frac{1 \times 3}{8 \times 3} = \frac{3}{24}$ Think: LCD is 24.

$+ \frac{1}{3} = \frac{1 \times 8}{3 \times 8} = \frac{8}{24}$

$\frac{11}{24}$ ← simplest form

Add. Write each sum in simplest form.

1. $\frac{5}{6}$
$+ \frac{5}{6}$

2. $\frac{3}{10}$
$+ \frac{1}{10}$

3. $\frac{4}{7}$
$+ \frac{3}{7}$

4. $\frac{8}{9}$
$+ \frac{4}{9}$

5. $\frac{11}{20}$
$+ \frac{3}{20}$

6. $\frac{2}{3}$
$+ \frac{2}{15}$

7. $\frac{2}{3}$
$+ \frac{1}{7}$

8. $\frac{4}{9}$
$+ \frac{3}{6}$

9. $\frac{1}{4}$
$+ \frac{1}{5}$

10. $\frac{3}{10}$
$+ \frac{1}{2}$

11. $\frac{3}{4}$
$+ \frac{5}{12}$

12. $\frac{2}{3}$
$+ \frac{4}{5}$

13. $\frac{5}{7}$
$+ \frac{3}{4}$

14. $\frac{3}{5}$
$+ \frac{7}{10}$

15. $\frac{8}{15}$
$+ \frac{5}{6}$

16. $\frac{5}{18} + \frac{4}{18} = $ _____

17. $\frac{3}{7} + \frac{5}{7} = $ _____

18. $\frac{1}{10} + \frac{7}{10} = $ _____

19. $\frac{1}{6} + \frac{1}{4} = $ _____

20. $\frac{1}{4} + \frac{5}{8} = $ _____

21. $\frac{2}{3} + \frac{1}{18} = $ _____

22. $\frac{4}{9} + \frac{2}{5} = $ _____

23. $\frac{3}{8} + \frac{2}{7} = $ _____

24. $\frac{3}{4} + \frac{1}{8} = $ _____

Problem Solving

25. Helena walks $\frac{5}{8}$ mi to her friend's house and then $\frac{1}{4}$ mi to school. How far does she walk? _____

26. What is the sum of three fourths and seven fourths? _____

Ⅽ Use with Lessons 5-1 and 5-2, pages 164–167 in the Student Book.
Ⅽ Then go to Lesson 5-1A, pages 185–186 in this Workbook.

Add Three Fractions

Name _____

Date _____

Add: $\frac{2}{3} + \frac{5}{6} + \frac{4}{9} = n$

Rename the fractions with like denominators.

Think: LCD is 18.

Then add.

$$\frac{2}{3} = \frac{2 \times 6}{3 \times 6} = \frac{12}{18}$$

$$\frac{5}{6} = \frac{5 \times 3}{6 \times 3} = \frac{15}{18}$$

$$+\ \frac{4}{9} = \frac{4 \times 2}{9 \times 2} = \frac{8}{18}$$

$$\frac{35}{18} \longrightarrow n = 1\frac{17}{18}$$

Add. Write each sum in simplest form.

1. $\frac{1}{7}$
    $\frac{3}{7}$
    $+\ \frac{1}{7}$

2. $\frac{2}{11}$
    $\frac{4}{11}$
    $+\ \frac{3}{11}$

3. $\frac{6}{14}$
    $\frac{4}{14}$
    $+\ \frac{4}{14}$

4. $\frac{2}{15}$
    $\frac{3}{15}$
    $+\ \frac{12}{15}$

5. $\frac{5}{17}$
    $\frac{4}{17}$
    $+\ \frac{7}{17}$

6. $\frac{3}{12}$
    $\frac{2}{3}$
    $+\ \frac{1}{4}$

7. $\frac{1}{2}$
    $\frac{1}{10}$
    $+\ \frac{1}{5}$

8. $\frac{2}{9}$
    $\frac{1}{6}$
    $+\ \frac{4}{18}$

9. $\frac{1}{3}$
    $\frac{3}{7}$
    $+\ \frac{4}{21}$

10. $\frac{1}{4}$
    $\frac{3}{16}$
    $+\ \frac{2}{8}$

11. $\frac{3}{10} + \frac{1}{5} + \frac{4}{15} =$ _____

12. $\frac{3}{4} + \frac{7}{12} + \frac{1}{6} =$ _____

13. $\frac{2}{9} + \frac{3}{9} + \frac{1}{3} =$ _____

14. $\frac{3}{4} + \frac{1}{2} + \frac{3}{8} =$ _____

15. $\frac{1}{5} + \frac{1}{4} + \frac{7}{10} =$ _____

16. $\frac{7}{18} + \frac{1}{3} + \frac{5}{6} =$ _____

Find the value of n. Then check by adding.

17. $\left(\frac{5}{8} + \frac{1}{8}\right) + \frac{3}{8} = \frac{5}{8} + \left(\frac{1}{8} + n\right)$

    $n =$ _____

18. $\left(\frac{2}{3} + n\right) + \frac{3}{4} = \left(\frac{3}{4} + \frac{1}{2}\right) + \frac{2}{3}$

    $n =$ _____

Problem Solving

19. A family used $\frac{5}{8}$, $\frac{3}{4}$, and $\frac{1}{2}$ gallons of water on 3 different days. How many gallons of water did the family use in all?

    _____

52

Use with Lesson 5-3, pages 168–169 in the Student Book.
C Then go to Lesson 5-4, pages 170–171 in the Student Book.

Copyright © by William H. Sadlier, Inc. All rights reserved.

Add Mixed Numbers

Name _____

Date _____

Find the LCD. Add the fractions.	→	Add the whole numbers.	→	Write the sum in simplest form.
$3\frac{1}{5} = 3\frac{2}{10}$ $+\ 5\frac{3}{10} = +\ 5\frac{3}{10}$ $\overline{\frac{5}{10}}$		$3\frac{1}{5}$ $+\ 5\frac{3}{10}$ $\overline{8\frac{5}{10}}$		$3\frac{1}{5}$ $+\ 5\frac{3}{10}$ $\overline{8\frac{5}{10} = 8\frac{1}{2}}$

Add. Write each sum in simplest form.

1. $2\frac{2}{5}$
$+\ 7\frac{1}{5}$

2. $5\frac{2}{15}$
$+\ 7\frac{1}{5}$

3. $3\frac{2}{9}$
$+\ 4\frac{4}{9}$

4. $\frac{1}{3}$
$+\ 2\frac{1}{6}$

5. $14\frac{7}{9}$
$+\ 9\frac{1}{18}$

6. $4\frac{8}{12}$
$+\ 2\frac{3}{4}$

7. $1\frac{1}{4}$
$3\frac{1}{4}$
$+\ 2\frac{3}{4}$

8. $4\frac{2}{12}$
$3\frac{1}{12}$
$+\ 1\frac{7}{12}$

9. $5\frac{1}{3}$
$3\frac{1}{12}$
$+\ 4\frac{1}{6}$

10. $7\frac{1}{6}$
$\frac{1}{3}$
$+\ 2\frac{1}{2}$

11. $8\frac{1}{3}$
$5\frac{1}{12}$
$+\ 3\frac{3}{4}$

12. $9\frac{1}{7}$
$1\frac{2}{21}$
$+\ \frac{2}{3}$

13. $7\frac{3}{5} + 5\frac{2}{15} =$ _____

14. $9\frac{2}{5} + 2\frac{7}{20} =$ _____

15. $4\frac{1}{3} + 1\frac{2}{9} + 1\frac{5}{18} =$ _____

16. $6\frac{1}{5} + 5\frac{4}{6} =$ _____

17. $\frac{1}{5} + 3\frac{2}{10} =$ _____

18. $4\frac{2}{5} + 2\frac{1}{4} + 3\frac{1}{20} =$ _____

19. $3\frac{3}{4} + 8\frac{1}{16} =$ _____

20. $5\frac{1}{4} + 7\frac{3}{8} =$ _____

21. $7\frac{2}{15} + 3\frac{3}{10} + 1\frac{1}{5} =$ _____

Problem Solving

22. Amiel weighs $12\frac{1}{2}$ pounds and Marthe weighs $21\frac{1}{4}$ pounds. What is the total weight of both babies?

_____

23. Nan bought $6\frac{1}{8}$ pounds of fish. Hank bought $3\frac{1}{2}$ pounds of fish. How much fish did the two buy altogether?

_____

24. Ms. Johnson bought $2\frac{3}{8}$ yd of fabric to make a dress and $1\frac{1}{3}$ yd of fabric to make a shirt. How much fabric did she buy?

_____

◯ Use with Lesson 5-4, pages 170–171 in the Student Book.
◯ Then go to Lesson 5-5, pages 172–173 in the Student Book.

53

Rename Mixed-Number Sums

Name _____

Date _____

$8\frac{2}{3} + 4\frac{7}{9} = n$

$$8\frac{2}{3} = \quad 8\frac{6}{9}$$
$$+ 4\frac{7}{9} = \quad + 4\frac{7}{9}$$
$$12\frac{13}{9} = 12 + 1\frac{4}{9} = 13\frac{4}{9}$$

$$n = 13\frac{4}{9}$$

$1\frac{5}{12} + 2\frac{1}{4} + 1\frac{1}{3} = n$

$$1\frac{5}{12} = \quad 1\frac{5}{12}$$
$$2\frac{1}{4} = \quad 2\frac{3}{12}$$
$$+ 1\frac{1}{3} = \quad + 1\frac{4}{12}$$
$$4\frac{12}{12} = 4 + 1 = 5$$

$$n = 5$$

Rename each as a whole number or a mixed number in simplest form.

1. $\frac{5}{3}$ _____
2. $6\frac{2}{2}$ _____
3. $5\frac{6}{4}$ _____
4. $6\frac{7}{4}$ _____
5. $8\frac{12}{10}$ _____

6. $7\frac{18}{14}$ _____
7. $2\frac{16}{15}$ _____
8. $5\frac{15}{11}$ _____
9. $7\frac{20}{15}$ _____
10. $42\frac{20}{20}$ _____

Add.

11. $\begin{array}{r} 8\frac{2}{3} \\ + 3\frac{2}{3} \\ \hline \end{array}$
12. $\begin{array}{r} 6\frac{4}{5} \\ + 2\frac{3}{5} \\ \hline \end{array}$
13. $\begin{array}{r} 4\frac{5}{8} \\ + 7\frac{3}{8} \\ \hline \end{array}$
14. $\begin{array}{r} 4\frac{7}{24} \\ + 7\frac{5}{6} \\ \hline \end{array}$
15. $\begin{array}{r} 9\frac{3}{4} \\ + 5\frac{1}{4} \\ \hline \end{array}$

16. $\begin{array}{r} 3\frac{3}{5} \\ + 3\frac{5}{12} \\ \hline \end{array}$
17. $\begin{array}{r} 2\frac{2}{15} \\ + 3\frac{3}{15} \\ \hline \end{array}$
18. $\begin{array}{r} 1\frac{4}{7} \\ + 5\frac{1}{2} \\ \hline \end{array}$
19. $\begin{array}{r} 13\frac{11}{12} \\ + 4\frac{5}{6} \\ \hline \end{array}$
20. $\begin{array}{r} 12\frac{7}{18} \\ + 3\frac{7}{9} \\ \hline \end{array}$

21. $\begin{array}{r} 2\frac{5}{8} \\ 4\frac{1}{2} \\ + 3\frac{3}{16} \\ \hline \end{array}$
22. $\begin{array}{r} 4\frac{1}{3} \\ 6\frac{5}{12} \\ + 1\frac{1}{4} \\ \hline \end{array}$
23. $\begin{array}{r} 3\frac{3}{20} \\ 4\frac{1}{5} \\ + 3\frac{3}{4} \\ \hline \end{array}$
24. $\begin{array}{r} 5\frac{2}{7} \\ 2\frac{4}{14} \\ + \frac{5}{7} \\ \hline \end{array}$
25. $\begin{array}{r} 1\frac{5}{15} \\ 8\frac{1}{10} \\ + 6\frac{5}{6} \\ \hline \end{array}$

26. $1\frac{3}{8} + 6\frac{2}{3} + 4\frac{7}{24} =$ _____

27. $3\frac{2}{5} + 2\frac{7}{15} + 5\frac{3}{10} =$ _____

Problem Solving

28. Charlene mixed $2\frac{5}{8}$ gal of lemonade with $3\frac{3}{4}$ gal of seltzer to make punch. How much punch did she make? _____

Use with Lesson 5-5, pages 172–173 in the Student Book.
Then go to Lessons 5-6 and 5-7, pages 174–177 in the Student Book.

Fraction Differences

Name _____

Date _____

$$\frac{9}{4} - \frac{3}{4} = \frac{9-3}{4} = \frac{6}{4} = 1\frac{1}{2}$$

simplest form

Rename the fractions with like denominators. Then subtract.

$$\frac{7}{10} \qquad\qquad = \frac{7}{10}$$
$$-\frac{1}{5} = \frac{1 \times 2}{5 \times 2} = \frac{2}{10}$$
$$\frac{5}{10} = \frac{1}{2}$$

Think: LCD is 10.

simplest form

Subtract. Write the difference in simplest form.

1. $\frac{7}{12}$ $-\frac{1}{12}$

2. $\frac{19}{13}$ $-\frac{5}{13}$

3. $\frac{23}{11}$ $-\frac{10}{11}$

4. $\frac{4}{9}$ $-\frac{4}{9}$

5. $\frac{4}{5}$ $-\frac{3}{5}$

6. $\frac{9}{10}$ $-\frac{4}{5}$

7. $\frac{7}{10}$ $-\frac{2}{5}$

8. $\frac{8}{9}$ $-\frac{1}{3}$

9. $\frac{5}{8}$ $-\frac{1}{4}$

10. $\frac{7}{9}$ $-\frac{2}{3}$

11. $\frac{11}{12}$ $-\frac{5}{6}$

12. $\frac{5}{6}$ $-\frac{1}{3}$

13. $\frac{7}{16}$ $-\frac{1}{4}$

14. $\frac{8}{15}$ $-\frac{1}{3}$

15. $\frac{9}{10}$ $-\frac{1}{2}$

16. $\frac{31}{25} - \frac{17}{25} =$ _____

17. $\frac{15}{7} - \frac{2}{7} =$ _____

18. $\frac{10}{16} - \frac{3}{8} =$ _____

19. $\frac{5}{8} - \frac{3}{40} =$ _____

Problem Solving

20. Josefina spent $\frac{1}{4}$ hour exercising and another $\frac{3}{20}$ hour shooting baskets. How much more time did she spend exercising? _____

21. Gareth ate $\frac{3}{8}$ c of soup. Dan ate $\frac{1}{4}$ c of soup. Who ate more soup? How much more? _____

Use with Lessons 5-6 and 5-7, pages 174–177 in the Student Book.
Then go to Lesson 5-6A, pages 187–188 in this Workbook.

More Subtraction of Fractions

Name _____

Date _____

Subtract: $\frac{5}{6} - \frac{6}{8} = n$

Rename the fractions with like denominators.

Think: LCD is 24.

Then subtract.

$$\frac{5}{6} = \frac{5 \times 4}{6 \times 4} = \frac{20}{24}$$

$$-\frac{6}{8} = \frac{6 \times 3}{8 \times 3} = \frac{18}{24}$$

$$\frac{2}{24} = \frac{1}{12} \longleftarrow \text{simplest form} \qquad n = \frac{1}{12}$$

Subtract.

1. $\frac{1}{6}$
   $-\frac{1}{10}$

2. $\frac{7}{10}$
   $-\frac{5}{12}$

3. $\frac{5}{6}$
   $-\frac{1}{8}$

4. $\frac{5}{8}$
   $-\frac{1}{20}$

5. $\frac{5}{8}$
   $-\frac{1}{3}$

6. $\frac{4}{5}$
   $-\frac{1}{2}$

7. $\frac{6}{11}$
   $-\frac{1}{2}$

8. $\frac{1}{12}$
   $-\frac{1}{15}$

9. $\frac{6}{7}$
   $-\frac{1}{3}$

10. $\frac{6}{10}$
   $-\frac{1}{4}$

11. $\frac{3}{4} - \frac{1}{3} =$ _____

12. $\frac{3}{8} - \frac{1}{5} =$ _____

13. $\frac{1}{2} - \frac{1}{7} =$ _____

14. $\frac{9}{10} - \frac{3}{4} =$ _____

Compare. Write <, =, or >.

15. $\frac{1}{2} - \frac{1}{3}$ _____ $\frac{1}{6} + \frac{1}{6}$

16. $\frac{1}{2} - \frac{1}{9}$ _____ $\frac{1}{3} + \frac{1}{18}$

Problem Solving

17. Esther had $\frac{7}{8}$ yd of ribbon. She cut off $\frac{1}{3}$ yd.

    How much ribbon did she have left? _____

18. In Guatemala, $\frac{6}{10}$ of an inch of rain fell in one week.

    In Honduras, $\frac{5}{8}$ of an inch fell in the same time.

    Where did more rain fall? How much more? _____

Use with Lesson 5-8, pages 178–179 in the Student Book.
Then go to Lesson 5-8A, pages 189–190 in this Workbook.

Subtract Mixed Numbers

Name _____

Date _____

$9\frac{5}{8}$

$-2\frac{1}{8}$

$7\frac{4}{8} = 7\frac{1}{2}$ ← simplest form

Remember: Subtract fractions, then subtract whole numbers.

$8\frac{5}{6} = 8\frac{20}{24}$

$-2\frac{2}{8} = -2\frac{6}{24}$

$6\frac{14}{24} = 6\frac{7}{12}$ ← simplest form

Think: LCD is 24.

Subtract.

1. $4\frac{7}{9}$
$-\ \ \frac{4}{9}$

2. $6\frac{8}{9}$
$-2\frac{2}{9}$

3. $7\frac{11}{12}$
$-5\frac{3}{12}$

4. $4\frac{7}{8}$
$-3\frac{5}{8}$

5. $9\frac{7}{20}$
$-4\frac{1}{20}$

6. $3\frac{13}{15}$
$-3\frac{5}{6}$

7. $7\frac{8}{9}$
$-5\frac{3}{4}$

8. $5\frac{9}{10}$
$-2\frac{3}{4}$

9. $8\frac{4}{7}$
$-8\frac{1}{3}$

10. $7\frac{5}{6}$
$-4\frac{2}{5}$

11. $8\frac{7}{8}$
$-3\frac{2}{7}$

12. $7\frac{4}{5}$
$-2\frac{1}{2}$

13. $5\frac{6}{12}$
$-1\frac{3}{7}$

14. $2\frac{9}{10}$
$-2\frac{1}{5}$

15. $4\frac{4}{15}$
$-3\frac{3}{30}$

Circle the letter of the correct answer.

16. $6\frac{7}{8} - 2\frac{7}{8}$ a. $4\frac{7}{8}$ b. 8 c. 4 d. 5

17. $8\frac{2}{3} - 1\frac{1}{15}$ a. $7\frac{8}{15}$ b. $7\frac{4}{5}$ c. $7\frac{1}{12}$ d. $7\frac{3}{5}$

18. $5\frac{2}{5} - 2\frac{1}{8}$ a. $3\frac{1}{3}$ b. $3\frac{1}{40}$ c. $3\frac{11}{40}$ d. $3\frac{1}{4}$

19. $5\frac{4}{7} - 4\frac{4}{7}$ a. $2\frac{1}{2}$ b. $2\frac{1}{7}$ c. $1\frac{2}{7}$ d. 1

Problem Solving

20. Clarissa bought $2\frac{2}{3}$ yd of wrapping paper. After wrapping a gift, she had $1\frac{1}{6}$ yd left. How much did she use? _____

21. Muni painted $4\frac{1}{2}$ feet of a $10\frac{3}{4}$ ft long fence. How much of the fence was not painted? _____

C Use with Lesson 5-9, pages 180–181 in the Student Book.
C Then go to Lesson 5-9A, pages 191–192 in this Workbook.

57

Subtraction With Renaming

Name _____

Date _____

Subtract: $8 - 3\frac{6}{8} = n$

$$8 \quad = 7\frac{8}{8}$$
$$- 3\frac{6}{8} = 3\frac{6}{8}$$
$$\overline{\qquad\qquad}$$
$$4\frac{2}{8} = 4\frac{1}{4}$$

$$8 = 7 + 1$$
$$= 7 + \frac{8}{8}$$
$$= 7\frac{8}{8}$$

simplest form

$$n = 4\frac{1}{4}$$

Rename each whole number as a mixed number.

1. $8 = 7\frac{}{3}$

2. $4 = 3\frac{}{6}$

3. $1 = \frac{}{8}$

4. $6 = 5\frac{}{4}$

5. $3 = 2\frac{}{2}$

6. $9 = 8\frac{}{10}$

7. $2 = 1\frac{}{9}$

8. $5 = 4\frac{}{7}$

Subtract.

9. $\begin{array}{r} 7 \\ - 4\frac{3}{4} \\ \hline \end{array}$

10. $\begin{array}{r} 10 \\ - 5\frac{3}{6} \\ \hline \end{array}$

11. $\begin{array}{r} 4 \\ - 1\frac{2}{10} \\ \hline \end{array}$

12. $\begin{array}{r} 6 \\ - 2\frac{5}{8} \\ \hline \end{array}$

13. $\begin{array}{r} 5 \\ - 3\frac{1}{3} \\ \hline \end{array}$

14. $\begin{array}{r} 4 \\ - 3\frac{2}{10} \\ \hline \end{array}$

15. $\begin{array}{r} 9 \\ - 7\frac{4}{5} \\ \hline \end{array}$

16. $\begin{array}{r} 2 \\ - 1\frac{8}{12} \\ \hline \end{array}$

17. $\begin{array}{r} 10 \\ - 3\frac{2}{8} \\ \hline \end{array}$

18. $\begin{array}{r} 7 \\ - 1\frac{9}{12} \\ \hline \end{array}$

19. $\begin{array}{r} 5 \\ - 4\frac{3}{5} \\ \hline \end{array}$

20. $\begin{array}{r} 6 \\ - 5\frac{1}{2} \\ \hline \end{array}$

21. $\begin{array}{r} 8 \\ - 6\frac{6}{10} \\ \hline \end{array}$

22. $\begin{array}{r} 12 \\ - 10\frac{2}{6} \\ \hline \end{array}$

23. $\begin{array}{r} 9 \\ - 5\frac{3}{8} \\ \hline \end{array}$

Find the difference.

24. $4 - \frac{1}{5} =$ _____

25. $1 - \frac{5}{6} =$ _____

26. $8 - 7\frac{2}{9} =$ _____

27. $6 - 2\frac{2}{3} =$ _____

28. $17 - 6\frac{7}{10} =$ _____

29. $5 - \frac{5}{6} =$ _____

30. $3 - \frac{6}{8} =$ _____

31. $10 - \frac{3}{9} =$ _____

32. $2 - \frac{8}{10} =$ _____

Problem Solving

33. Charise had 10 ft of twine. She used $4\frac{3}{4}$ ft to tie up a package. Does she have enough twine left to tie up another package if she needs $6\frac{1}{4}$ ft of twine? _____

58

Use with Lesson 5-10, pages 182–183 in the Student Book.
Then go to Lesson 5-11, pages 184–185 in the Student Book.

More Renaming in Subtraction

Name _____

Date _____

Subtract: $5\frac{1}{3} - 3\frac{5}{6} = n$

$$5\frac{1}{3} = 5\frac{4}{12}$$
$$-3\frac{5}{6} = -3\frac{10}{12}$$

$$5\frac{4}{12} = 4 + 1 + \frac{4}{12}$$
$$= 4 + \frac{12}{12} + \frac{4}{12}$$
$$= 4 + \frac{16}{12}$$

$$4\frac{16}{12}$$
$$-3\frac{10}{12}$$
$$\overline{1\frac{6}{12}} = 1\frac{1}{2} \quad n = 1\frac{1}{2}$$

Rename each mixed number.

1. $6\frac{3}{4} = 5 + 1 + \frac{3}{4}$

$= 5 + \frac{4}{4} + \frac{3}{4}$

$= 5\frac{}{4}$

2. $4\frac{7}{10} = \underline{\ \ } + 1 + \frac{7}{10}$

$= \underline{\ \ } + \frac{10}{10} + \frac{7}{10}$

$= \underline{\ \ }\frac{}{10}$

3. $9\frac{5}{8} = 8 + \frac{}{8} + \frac{5}{8}$

$= \underline{\ \ } + \frac{}{8} + \frac{5}{8}$

$= \underline{\ \ } + \frac{}{8}$

Subtract.

4. $\begin{array}{r} 6\frac{3}{4} \\ -\ 2\frac{7}{8} \\ \hline \end{array}$

5. $\begin{array}{r} 5\frac{1}{6} \\ -\ 2\frac{1}{2} \\ \hline \end{array}$

6. $\begin{array}{r} 5\frac{1}{4} \\ -\ \frac{3}{8} \\ \hline \end{array}$

7. $\begin{array}{r} 9\frac{2}{3} \\ -\ 7\frac{5}{6} \\ \hline \end{array}$

8. $\begin{array}{r} 7\frac{1}{2} \\ -\ \frac{4}{5} \\ \hline \end{array}$

9. $\begin{array}{r} 4\frac{3}{4} \\ -\ 3\frac{5}{6} \\ \hline \end{array}$

10. $\begin{array}{r} 8\frac{1}{3} \\ -\ 4\frac{7}{8} \\ \hline \end{array}$

11. $\begin{array}{r} 3\frac{3}{9} \\ -\ 1\frac{5}{6} \\ \hline \end{array}$

12. $\begin{array}{r} 11\frac{1}{12} \\ -\ 2\frac{5}{12} \\ \hline \end{array}$

13. $\begin{array}{r} 8\frac{1}{4} \\ -\ 1\frac{9}{14} \\ \hline \end{array}$

14. $\begin{array}{r} 6\frac{5}{8} \\ -\ 1\frac{4}{5} \\ \hline \end{array}$

15. $\begin{array}{r} 7\frac{5}{9} \\ -\ 6\frac{5}{6} \\ \hline \end{array}$

16. $\begin{array}{r} 9\frac{5}{6} \\ -\ 2\frac{7}{8} \\ \hline \end{array}$

17. $\begin{array}{r} 12\frac{5}{7} \\ -\ 9\frac{5}{6} \\ \hline \end{array}$

18. $\begin{array}{r} 9\frac{1}{8} \\ -\ 3\frac{5}{12} \\ \hline \end{array}$

19. $8\frac{2}{3} - 6\frac{3}{4} =$ _____

20. $4\frac{1}{5} - \frac{4}{5} =$ _____

21. $3\frac{3}{8} - 2\frac{9}{10} =$ _____

22. $10\frac{1}{5} - \frac{12}{15} =$ _____

23. $7\frac{1}{2} - \frac{9}{12} =$ _____

24. $9\frac{1}{4} - \frac{5}{6} =$ _____

Problem Solving

25. Mr. Lin drove $18\frac{1}{2}$ mi to work. Then he moved $6\frac{8}{10}$ mi closer to work. How far does he drive to work now? _____

C Use with Lesson 5-11, pages 184–185 in the Student Book.
C Then go to Lesson 5-12, pages 186–187 in the Student Book.

59

Estimate Sums and Differences of Mixed Numbers

Name _____

Date _____

Estimate the sum or difference by rounding.	**Use front-end estimation.**
Round each fraction to the nearest whole number. Then add or subtract.	Add the whole number parts, then adjust the estimate with the fraction parts.

$$8\frac{1}{3} + 2\frac{5}{7} + 11\frac{3}{10} \qquad\qquad 9\frac{3}{4} - 2\frac{4}{5}$$

$$\downarrow \quad\quad \downarrow \quad\quad \downarrow \qquad\qquad\qquad \downarrow \quad\quad \downarrow$$

$$8 + 3 + 11 = 22 \qquad 10 - 3 = 7$$

$$7\frac{1}{5} + 6\frac{9}{10}$$

$$\downarrow \quad\quad \downarrow \quad\quad\searrow$$

$$7 + 6 + 1 = 14$$

Estimate the sum or difference by rounding.

1. $4\frac{7}{12}$
   $+\ 3\frac{2}{3}$

2. $8\frac{3}{10}$
   $+\ 2\frac{2}{5}$

3. $17\frac{5}{7}$
   $+\ 4\frac{1}{2}$

4. $13\frac{5}{8}$
   $+\ 4\frac{1}{8}$

5. $9\frac{2}{5}$
   $+\ 3\frac{4}{7}$

6. $16\frac{1}{2}$
   $+\ 4\frac{3}{4}$

7. $18\frac{7}{12}$
   $-\ 1\frac{5}{12}$

8. $9\frac{9}{10}$
   $-\ 4\frac{4}{5}$

9. $4\frac{4}{5}$
   $-\ \frac{2}{3}$

10. $13\frac{3}{4}$
    $-\ 6\frac{1}{2}$

11. $7\frac{1}{6}$
    $-\ 3\frac{5}{6}$

12. $6\frac{5}{9}$
    $-\ 2\frac{12}{19}$

Estimate the sum or difference. Use front-end estimation.

13. $4\frac{1}{3}$
    $+\ 2\frac{7}{12}$

14. $8\frac{2}{5}$
    $+\ 4\frac{5}{6}$

15. $12\frac{1}{4}$
    $+\ 5\frac{3}{4}$

16. $6\frac{1}{8}$
    $+\ 2\frac{7}{11}$

17. $7\frac{2}{9}$
    $+\ 2\frac{1}{2}$

18. $4\frac{2}{3}$
    $+\ 9\frac{5}{8}$

19. $19\frac{4}{5}$
    $-\ 12\frac{7}{8}$

20. $16\frac{7}{9}$
    $-\ 4\frac{4}{11}$

21. $8\frac{4}{9}$
    $-\ 6\frac{2}{3}$

22. $11\frac{4}{5}$
    $-\ 2\frac{1}{5}$

23. $13\frac{7}{10}$
    $-\ 9\frac{4}{9}$

24. $17\frac{7}{9}$
    $-\ 6\frac{3}{10}$

Choose a method to estimate the sum or difference. Then estimate.

25. $12\frac{2}{5} + 3\frac{2}{3} + 3\frac{7}{9}$ _____

26. $14\frac{1}{2} + 5\frac{3}{11} + 2\frac{4}{13}$ _____

27. $9\frac{1}{7} + 8\frac{4}{5} + 3\frac{3}{8}$ _____

28. $18\frac{2}{3} + 7\frac{1}{6} + 3\frac{7}{10}$ _____

29. $22\frac{1}{3} - 17\frac{1}{2}$ _____

30. $14\frac{7}{11} - 4\frac{2}{11}$ _____

31. $8\frac{3}{5} - 1\frac{11}{12}$ _____

32. $19\frac{9}{10} - 4\frac{8}{9}$ _____

33. $17\frac{3}{8} - 8\frac{1}{7}$ _____

Use with Lesson 5-12, pages 186–187 in the Student Book.
Then go to Lesson 5-13, pages 188–189 in the Student Book.

Problem-Solving Strategy: Work Backward

Name _____

Date _____

Lisa bought a blouse for $24.95 and a scarf for $9.95.
She gave the clerk 2 bills and received $5.10 change.
What bills did Lisa give the clerk?

| Start with the change and work backward. | $5.10 |

Add the amount she paid for the scarf. $5.10 + $9.95 = $15.05

Add the amount she paid for the blouse. $15.05 + $24.95 = $40.00

Lisa gave $40.00 to the clerk.

Two 20-dollar bills equal $40.00.

Lisa gave two 20-dollar bills to the clerk.

Solve. Do your work on a separate sheet of paper.

1. Francine and Franklin baked some granola bars. The first customer bought $\frac{1}{2}$ dozen. The next customer bought 2 dozen. The third customer bought $1\frac{1}{2}$ dozen. There were 1 dozen left. How many granola bars did Francine and Franklin bake?

2. A bus leaves the school with some students on board. At the first stop, 4 students get off. At the second stop, 6 students get off. At each of the next 3 stops, 8 students get off. There are 10 students still on the bus. How many students were on the bus when it left the school?

3. Marlena says that if you add 8 to her age and then divide by 2, the answer is 10. How old is Marlena?

4. Sean says that if you double his age and then add 2, the answer is 30. How old is Sean?

5. Carmella spent $6.95 for a book and $1.50 for a birthday card. She had $1.55 left. How much money did she have before she bought anything?

6. Brendan gathered seashells on the beach. He gave 7 to his younger sister and 7 to his older brother. He has 17 left. How many shells did he gather?

7. Gary baked some bran muffins. His mother ate 1, his father ate 2, his sister and brother each ate 1, and his friends ate 8. There are 11 muffins left. How many did Gary bake?

8. Patty ties a bow on each basket she is making. She cuts 2 pieces of ribbon that are $1\frac{1}{2}$ feet long each and 2 pieces that are $1\frac{3}{4}$ feet long each. She has $8\frac{1}{2}$ feet of ribbon left. How much ribbon did she have in the beginning?

C Use with Lesson 5-13, pages 188–189 in the Student Book.

C Then go to Lesson 5-14, pages 190–191 in the Student Book.

61

Problem-Solving Applications: Mixed Review

Name _____

Date _____

Read ▶ Plan ▶ Solve ▶ Check

Solve each problem and explain the method you used. If needed, do all your work on a separate sheet of paper.

Strategy File

Use These Strategies
Work Backward
Guess and Test
Use More Than One Step
Logical Reasoning
Find a Pattern
Use a Graph

1. Sal, Ron, and Jose are long-distance runners. One ran $14\frac{4}{8}$ mi, another ran $13\frac{5}{6}$ mi, and the other ran $14\frac{4}{5}$ mi. If you double Ron's distance it is a whole number. Jose ran the farthest. How far did each run?

   _____

2. Sandy worked $5\frac{1}{3}$ hours on Friday. If she worked 14 hours for the weekend and worked $4\frac{1}{2}$ hours on Sunday, how much did she work on Saturday?

   _____

3. Lois used $\frac{3}{5}$ of a can of tuna in the afternoon and $\frac{1}{4}$ of that can in the evening. At the end of the day, how much of the can was left?

4. It was $68\frac{1}{2}°$ at 6 A.M. If the temperature rose $1\frac{1}{2}°$ every hour, what was the temperature at 2 P.M?

   _____

5. Avi's bike and Todd's bike together weigh 74 lbs. Todd's bike weighs $6\frac{1}{2}$ lbs more than Avi's. How much does each bike weigh?

   _____

6. Gia's friends drank $3\frac{1}{3}$ gallons of punch at a party, and then another $\frac{1}{2}$ gallon the next morning. If Gia has $2\frac{1}{3}$ gallons of punch left, how much did she buy originally?

   _____

7. Yuri got to the movie 20 minutes early. If the movie starts at 5:30 and it took him half an hour to walk from his house to the theatre, what time did he leave his house?

   _____

Sale of Cookies at the Fair

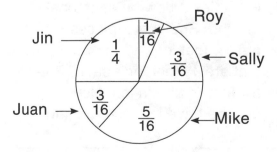

Use the graph at left to solve.

8. What fractional part did Jin and Sally sell together?

   _____

9. If Juan sold 30 cookies, how many did Mike sell?

   _____

Use with Lesson 5-14, pages 190–191 in the Student Book.

Multiply Fractions

Name _____

Date _____

Find: $\frac{1}{2}$ of $\frac{1}{3} = n$

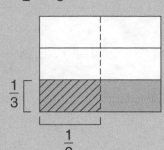

$\frac{1}{3}$ [ ] $\frac{1}{2}$ of $\frac{1}{3} = \frac{1}{6}$

$\frac{1}{2}$ $n = \frac{1}{6}$

Multiply: $\frac{2}{3} \times \frac{2}{5} = n$

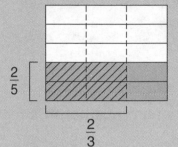

$\frac{2}{5}$ [ ] $\frac{2}{3} \times \frac{2}{5} = \frac{4}{15}$

$\frac{2}{3}$ $n = \frac{4}{15}$

Use the diagram to complete each statement.

1.
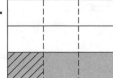

$\frac{3}{4}$ of $\frac{1}{3} =$ ____

2.
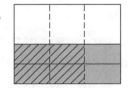

$\frac{2}{3}$ of $\frac{1}{4} =$ ____

3.
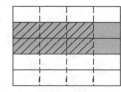

$\frac{2}{5}$ of $\frac{1}{4} =$ ____

4.
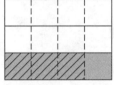

$\frac{2}{3} \times \frac{2}{3} =$ ____

5.
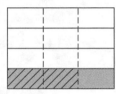

$\frac{1}{5} \times \frac{1}{4} =$ ____

6.

____ $\times \frac{4}{5} = \frac{4}{15}$

7.
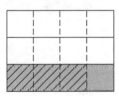

$\frac{3}{4} \times$ ____ $= \frac{3}{12}$

8.
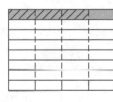

____ $\times$ ____ $=$ ____

9.
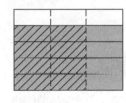

____ $\times$ ____ $=$ ____

Find the diagram that matches each statement. Then complete.

10. $\frac{3}{4}$ of $\frac{2}{5} =$ ____

11. $\frac{1}{4}$ of $\frac{2}{3} =$ ____

12. $\frac{1}{3}$ of $\frac{1}{3} =$ ____

13. $\frac{2}{3}$ of $\frac{1}{2} =$ ____

a.
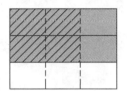

b.
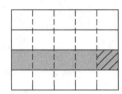

c.
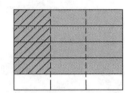

d.
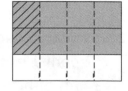

Use with Lesson 6-1, pages 198–199 in the Student Book.
Then go to Lesson 6-2, pages 200–201 in the Student Book.

Multiply Fractions by Fractions

Name _____

Date _____

Multiply: $\frac{2}{3} \times \frac{1}{4} = n$

$$\frac{2}{3} \times \frac{1}{4} = \frac{2 \times 1}{3 \times 4} = \frac{2}{12}$$

$$n = \frac{2}{12} = \frac{1}{6} \longleftarrow \boxed{\text{simplest form}}$$

Multiply. Write each product in simplest form.

1. $\frac{1}{2} \times \frac{3}{4} =$ _____

2. $\frac{5}{6} \times \frac{1}{2} =$ _____

3. $\frac{1}{2} \times \frac{2}{5} =$ _____

4. $\frac{2}{3} \times \frac{1}{3} =$ _____

5. $\frac{3}{4} \times \frac{1}{3} =$ _____

6. $\frac{1}{3} \times \frac{1}{4} =$ _____

7. $\frac{4}{5} \times \frac{3}{4} =$ _____

8. $\frac{1}{4} \times \frac{2}{5} =$ _____

9. $\frac{3}{5} \times \frac{1}{2} =$ _____

10. $\frac{1}{9} \times \frac{2}{3} =$ _____

11. $\frac{2}{3} \times \frac{3}{4} =$ _____

12. $\frac{3}{7} \times \frac{1}{4} =$ _____

Compare. Write <, =, or >.

13. $\frac{1}{3} \times \frac{1}{5}$ ____ $\frac{1}{4} \times \frac{1}{3}$

14. $\frac{1}{2} \times \frac{1}{2}$ ____ $\frac{3}{4} \times \frac{1}{6}$

15. $\frac{1}{2} \times \frac{2}{3}$ ____ $\frac{2}{4} \times \frac{2}{3}$

16. $\frac{3}{4} \times \frac{1}{3}$ ____ $\frac{3}{5} \times \frac{1}{2}$

17. $\frac{3}{6} \times \frac{3}{6}$ ____ $\frac{1}{2} \times \frac{1}{2}$

18. $\frac{3}{4} \times \frac{3}{4}$ ____ $\frac{1}{2} \times \frac{5}{8}$

Find the missing fraction.

19. $\frac{4}{5} \times$ ____ $= \frac{2}{5} \times \frac{4}{5}$

20. $\frac{5}{7} \times \frac{1}{3} =$ ____ $\times \frac{5}{7}$

21. ____ $\times \frac{2}{3} = \frac{2}{3} \times \frac{4}{7}$

Problem Solving

22. Conrad has a book about the outdoors, and $\frac{2}{5}$ of the book is about camping. Conrad has read $\frac{1}{3}$ of the section on camping. What part of the book has Conrad read? _____

23. Lucy created a design with different shapes. Stars made up $\frac{1}{4}$ of all the shapes in the design. Eight ninths of the stars are red. What fraction of all the shapes are red stars? _____

24. Hector used $\frac{3}{4}$ of the money he earned to buy presents. He spent $\frac{1}{6}$ of the present money for his brother's gift. What part of his money did he spend on a gift for his brother? _____

Use with Lesson 6-2, pages 200–201 in the Student Book.
Then go to Lessons 6-2A and 6-2B, pages 193–196 in this Workbook.

Multiply Fractions and Whole Numbers

Name _____

Date _____

$$5 \times \frac{2}{5} = \frac{5}{1} \times \frac{2}{5}$$

$$= \frac{5 \times 2}{1 \times 5}$$

$$= \frac{10}{5} = 2$$

$$3 \times \frac{2}{5} = \frac{3}{1} \times \frac{2}{5}$$

$$= \frac{3 \times 2}{1 \times 5}$$

$$= \frac{6}{5} = 1\frac{1}{5}$$

$$\frac{3}{4} \text{ of } \$8 = \frac{3}{4} \times \frac{8}{1}$$

$$= \frac{3 \times 8}{4 \times 1}$$

$$= \frac{24}{4} = \$6$$

Multiply.

1. $6 \times \frac{1}{2} =$ _____

2. $10 \times \frac{5}{8} =$ _____

3. $12 \times \frac{1}{7} =$ _____

4. $18 \times \frac{1}{3} =$ _____

5. $20 \times \frac{2}{5} =$ _____

6. $8 \times \frac{1}{4} =$ _____

7. $9 \times \frac{5}{9} =$ _____

8. $32 \times \frac{1}{4} =$ _____

9. $12 \times \frac{1}{3} =$ _____

10. $52 \times \frac{3}{4} =$ _____

11. $30 \times \frac{3}{10} =$ _____

12. $21 \times \frac{3}{7} =$ _____

13. $12 \times \frac{5}{6} =$ _____

14. $20 \times \frac{3}{5} =$ _____

15. $30 \times \frac{3}{5} =$ _____

16. $\frac{1}{5}$ of $\$10 =$ _____

17. $\frac{3}{12}$ of $\$36 =$ _____

18. $\frac{3}{4}$ of $\$12 =$ _____

19. $\frac{2}{3}$ of $\$18 =$ _____

20. $\frac{1}{3}$ of $\$9 =$ _____

21. $\frac{2}{5}$ of $\$10 =$ _____

22. $\frac{1}{2}$ of $19 =$ _____

23. $\frac{5}{6}$ of $9 =$ _____

24. $\frac{3}{7}$ of $63 =$ _____

Problem Solving

25. Arthur walks $\frac{5}{8}$ mi to school. Jonathan rides a bus 8 times that far. How far does Jonathan ride to school?

26. A recipe to serve 4 people requires $\frac{2}{3}$ cup of flour. Jamika needs 5 times as much flour. How much flour does she need?

27. Delores read $\frac{2}{5}$ of the books on her reading list. There were 10 books on her list. How many books did Delores read?

28. Alex had 4 yd of cloth. He used $\frac{3}{8}$ of it to make a shirt. How many yards of cloth did Alex use to make the shirt?

_____

_____

_____

_____

Use with Lesson 6-3, pages 202–203 in the Student Book.
Then go to Lesson 6-4, pages 204–205 in the Student Book.

Multiply Fractions Using the GCF

Name _____

Date _____

Simplify fractions using the GCF.

$$\frac{3}{4} \times \frac{8}{9} = \frac{3 \times \overset{2}{\cancel{8}}}{\cancel{4} \times 9}$$ | GCF of 4 and 8: 4 | $$\frac{3}{4} \times 20 = \frac{3}{4} \times \frac{20}{1}$$ | GCF of 4 and 20: 4 |
| GCF of 3 and 9: 3 |

$$= \frac{\overset{1}{\cancel{3}} \times \overset{2}{\cancel{8}}}{\underset{1}{\cancel{4}} \times \underset{3}{\cancel{9}}} = \frac{1 \times 2}{1 \times 3} = \frac{2}{3}$$

$$= \frac{3 \times \overset{5}{\cancel{20}}}{\underset{1}{\cancel{4}} \times 1} = \frac{3 \times 5}{1 \times 1} = \frac{15}{1} = 15$$

Complete each multiplication.

1. $\frac{4}{9} \times \frac{7}{24} = \frac{\overset{\square}{\cancel{4}} \times 7}{9 \times \underset{\square}{\cancel{24}}}$

   $= \frac{1 \times}{9 \times} = -$

2. $\frac{1}{4} \times 12 = \frac{1}{\underset{\square}{\cancel{4}}} \times \frac{\overset{\square}{\cancel{12}}}{1}$

   $= \frac{1 \times}{1 \times} = \underline{} = \underline{}$

Multiply using the GCF.

3. $\frac{2}{3} \times \frac{3}{5} = $ _____

4. $\frac{2}{5} \times \frac{1}{2} = $ _____

5. $\frac{7}{8} \times \frac{4}{7} = $ _____

6. $\frac{3}{5} \times \frac{5}{6} = $ _____

7. $\frac{2}{3} \times \frac{9}{10} = $ _____

8. $\frac{1}{2} \times \frac{4}{7} = $ _____

9. $\frac{6}{7} \times \frac{3}{10} = $ _____

10. $\frac{2}{5} \times \frac{5}{6} = $ _____

11. $\frac{1}{6} \times \frac{8}{9} = $ _____

12. $\frac{5}{12} \times \frac{6}{25} = $ _____

13. $\frac{4}{7} \times \frac{7}{10} = $ _____

14. $\frac{9}{10} \times \frac{10}{27} = $ _____

15. $\frac{5}{12} \times \frac{12}{35} = $ _____

16. $\frac{2}{3} \times 15 = $ _____

17. $\frac{3}{8} \times 32 = $ _____

18. $40 \times \frac{4}{5} = $ _____

19. $50 \times \frac{7}{10} = $ _____

20. $\frac{3}{4} \times 6 = $ _____

21. $8 \times \frac{5}{12} = $ _____

22. $\frac{5}{6} \times 9 = $ _____

23. $15 \times \frac{9}{10} = $ _____

Problem Solving

24. Donald bought 50 lb of grass seed. He used $\frac{4}{5}$ of it for a new lawn. How many pounds did he use?

    _____

25. Ralph's dog weighs 24 lb and his cat weighs $\frac{5}{8}$ as much. How much does Ralph's cat weigh?

    _____

Use with Lesson 6-4, pages 204–205 in the Student Book.
Then go to Lesson 6-5, pages 206–207 in the Student Book.

Rename Mixed Numbers as Fractions

Name _____

Date _____

Rename $4\frac{1}{3}$ as an improper fraction.

$$4\frac{1}{3} = \frac{(3 \times 4) + 1}{3}$$

$$= \frac{12 + 1}{3}$$

$$= \frac{13}{3}$$

Remember: An improper fraction is a fraction with its numerator equal to or greater than its denominator.

Rename each as a fraction greater than one.

1. $2\frac{1}{4} = $ _____

2. $6\frac{1}{2} = $ _____

3. $5\frac{1}{3} = $ _____

4. $3\frac{1}{8} = $ _____

5. $5\frac{3}{7} = $ _____

6. $3\frac{6}{7} = $ _____

7. $2\frac{7}{8} = $ _____

8. $7\frac{3}{5} = $ _____

9. $1\frac{5}{9} = $ _____

10. $6\frac{2}{3} = $ _____

11. $5\frac{3}{4} = $ _____

12. $4\frac{5}{6} = $ _____

13. $8\frac{3}{5} = $ _____

14. $13\frac{1}{3} = $ _____

15. $8\frac{1}{2} = $ _____

16. $15\frac{1}{2} = $ _____

17. $9\frac{5}{6} = $ _____

18. $12\frac{5}{7} = $ _____

19. $11\frac{3}{5} = $ _____

20. $10\frac{6}{7} = $ _____

21. $3\frac{1}{3} = $ _____

22. $4\frac{1}{2} = $ _____

23. $10\frac{2}{9} = $ _____

24. $7\frac{3}{4} = $ _____

25. $9\frac{2}{3} = $ _____

26. $1\frac{3}{8} = $ _____

27. $5\frac{3}{5} = $ _____

28. $6\frac{1}{7} = $ _____

Problem Solving

Write each as an improper fraction.

29. A plumber needs to cut $7\frac{11}{16}$ inches from a piece of pipe.
_____

30. Daryl cuts a board that is $9\frac{1}{3}$ ft long.
_____

31. A pencil is $3\frac{5}{16}$ inches long.
_____

32. Lyall has a piece of rope that is $8\frac{4}{9}$ yd long.
_____

33. Jessica is $4\frac{3}{4}$ ft tall.
_____

34. Lamont jogs $2\frac{3}{10}$ mi everyday.
_____

Ⓒ Use with Lesson 6-5, pages 206–207 in the Student Book.
Ⓒ Then go to Lesson 6-6, pages 208–209 in the Student Book.

Multiply Fractions and Mixed Numbers

Name _____

Date _____

Multiply: $\frac{3}{4} \times 1\frac{1}{5} = n$

$$\frac{3}{4} \times 1\frac{1}{5} = \frac{3}{4} \times \frac{6}{5}$$

$$= \frac{3 \times \overset{3}{\cancel{6}}}{\underset{2}{\cancel{4}} \times 5}$$

$$= \frac{3 \times 3}{2 \times 5} = \frac{9}{10} \longrightarrow n = \frac{9}{10}$$

Multiply: $7\frac{1}{2} \times \frac{4}{5} = n$

Use the distributive property.

$$= \left(7 + \frac{1}{2}\right) \times \frac{4}{5}$$

$$= \left(\frac{7}{1} \times \frac{4}{5}\right) + \left(\frac{1}{2} \times \frac{4}{5}\right)$$

$$= \frac{7 \times 4}{1 \times 5} + \frac{1 \times \overset{2}{\cancel{4}}}{\underset{1}{\cancel{2}} \times 5}$$

$$= \frac{28}{5} + \frac{2}{5} = \frac{30}{5} = 6 \longrightarrow n = 6$$

Find the product.

1. $2\frac{1}{4} \times \frac{1}{3} =$ _____

2. $3\frac{1}{3} \times \frac{1}{2} =$ _____

3. $\frac{1}{8} \times 2\frac{2}{5} =$ _____

4. $1\frac{1}{3} \times \frac{1}{6} =$ _____

5. $\frac{5}{6} \times 3\frac{1}{5} =$ _____

6. $7\frac{1}{2} \times \frac{1}{4} =$ _____

7. $\frac{1}{8} \times 3\frac{1}{4} =$ _____

8. $\frac{3}{8} \times 1\frac{5}{7} =$ _____

Multiply. Use the distributive property.

9. $\frac{3}{5} \times 3\frac{1}{2} =$ _____

10. $\frac{6}{7} \times 4\frac{2}{3} =$ _____

11. $\frac{3}{5} \times 1\frac{3}{5} =$ _____

12. $\frac{4}{9} \times 3\frac{3}{5} =$ _____

Problem Solving

13. Frank lives $\frac{3}{10}$ mile from school. Michelle lives $2\frac{1}{3}$ times as far from school as Frank. How far does Michelle live from school? _____

14. Jennifer had $3\frac{3}{4}$ lb of tomatoes. She used $\frac{1}{3}$ of that amount to make a salad. How many pounds did she use? _____

15. Daniel had $7\frac{3}{5}$ qt of strawberries. He used $\frac{1}{2}$ of that amount to make jam. How many quarts did he have left? _____

16. Shaya bought $2\frac{2}{3}$ lb of apples. She gave $\frac{1}{8}$ of that amount to her friend. How many pounds did she give to her friend? _____

68

Use with Lesson 6-6, pages 208–209 in the Student Book.
Then go to Lesson 6-7, pages 210–211 in the Student Book.

Multiply Mixed Numbers

Name _____

Date _____

Multiply: $2\frac{1}{2} \times 2\frac{3}{5}$

$$2\frac{1}{2} \times 2\frac{3}{5} = \frac{5}{2} \times \frac{13}{5}$$

$$= \frac{\overset{1}{\cancel{5}} \times 13}{2 \times \underset{1}{\cancel{5}}} = \frac{1 \times 13}{2 \times 1}$$

$$= \frac{13}{2} = 6\frac{1}{2}$$

Multiply: $6 \times 2\frac{1}{8}$

$$6 \times 2\frac{1}{8} = \frac{6}{1} \times \frac{17}{8}$$

$$= \frac{\overset{3}{\cancel{6}} \times 17}{1 \times \underset{4}{\cancel{8}}} = \frac{3 \times 17}{1 \times 4}$$

$$= \frac{51}{4} = 12\frac{3}{4}$$

Multiply.

1. $1\frac{7}{8} \times 18$ = _____

2. $3\frac{3}{4} \times 4\frac{2}{3}$ = _____

3. $7\frac{3}{10} \times 2\frac{1}{3}$ = _____

4. $5\frac{1}{2} \times 2\frac{1}{2}$ = _____

5. $3\frac{3}{8} \times 4\frac{1}{4}$ = _____

6. $4\frac{2}{5} \times 25$ = _____

7. $2\frac{1}{3} \times 3$ = _____

8. $5\frac{1}{2} \times 5$ = _____

9. $4 \times 1\frac{1}{4}$ = _____

10. $6 \times 1\frac{1}{5}$ = _____

11. $2\frac{1}{3} \times 4\frac{2}{3}$ = _____

12. $3\frac{1}{5} \times 1\frac{7}{8}$ = _____

Compare. Write <, =, or >.

13. $1\frac{3}{5} \times 10$ _____ $1\frac{1}{2} \times 12$

14. $7 \times 2\frac{3}{7}$ _____ $3\frac{1}{8} \times 4$

15. $2\frac{1}{5} \times 1\frac{2}{3}$ _____ $1\frac{1}{4} \times 3\frac{1}{5}$

16. $4\frac{2}{3} \times 3\frac{3}{4}$ _____ $7\frac{1}{2} \times 2\frac{1}{3}$

Problem Solving

17. Midori jogs on weekdays. If she jogs $3\frac{1}{10}$ miles on each of the 5 days, what is her total distance per week?

_____

18. Emil jumped $4\frac{1}{2}$ ft in the high jump event at a track meet. Bill jumped $\frac{8}{9}$ as high as Emil. How high did Bill jump?

_____

© Use with Lesson 6-7, pages 210–211 in the Student Book.
© Then go to Lesson 6-7A, pages 197–198 in this Workbook.

Division of Fractions

Name _____

Date _____

 How many fourths in 2?

$2 \div \frac{1}{4} = 8$

 How many twelfths in $\frac{5}{6}$?

$\frac{5}{6} \div \frac{1}{12} = 10$

Use each diagram to find the quotient.

1.

How many fourths in 4?

$4 \div \frac{1}{4} =$ _____

2.

How many fourths in 3?

$3 \div \frac{1}{4} =$ _____

3.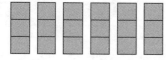

How many thirds in 6?

$6 \div \frac{1}{3} =$ _____

4.

How many eighths in 3?

$3 \div \frac{1}{8} =$ _____

5.

How many halves in 1?

$1 \div \frac{1}{2} =$ _____

6.

How many halves in 5?

$5 \div \frac{1}{2} =$ _____

Write a division sentence for each diagram.

7.

_____

8.

_____

9.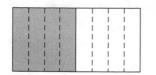

_____

10.

_____

Use with Lesson 6-8, pages 212–213 in the Student Book.
Then go to Lesson 6-9, pages 214–215 in the Student Book.

Reciprocals

Name _____

Date _____

Find the reciprocal.

$9 = \frac{9}{1}$ $\frac{9}{1} \diagdown \frac{1}{9}$

$\frac{\overset{1}{9}}{1} \times \frac{1}{\underset{1}{9}} = \frac{1}{1} = 1$

$\frac{1}{9}$ is the reciprocal of 9.

$\frac{2}{3} \diagdown \frac{3}{2}$

$\frac{\overset{1}{2}}{\underset{1}{3}} \times \frac{\overset{1}{3}}{\underset{1}{2}} = \frac{1}{1} = 1$

$\frac{3}{2}$ is the reciprocal of $\frac{2}{3}$.

$1\frac{1}{4} = \frac{5}{4}$ $\frac{5}{4} \diagdown \frac{4}{5}$

$\frac{\overset{1}{5}}{\underset{1}{4}} \times \frac{\overset{1}{4}}{\underset{1}{5}} = \frac{1}{1} = 1$

$\frac{4}{5}$ is the reciprocal of $1\frac{1}{4}$.

Write the missing reciprocal in each statement.

1. $8 \times$ _____ $= 1$ 2. $3 \times$ _____ $= 1$ 3. $\frac{1}{2} \times$ _____ $= 1$ 4. $\frac{1}{5} \times$ _____ $= 1$

5. $\frac{7}{8} \times$ _____ $= 1$ 6. $\frac{4}{5} \times$ _____ $= 1$ 7. $1\frac{1}{2} \times$ _____ $= 1$ 8. $2\frac{1}{4} \times$ _____ $= 1$

Are the numbers reciprocals? Write *Yes* or *No*.

9. $12, \frac{1}{12}$ _____   10. $\frac{1}{3}, \frac{2}{6}$ _____   11. $\frac{4}{9}, \frac{9}{4}$ _____   12. $\frac{5}{8}, \frac{8}{5}$ _____

13. $\frac{1}{10}, 10$ _____   14. $2\frac{1}{5}, \frac{5}{11}$ _____   15. $3\frac{1}{2}, \frac{2}{5}$ _____   16. $1\frac{7}{8}, \frac{8}{15}$ _____

Write the reciprocal of each number.

17. 1 _____   18. 20 _____   19. $\frac{1}{3}$ _____   20. $\frac{1}{8}$ _____

21. $\frac{9}{10}$ _____   22. $\frac{7}{12}$ _____   23. $\frac{10}{3}$ _____   24. $\frac{9}{5}$ _____

25. $\frac{14}{9}$ _____   26. $1\frac{1}{6}$ _____   27. $2\frac{3}{4}$ _____   28. $3\frac{1}{5}$ _____

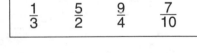 **Use the numbers in the box.**

| $\frac{1}{3}$ | $\frac{5}{2}$ | $\frac{9}{4}$ | $\frac{7}{10}$ |

29. Write the fractions that are less than 1. Then write their reciprocals.

_____

30. Write the fractions that are greater than 1. Then write their reciprocals.

_____

31. What number times $\frac{5}{16}$ equals 1?

_____

32. What number times 100 equals 1?

_____

33. Use the numbers 7 and 11 to write a multiplication sentence with a product of 1.

_____

Divide Whole Numbers by Fractions

Name _____

Date _____

Divide: $6 \div \frac{3}{8} = n$

$$6 \div \frac{3}{8} = \frac{6}{1} \div \frac{3}{8}$$

$$= \frac{6}{1} \times \frac{8}{3}$$

$$= \frac{\overset{2}{6} \times 8}{1 \times \underset{1}{3}} = \frac{16}{1} = 16$$

$$n = 16$$

Multiply by the reciprocal of the divisor.

Divide: $7 \div \frac{2}{5} = n$

$$7 \div \frac{2}{5} = \frac{7}{1} \div \frac{2}{5}$$

$$= \frac{7}{1} \times \frac{5}{2}$$

$$= \frac{7 \times 5}{1 \times 2} = \frac{35}{2} = 17\frac{1}{2}$$

$$n = 17\frac{1}{2}$$

Complete each division.

1. $6 \div \frac{1}{4} = \frac{6}{1} \div \frac{1}{4}$

$\qquad = \frac{6}{1} \times \text{——}$

$\qquad = \text{_____}$

2. $3 \div \frac{2}{7} = \frac{3}{1} \div \frac{2}{7}$

$\qquad = \frac{3}{1} \times \text{——}$

$\qquad = \text{_____}$

Divide.

3. $12 \div \frac{2}{3} =$ _____

4. $16 \div \frac{5}{8} =$ _____

5. $6 \div \frac{1}{3} =$ _____

6. $10 \div \frac{1}{3} =$ _____

7. $9 \div \frac{4}{5} =$ _____

8. $18 \div \frac{3}{4} =$ _____

9. $8 \div \frac{2}{5} =$ _____

10. $21 \div \frac{2}{5} =$ _____

11. $1 \div \frac{1}{3} =$ _____

12. $25 \div \frac{1}{8} =$ _____

13. $2 \div \frac{7}{10} =$ _____

14. $15 \div \frac{3}{4} =$ _____

15. $7 \div \frac{2}{5} =$ _____

16. $14 \div \frac{1}{3} =$ _____

Problem Solving

17. Lee needs pieces of wire that are each $\frac{2}{5}$ ft long. How many pieces can he cut from a 6-ft length of wire?

_____

18. A pie is divided into eight equal pieces. How many pieces would there be if it were divided into pieces only $\frac{1}{2}$ that size?

_____

Use with Lesson 6-10, pages 216–217 in the Student Book.
Then go to Lessons 6-10A and 6-10B, pages 199–202 in this Workbook.

Divide Fractions by Fractions

Name _____

Date _____

Divide: $\frac{3}{4} \div \frac{1}{8} = n$

$$\frac{3}{4} \div \frac{1}{8} = \frac{3}{4} \times \frac{8}{1}$$

$$= \frac{3 \times \overset{2}{8}}{\underset{1}{4} \times 1} = \frac{3 \times 2}{1 \times 1}$$

$$= \frac{6}{1} = 6$$

$$n = 6$$

Divide: $\frac{4}{5} \div \frac{2}{3} = n$

$$\frac{4}{5} \div \frac{2}{3} = \frac{4}{5} \times \frac{3}{2}$$

$$= \frac{\overset{2}{4} \times 3}{5 \times \underset{1}{2}} = \frac{2 \times 3}{5 \times 1}$$

$$= \frac{6}{5} = 1\frac{1}{5}$$

$$n = 1\frac{1}{5}$$

Complete each division.

1. $\frac{2}{3} \div \frac{2}{9} = \frac{2}{3} \times \frac{9}{2} =$ _____

2. $\frac{4}{5} \div \frac{1}{10} = \frac{4}{5} \times \frac{10}{1} =$ _____

3. $\frac{7}{8} \div \frac{3}{4} = \frac{7}{8} \times$ ___ $=$ _____

4. $\frac{5}{8} \div \frac{1}{3} =$ ___ $\times$ ___ $=$ _____

Divide.

5. $\frac{1}{2} \div \frac{1}{10} =$ _____

6. $\frac{1}{4} \div \frac{1}{8} =$ _____

7. $\frac{5}{6} \div \frac{2}{3} =$ _____

8. $\frac{7}{8} \div \frac{1}{2} =$ _____

9. $\frac{2}{5} \div \frac{4}{15} =$ _____

10. $\frac{7}{12} \div \frac{1}{3} =$ _____

11. $\frac{1}{9} \div \frac{2}{3} =$ _____

12. $\frac{3}{8} \div \frac{1}{2} =$ _____

13. $\frac{2}{7} \div \frac{6}{7} =$ _____

14. $\frac{4}{5} \div \frac{9}{10} =$ _____

Compare. Write <, =, or >.

15. $\frac{5}{8} \div \frac{2}{3}$ _____ $\frac{7}{8} \div \frac{7}{9}$

16. $\frac{5}{6} \div \frac{1}{6}$ _____ $\frac{1}{6} \div \frac{5}{6}$

17. $\frac{1}{10} \div \frac{2}{5}$ _____ $\frac{1}{20} \div \frac{1}{5}$

18. $\frac{7}{10} \div \frac{1}{3}$ _____ $\frac{5}{18} \div \frac{1}{9}$

Problem Solving

19. How many glasses, each containing $\frac{1}{8}$ liter, can be poured from a half liter of milk?

_____

20. Tom has a board $\frac{2}{3}$ yd long. How many $\frac{1}{8}$-yd-long sections can he cut from the board?

_____

Use with Lesson 6-11, pages 218–219 in the Student Book.
Then go to Lesson 6-12, pages 220–221 in the Student Book.

73

Divide Fractions by Whole Numbers

Name _____

Date _____

Divide: $\frac{1}{5} \div 2 = n$

$\frac{1}{5} \div 2 = \frac{1}{5} \div \frac{2}{1}$

$= \frac{1}{5} \times \frac{1}{2}$

$= \frac{1 \times 1}{5 \times 2} = \frac{1}{10}$

$n = \frac{1}{10}$

Divide: $\frac{2}{7} \div 4 = n$

$\frac{2}{7} \div 4 = \frac{2}{7} \div \frac{4}{1}$

$= \frac{2}{7} \times \frac{1}{4} = \frac{\overset{1}{\cancel{2}} \times 1}{7 \times \underset{2}{\cancel{4}}}$

$= \frac{1 \times 1}{7 \times 2} = \frac{1}{14}$

$n = \frac{1}{14}$

Complete each division.

1. $\frac{1}{2} \div 3 = \frac{1}{2} \div \frac{3}{1}$

    $= \frac{1}{2} \times \underline{} = \underline{}$

2. $\frac{3}{5} \div 15 = \frac{3}{5} \div \frac{15}{1}$

    $= \frac{3}{5} \times \underline{} = \underline{}$

Divide.

3. $\frac{1}{2} \div 5 =$ _____

4. $\frac{2}{3} \div 5 =$ _____

5. $\frac{5}{8} \div 3 =$ _____

6. $\frac{4}{7} \div 2 =$ _____

7. $\frac{2}{3} \div 6 =$ _____

8. $\frac{1}{4} \div 4 =$ _____

9. $\frac{3}{8} \div 3 =$ _____

10. $\frac{7}{10} \div 2 =$ _____

11. $\frac{1}{2} \div 7 =$ _____

12. $\frac{9}{10} \div 5 =$ _____

13. $\frac{4}{5} \div 8 =$ _____

14. $\frac{7}{16} \div 14 =$ _____

Problem Solving

15. Mrs. Jamison has a garden that is $\frac{1}{3}$ of an acre.
    She wants to divide it into 6 equal sections.
    What part of an acre will each section be? _____

16. During the fair, the fifth grade class uses $\frac{1}{4}$ of the gym.
    They divide the space into 5 equal sections for displays.
    What part of the gym is used for each display? _____

Use with Lesson 6-12, pages 220–221 in the Student Book.
Then go to Lesson 6-13, pages 222–223 in the Student Book.

Divide Mixed Numbers by Fractions

Name _____

Date _____

Divide: $3\frac{1}{5} \div \frac{1}{10} = n$

$3\frac{1}{5} \div \frac{1}{10} = \frac{16}{5} \div \frac{1}{10} = \frac{16}{5} \times \frac{10}{1}$

$= \frac{16 \times \overset{2}{\cancel{10}}}{\underset{1}{\cancel{5}} \times 1} = \frac{16 \times 2}{1 \times 1}$

$= \frac{32}{1} = 32$

$n = 32$

Divide: $2\frac{1}{3} \div \frac{2}{5} = n$

$2\frac{1}{3} \div \frac{2}{5} = \frac{7}{3} \div \frac{2}{5}$

$= \frac{7}{3} \times \frac{5}{2}$

$= \frac{35}{6} = 5\frac{5}{6}$

$n = 5\frac{5}{6}$

Divide.

1. $2\frac{1}{2} \div \frac{1}{4} =$ _____

2. $1\frac{5}{6} \div \frac{1}{12} =$ _____

3. $6\frac{1}{2} \div \frac{1}{2} =$ _____

4. $7\frac{3}{4} \div \frac{1}{4} =$ _____

5. $1\frac{1}{2} \div \frac{1}{3} =$ _____

6. $3\frac{1}{3} \div \frac{1}{4} =$ _____

7. $2\frac{1}{2} \div \frac{4}{9} =$ _____

8. $6\frac{1}{3} \div \frac{2}{5} =$ _____

9. $2\frac{1}{3} \div \frac{4}{9} =$ _____

10. $7\frac{1}{5} \div \frac{8}{15} =$ _____

Compare. Write <, =, or >.

11. $4\frac{1}{4} \div \frac{3}{4}$ _____ $3\frac{1}{2} \div \frac{1}{4}$

12. $3\frac{1}{3} \div \frac{1}{6}$ _____ $8\frac{1}{2} \div \frac{5}{6}$

13. $2\frac{1}{5} \div \frac{3}{10}$ _____ $4\frac{1}{2} \div \frac{2}{5}$

14. $4\frac{5}{6} \div \frac{1}{3}$ _____ $9\frac{2}{3} \div \frac{2}{3}$

Problem Solving

15. Chris needs pieces of yarn $\frac{1}{2}$ dm long to use as strands of hair for a rag doll she is making. She has a $16\frac{1}{2}$-dm length of yarn. How many strands of hair can she make?

_____

16. A shop teacher had a board that was $8\frac{1}{2}$ feet long. He cut it into $\frac{1}{2}$-ft sections. How many sections were there?

_____

Use with Lesson 6-13, pages 222–223 in the Student Book.
Then go to Lesson 6-14, pages 224–225 in the Student Book.

75

Divide Mixed Numbers

Name _____

Date _____

Divide: $2\frac{1}{2} \div 3\frac{1}{3} = n$

$2\frac{1}{2} \div 3\frac{1}{3} = \frac{5}{2} \div \frac{10}{3}$

$= \frac{5}{2} \times \frac{3}{10}$

$= \frac{\overset{1}{\cancel{5}} \times 3}{2 \times \underset{2}{\cancel{10}}} = \frac{1 \times 3}{2 \times 2}$

$= \frac{3}{4}$

$n = \frac{3}{4}$

Divide: $7 \div 1\frac{3}{4} = n$

$7 \div 1\frac{3}{4} = \frac{7}{1} \div \frac{7}{4}$

$= \frac{7}{1} \times \frac{4}{7}$

$= \frac{\overset{1}{7} \times 4}{1 \times \underset{1}{7}} = \frac{1 \times 4}{1 \times 1}$

$= 4$

$n = 4$

Divide.

1. $4\frac{1}{4} \div 2\frac{1}{8} =$ _____

2. $1\frac{1}{2} \div 4\frac{1}{2} =$ _____

3. $5 \div 1\frac{2}{3} =$ _____

4. $7 \div 1\frac{2}{5} =$ _____

5. $3\frac{1}{2} \div \frac{1}{3} =$ _____

6. $5\frac{1}{8} \div \frac{1}{16} =$ _____

7. $5\frac{1}{2} \div 1\frac{2}{3} =$ _____

8. $8\frac{1}{8} \div \frac{1}{8} =$ _____

9. $4\frac{2}{5} \div 2\frac{3}{4} =$ _____

10. $5 \div 6\frac{1}{4} =$ _____

11. $3\frac{3}{4} \div 5 =$ _____

12. $12 \div 1\frac{1}{3} =$ _____

13. $4\frac{3}{4} \div 2\frac{1}{4} =$ _____

14. $2\frac{1}{5} \div 1\frac{1}{10} =$ _____

Problem Solving

15. Charlie is cutting wire into $2\frac{1}{4}$-ft pieces. How many pieces can he cut from a 45-ft roll? _____

16. Pablo took $9\frac{1}{2}$ hours to paint 5 pictures. How long did it take him to paint each picture if he spent the same amount of time on each? _____

17. Loren studied for $3\frac{1}{3}$ h. She took a break every $\frac{2}{3}$ h. How many breaks did she take? _____

Use with Lesson 6-14, pages 224–225 in the Student Book.
Then go to Lesson 6-15, pages 226–227 in the Student Book.

Estimate Products and Quotients with Mixed Numbers

Name _____

Date _____

Estimate each product or quotient by rounding.	Estimate each product or quotient by using compatible numbers.
$1\frac{2}{3} \times 4\frac{1}{6}$ $55\frac{8}{9} \div 6\frac{2}{3}$	$8 \div 2\frac{2}{3}$ $3\frac{7}{8} \times 5$
$\downarrow$ $\downarrow$ $\downarrow$ $\downarrow$	$\downarrow$ $\downarrow$ $\downarrow$ $\downarrow$
$2 \times 4 = 8$ $56 \div 7 = 8$	$8 \div 2 = 4$ $3 \times 5 = 15$

Estimate each product or quotient by rounding.

1. $7 \times 2\frac{1}{4}$ _____

2. $5 \times 3\frac{1}{2}$ _____

3. $6 \times 1\frac{2}{3}$ _____

4. $6 \div 1\frac{1}{3}$ _____

5. $24\frac{5}{6} \div 4\frac{3}{4}$ _____

6. $8\frac{1}{9} \div 4$ _____

7. $5 \times 2\frac{3}{8}$ _____

8. $4\frac{1}{5} \times 1\frac{3}{7}$ _____

9. $2\frac{5}{8} \times 6\frac{9}{10}$ _____

10. $81\frac{2}{7} \div 8\frac{9}{11}$ _____

11. $14 \div 6\frac{7}{8}$ _____

12. $26\frac{6}{7} \div 2\frac{2}{3}$ _____

Estimate to compare. Write <, = or >.

13. $\frac{3}{8} \times 23\frac{5}{6}$ _____ $\frac{1}{5} \times 34\frac{2}{3}$

14. $17\frac{2}{3} \times \frac{1}{6}$ _____ $8\frac{3}{4} \times \frac{1}{3}$

15. $25\frac{1}{3} \div 4\frac{5}{7}$ _____ $39\frac{3}{5} \div 7\frac{3}{4}$

16. $26\frac{1}{2} \div 3\frac{2}{5}$ _____ $39\frac{4}{5} \div 4\frac{1}{4}$

17. $11 \times \frac{3}{4}$ _____ $17 \times \frac{5}{6}$

18. $15 \div 1\frac{3}{5}$ _____ $83\frac{1}{2} \div \frac{1}{7}$

Use compatible numbers to estimate. Then write whether the actual product is *less than* or *greater than* the estimated product or quotient.

19. $\frac{1}{2} \times 19\frac{1}{4}$

20. $\frac{3}{4} \times 24\frac{3}{8}$

_____

_____

21. $18 \div 2\frac{2}{5}$

22. $28 \div 1\frac{1}{7}$

_____

_____

Use with Lesson 6-15, pages 226–227 in the Student Book.
Then go to Lesson 6-16, pages 228–229 in the Student Book.

77

Problem-Solving Strategy: Use Simpler Numbers

Name _____

Date _____

Harvey lives $\frac{3}{4}$ mile from school. He walks to school each school-day morning and back home again in the afternoon. How many miles does Harvey walk in $2\frac{1}{2}$ days?

Use simpler numbers in order to decide how to solve the problems. Use 1 mile for $\frac{3}{4}$ mile and 3 days for $2\frac{1}{2}$ days.
Find the number of miles he walks each day and then multiply by the number of days.

$$2 \times 1 \times 3$$

Now use the numbers given to solve the problem.

NUMBER OF MILES A DAY		NUMBER OF DAYS		TOTAL MILES
$2 \times \frac{3}{4}$	$\times$	$2\frac{1}{2}$	$=$	t
$\frac{2}{1} \times \frac{3}{4}$	$\times$	$\frac{5}{2}$	$=$	t
$\frac{\overset{1}{2}}{1} \times \frac{3}{\underset{2}{2}}$	$\times$	$\frac{5}{2}$	$=$	$\frac{15}{4}$
			$=$	$3\frac{3}{4}$

Harvey walks $3\frac{3}{4}$ miles in $2\frac{1}{2}$ days.

Solve. Do your work on a separate sheet of paper.

1. How many hours will it take Wendy to make $4\frac{2}{3}$ batches of cookies if she can make $1\frac{1}{3}$ batches in 1 hour?

2. Terrell drove at a speed of $48\frac{1}{2}$ miles per hour for $2\frac{1}{4}$ hours. How far did he travel?

3. Ronny unpacks pears and stacks them in a bin at the grocery store. Each carton contains $3\frac{1}{2}$ dozen pears. How many cartons will Ronny unpack if he fills a bin that holds $10\frac{1}{2}$ dozen pears?

4. Nina practices her guitar every week-night for $\frac{3}{4}$ hour. On Saturday and Sunday, she practices $1\frac{1}{4}$ hours each day. How many hours does Nina practice in 2 weeks?

5. It takes Leon $\frac{1}{3}$ h to ride his bicycle from his home to John's home. One day, after he arrived at John's home, Leon realized he had forgotten to bring a book. So he returned home to get the book and then rode back to John's. After visiting, he rode home again. How many hours did Leon ride in all?

6. A recipe for fruit punch calls for $2\frac{1}{2}$ c of orange juice, $1\frac{1}{3}$ c of pineapple juice, and $1\frac{3}{4}$ c of soda water. If June makes 4 times the recipe, how many cups of fruit punch will she have?

Use with Lesson 6-16, pages 228–229 in the Student Book.
Then go to Lesson 6-17, pages 230–231 in the Student Book.

Problem-Solving Applications: Mixed Review

Name _____

Date _____

Solve each problem and explain the method you used. If needed, do all your work on a separate sheet of paper.

Read ▶ Plan ▶ Solve ▶ Check ▶

Strategy File

Use These Strategies
Work Backward
Use Simpler Numbers
Make an Organized List
Use More Than One Step
Make a Table/Find a Pattern

1. Dottie walks $\frac{3}{5}$ mi from her house. She is a third of the way to school. How far is it from her house to school?

   _____

2. Del and his 5 friends eat 4 pizzas. If each has the same amount and there is $\frac{1}{4}$ of a pizza left over, how much did each person eat?

   _____

3. At the restaurant, Randy washes 44 pots per hour. If he works for $1\frac{3}{4}$ hours, how many pots will Randy clean?

   _____

4. Sylvie's cake recipe calls for $2\frac{2}{3}$ cups of walnuts. If 8 people share the cake equally, how many cups of walnuts does each person eat?

   _____

5. In January, Todd was able to lift $127\frac{1}{2}$ lb. In February he could lift 135 lb, and in March he could lift $142\frac{1}{2}$ lb. If he continues at this rate, what will Todd be able to lift in July?

   _____

6. Raul is serving lunch. Each guest will get a sandwich, juice, and ice cream. If he has two types of sandwiches, 3 kinds of juice, and 3 flavors of ice cream, how many different lunch combinations will there be?

   _____

7. Jerry spent $5\frac{1}{3}$ hours cleaning the house. If he spent half that time cleaning the bathroom and 40 minutes cleaning his room, how much time did Jerry spend cleaning the rest of the house?

   _____

8. Sheri bought 3 lb of topping. If each meal takes 2 oz of topping, how many meals could Sheri make?

   _____

9. Sasha has $7\frac{4}{5}$ gal of paint. If he shares it equally with three friends, how much will each friend get? Will Sasha have more than 2 gal of paint left for himself?

   _____

Probability

Name _____

Date _____

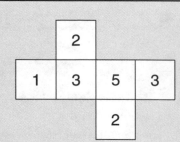

$P(1) = \dfrac{1}{6}$ ← 1

$P(2) = \dfrac{2}{6} = \dfrac{1}{3}$ ← 2, 2

$P(2 \text{ or } 3) = \dfrac{4}{6} = \dfrac{2}{3}$ ← 2, 2, 3, 3

$P(\text{not } 3) = \dfrac{4}{6} = \dfrac{2}{3}$ ← 1, 2, 2, 5

Use the number cube. Find the probability of each event.

1a. $P(2) =$ _____

  b. $P(4) =$ _____

  c. $P(3) =$ _____

  d. $P(not\ 3) =$ _____

  e. $P(not\ 4) =$ _____

  f. $P(not\ 2) =$ _____

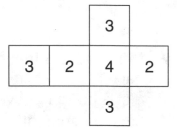

2. In 600 rolls, predict how many times you will roll

  a. 2 _____   b. 3 _____   c. 4 _____

Use the spinner at the right to find the probability of each event.

3. $P(3) =$ _____

4. $P(8) =$ _____

5. $P(4) =$ _____

6. $P(2) =$ _____

7. $P(1) =$ _____

8. $P(not\ 1) =$ _____

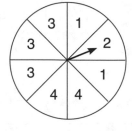

A bag contains 2 black marbles, 3 white marbles, 4 green marbles, 5 red marbles, and 6 blue marbles. Find each probability.

9. $P(not\ \text{black}) =$ _____   10. $P(\text{orange}) =$ _____

11. $P(\text{red or blue}) =$ _____   12. $P(\text{red or green}) =$ _____

13. $P(\text{black or white}) =$ _____   14. $P(not\ \text{red}) =$ _____

15. $P(\text{white or red}) =$ _____   16. $P(not\ \text{blue}) =$ _____

17. $P(\text{black or red}) =$ _____   18. $P(not\ \text{purple}) =$ _____

Problem Solving

19. Tim has 2 dimes, 1 nickel, and 1 quarter in his pocket. He picks out a coin at random. What is the probability that the coin is worth exactly 10¢? _____

Use with Lesson 7-1, pages 238–239 in the Student Book.
Then go to Lesson 7-2, pages 240–41 in the Student Book.

Tree Diagrams

Name _____

Date _____

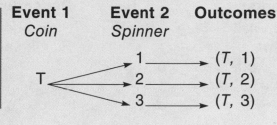

Toss a coin and spin the spinner. Find: $P(H, 3)$

Event 1 Coin	Event 2 Spinner	Outcomes	Event 1 Coin	Event 2 Spinner	Outcomes

H →
1 → (H, 1)
2 → (H, 2)
3 → (H, 3)

T →
1 → (T, 1)
2 → (T, 2)
3 → (T, 3)

$$P(H, 3) = \frac{1}{6}$$

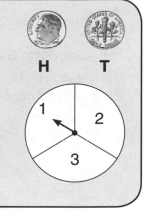

H   T

            A   B   C   D

Find each probability. Use the spinner and the cards above.

1. $P(2, A)$ **2.** $P(\text{odd}, B)$ **3.** $P(\text{even}, D)$ **4.** $P(1, A \text{ or } C)$ **5.** $P(\text{not } 2, \text{not } A)$

_____   _____   _____   _____   _____

Draw a tree diagram on a separate sheet of paper. Then find the probability.

6. $P(H, 5)$ _____   **7.** $P(T, 2)$ _____

8. $P(T, \text{even})$ _____   **9.** $P(H, \text{odd})$ _____

10. $P(T, 2 \text{ or } 3)$ _____   **11.** $P(H, \text{not } 2)$ _____

Heads (H)

Problem Solving   You may draw a tree diagram on a separate sheet of paper.

12. Candace has 5 T-shirts: 1 pink, 2 blue, 1 red, and 1 white. She also has 2 hats: 1 white and 1 blue. If she selects a shirt and a hat without looking, what is the probability that she will get a pink shirt and a white hat? _____

13. Derek has 2 pairs of socks in his drawer: 1 blue pair and 1 brown pair. He also has 2 pairs of shoes: 1 black pair and 1 brown pair. If he picks 1 pair of socks and 1 pair of shoes at random, what is the probability that he picks socks and shoes of the same color? _____

Use with Lesson 7-2, pages 240–241 in the Student Book.
Then go to Lesson 7-3, pages 242–243 in the Student Book.

81

Independent and Dependent Events

Name _____

Date _____

A bank contains 1 penny (*p*), 1 nickel (*n*), and 1 dime (*d*).

Independent Events:
Pick a coin. Return it.
Pick a second coin.

p⟨ p n d n⟨ p n d d⟨ p n d

$P(p, n) = \dfrac{1}{9}$

Dependent Events:
Pick a coin. *Do not* return it.
Pick a second coin.

p⟨ n d n⟨ p d d⟨ p n

$P(p, n) = \dfrac{1}{6}$

Find the probability. You may draw a tree diagram.

A bank contains 1 nickel (*n*), 1 dime (*d*) and 2 quarters (*q*).

1. Pick a coin. Put it back. Then pick another coin.

   a. $P(n, d) =$ _____

   b. $P(q, d) =$ _____

   c. $P(q, q) =$ _____

   d. $P(not\ n, d) =$ _____

   e. $P(q, not\ d) =$ _____

   f. $P(n, not\ q) =$ _____

2. Pick a coin. Do *not* put it back. Then pick another coin.

   a. $P(n, d) =$ _____

   b. $P(q, d) =$ _____

   c. $P(q, q) =$ _____

   d. $P(not\ n, d) =$ _____

   e. $P(q, not\ d) =$ _____

   f. $P(n, not\ q) =$ _____

In a bag are 1 red marble (*R*), 1 blue marble (*B*), 1 white marble (*W*),
and 1 green marble (*G*).

3. Pick a marble. Put it back. Then pick another marble.

   a. $P(W, G) =$ _____

   b. $P(R, not\ B) =$ _____

   c. $P(not\ G, R) =$ _____

4. Pick a marble. Do not put it back. Then pick another marble.

   a. $P(W, G) =$ _____

   b. $P(R, not\ B) =$ _____

   c. $P(not\ G, R) =$ _____

Problem Solving

5. Suppose there are 2 dimes and 3 quarters in a
bank. You shake it so that 2 coins fall out.
What is the probability that

   a. both coins are quarters? _____

   b. both coins are dimes? _____

   c. both coins are the same? _____

   d. you shake out one of each coin? _____

Use with Lesson 7-3, pages 242–243 in the Student Book.
Then go to Lessons 7-4 and 7-5, pages 244–247 in the Student Book.

Collect and Organize Data; Range, Median, Mean, and Mode

Name _____

Date _____

Favorite Pet			
Pet	**Tally**	**Frequency**	**Cumulative Frequency**
Horse	ЖН //	7	7
Cat	ЖН ЖН	10	17
Dog	ЖН ЖН	10	27
Bird	ЖН	5	32

Range: $10 - 5 = 5$

Median: $\dfrac{7 + 10}{2} = 8\dfrac{1}{2}$

Mean: $\dfrac{5 + 7 + 10 + 10}{4} = 8$

Mode: 10

Make a frequency table.

1. Abra asked friends to name their favorite fruit. The responses are listed below.

pear	orange	apple
orange	apple	grapes
apple	orange	banana
apple	banana	grapes
apple	pear	orange
orange	banana	orange
banana	orange	banana
kiwi	apple	grapes

Favorite Fruit			
Fruit	**Tally**	**Frequency**	**Cumulative Frequency**
pear			
grapes			
apple			
orange			
banana			
kiwi			

Use the data in exercise 1 for exercises 2–4.

2. Organize the data from least to greatest in the table at the right.

3. How many friends did Abra ask? What section of the original table answers this question?

    _____

4. Which fruit was the favorite of the greatest number of Abra's friends? the least number?

    _____

Favorite Fruit	
Kind	**Numbers**

Find the range, median, mean, and mode for each set of data.
Do your work on a separate sheet of paper.

5. 48, 45, 50, 52

    _____

6. 82°F, 85°F, 81°F, 88°F, 79°F

    _____

7. 23, 44, 28, 64, 32, 44, 38

    _____

8. 120, 94, 78, 94, 88, 94, 97

    _____

9. $22, $9, $54, $36, $38, $29, $36

    _____

10. $135, $120, $144, $136, $95

    _____

Use with Lessons 7-4 and 7-5, pages 244–247 in the Student Book.
Then go to Lesson 7-6, pages 248–249 in the Student Book.

83

Graphing Sense

Name _____

Date _____

Hours Worked in One Week

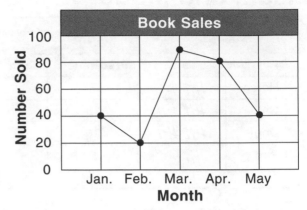

Book Sales

Tickets Sold For Picnic

Pony Club	☐	☐	☐	☐	☐	⬚
Little League	☐	☐	☐	⬚		
Dance Club	☐	☐	☐	☐		
Key: ☐ = 10 tickets ⬚ = 5 tickets						

Movie Choices

Mystery ▶ 3   Comedy 15   Science Fiction 9   Adventure 9

Problem Solving   **Use the graphs above.**

1. How many hours worked does each unit on the vertical scale represent? _____

2. Who worked the greatest number of hours in one week? How many hours? _____

3. How many hours did Ron work in one week? _____

4. During which month were the greatest number of books sold? How many were sold? _____

5. Between which two months was the decrease in book sales the greatest? _____

6. Between which two months did the book sales increase? _____

7. How many tickets does the symbol ⬚ represent? _____

8. How many tickets did the Dance Club sell? _____

9. Which group sold the most tickets? How many did they sell? _____

10. How many movie club members prefer adventure movies? _____

11. What fractional part of the movie club prefer science fiction movies? _____

12. Which type of movies is preferred by the fewest movie club members? _____

13. Which graph compares three sets of data? _____

14. Which graph shows parts of a whole? _____

15. Which graphs compare four sets of data? _____

Use with Lesson 7-6, pages 248–249 in the Student Book.
Then go to Lesson 7-7, pages 250–251 in the Student Book.

Line Plots

Name _____

Date _____

The line plot shows the number of push-ups the members of the soccer team were able to do.

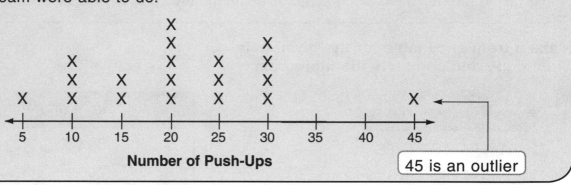

Number of Push-Ups

45 is an outlier

Use the line plot above to answer questions 1–5.

1. What is the mode of the data? _____

2. What is the range of the data? _____

3. Around which number do the data seem to cluster? _____

4. How many team members could do 20 or more push-ups? _____

5. How many team members could do fewer than 20 push-ups? _____

Draw a line plot for each set of data. Find the range, mode, and an outlier.

6. Donovan's basketball scores: 14, 17, 19, 18, 16, 18, 17, 21, 15, 18, 16, 14, 16, 18, 15

Range: _____

Mode: _____

Outlier: _____

7. Edie's math scores: 83, 93, 78, 85, 85, 87, 88, 90, 84

Range: _____

Mode: _____

Outlier: _____

Use with Lesson 7-7, pages 250–251 in the Student Book.
Then go to Lesson 7-8, pages 252–253 in the Student Book.

Histograms

Name _____

Date _____

> A histogram is a bar graph that shows the frequency of equal intervals of data.
> In a histogram, the intervals must not overlap and the bars are not separated by spaces.

Make a frequency table for the given data.
Then copy and complete the histogram.

1.

Scores on Tuesday's Math Test			
91	85	77	88
	68	94	78
70	86	97	85
	62	80	91
84	79	69	78

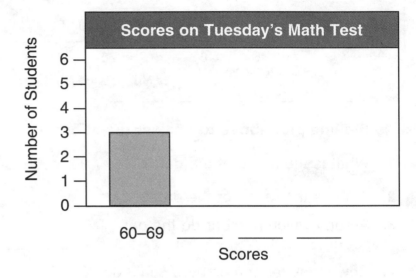

Use the histogram above.

2. Which interval has the least frequency?

_____

3. Which interval has the greatest frequency?

_____

4. How many students got a score greater than 79?

_____

5. How many students got a score lower than 80?

_____

6. If two students were out sick on Tuesday, how many students are in the class?

_____

7. If two of the students in the 60–69 interval raise their score by 10 points, which interval would have the greatest frequency?

_____

Use with Lesson 7-8, pages 252–253 in the Student Book.
Then go to Lesson 7-9, pages 254–255 in the Student Book.

Make Line Graphs

Name _____

Date _____

Use the table to complete the line graph. Then answer problems 2–4.

1.

Shoe Shack	
Day	**Pairs Sold**
Mon.	16
Tue.	32
Wed.	22
Thu.	28
Fri.	12

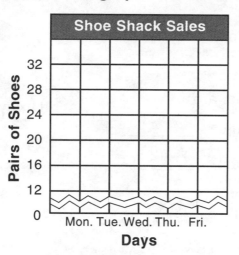

2. Between which two days was the difference in sales the least?

_____

3. Between which two days was the increase in sales the most?

_____

4. On the average, about how many pairs of shoes were sold daily?

_____

Make a line graph for the data below.

5.

Average Monthly Temperature in Washington, DC (°F)	
Month	**Temperature**
Sept.	67
Oct.	55
Nov.	45
Dec.	35
Jan.	31
Feb.	34
Mar.	43

Use the graph you made in problem 5.

6. Which month is the warmest? the coldest?

_____

7. About how many degrees difference is there between the average temperatures in February and October?

_____

8. About what is the average monthly temperature for these months?

_____

9. Between which consecutive months was there an increase of about 10°F?

_____

Use with Lesson 7-9, pages 254–255 in the Student Book.
Then go to Lesson 7-10, pages 256–257 in the Student Book.

87

Interpret Circle Graphs

Name _____

Date _____

Use the circle graph at the right to answer problems 1–3.

Number of Cars Purchased

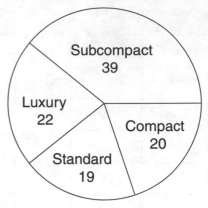

1. How many cars in all are represented by the graph? _____

2. What fractional part of all the cars are

   compact? _____   luxury? _____

   standard? _____   subcompact? _____

3. Which two types of cars together equal the number of subcompact cars purchased?

   _____

Use the circle graph at the right to answer problems 4–9.

Hank's Weekly Budget

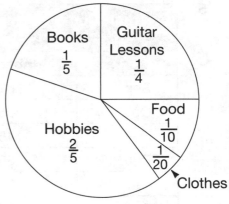

4. Hank earns $120 each week. How much does he spend on guitar lessons? _____

5. How much does he spend for food? _____

6. How much more does he spend for guitar lessons than books? _____

7. What fractional part of Hank's budget does he spend for books, clothes, and food? _____

8. How much does he spend on books, clothes, and food? _____

9. What fractional part of Hank's budget does he spend for his hobbies and guitar lessons? _____

Use the circle graph at the right to answer problems 10–12.

Favorite Sport

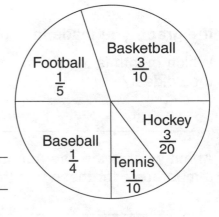

10. Which sport does the greatest number of students favor? _____

11. Which sport is the least favored? _____

12. If 200 students took part in the survey, how many chose:

    a. football? _____   **b.** baseball? _____

    c. hockey? _____   **d.** tennis? _____

    e. basketball? _____

Use with Lesson 7-10, pages 256–257 in the Student Book.
Then go to Lesson 7-11, pages 258–259 in the Student Book.

Problem-Solving Strategy: Use a Model/Diagram

Name _____

Date _____

In a group of 25 students, $\frac{2}{5}$ of them play only basketball, 7 play only soccer, and 5 play neither sport. How many students play both basketball and soccer?

Draw a diagram.
To find how many students just play basketball, multiply:
$\frac{2}{5} \times 25 = 10$
To find how many students play both sports, subtract:
$25 - 5 - 10 - 7 = 3$.
Three students play both basketball and soccer.

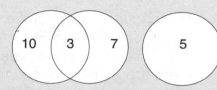

Basketball   Soccer   Neither sport

Solve. Do your work on a separate sheet of paper.

1. Of 18 students, $\frac{1}{3}$ can play guitar and piano, 6 can play only the guitar, and 4 can play neither instrument. How many students can play only the piano?

2. The History Club can go to Boston, Philadelphia, or Washington, DC. They can travel by plane or by train. Draw a tree diagram to find the number of travel choices they have.

3. Use the diagram below. What is the total number of students who play at least 1 of the 3 sports? the number of students who play only 1 of the 3 sports? the number of students who play all 3 sports?

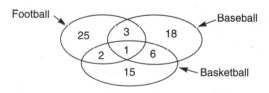

4. You toss a coin that can land heads or tails. Then you roll a number cube that has 2 red faces, 1 green face and 3 blue faces. Draw a tree diagram to show the possible outcomes. What is the probability that you will toss a head and roll a blue face?

5. There are 18 bottles of fruit juice on a shelf. Four bottles contain only apple juice. Nine bottles contain orange juice, and 7 contain grapefruit juice. How many bottles contain both orange and grapefruit juice?

6. Alice, Bruce, and Charlene each borrow a mystery book from the library. Alice, Doug, and Pat each borrow a biography. Charlene, Elaine, and Pat each borrow a travel book. How many different students borrow at least 2 books from the library?

Use with Lesson 7-11, pages 258–259 in the Student Book.
Then go to Lesson 7-12, pages 260–261 in the Student Book.

89

Problem-Solving Applications: Mixed Review

Solve each problem and explain the method you used. If needed, do all your work on a separate sheet of paper.

Name _____

Date _____

Strategy File

Use These Strategies
Use a Model/Diagram
Make an Organized List
Work Backward
Use Simpler Numbers
Logical Reasoning

1. In the tour group, $\frac{1}{4}$ of the people can speak Spanish and French, 8 can speak only Spanish, and 6 speak neither. If there are 24 people in the group, how many can speak only French?

_____

2. Sandi can only take two CDs on vacation. She narrows her choice down to 3 jazz and 4 rap CDs. If she takes 1 from each type of music, how many different combinations can she make?

_____

3. $\frac{3}{4}$ of a whole cake was eaten on Sunday. If two pieces are eaten Monday and three pieces are left, how many pieces of cake were there to start?

_____

4. Dar holds a bag with two nickels and three pennies. What is the probability of picking a nickel first, holding it, then picking a penny?

_____

5. Sharon, Kai, Todd, and Mary stand in line. Sharon is not first. Mary is right before Todd. Kai is right after Sharon. In what order do they stand in line?

_____

6. Alejandro reads $3\frac{1}{2}$ books a week. On average, how many books does he read a day?

_____

7. Sadie ran $5\frac{1}{4}$ miles per hour for an hour and a half. How far did she run?

_____

Favorite Section of the Newspaper

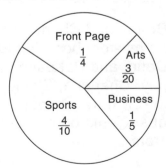

Use the graph at the left to solve.

8. If 120 people were polled, how many chose Arts as their favorite section of the paper?

_____

9. If 24 people chose Business as their favorite, how many people chose Sports?

_____

Decimal Sense

Name _____

Date _____

As with whole numbers, a greater decimal is located to the right of a lesser decimal on a number line.

Point *A* represents 1.7

Point *B* represents 2.1

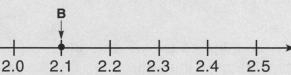

Point *A* represents 0.71

Point *B* represents 0.745

Point *C* represents 0.782

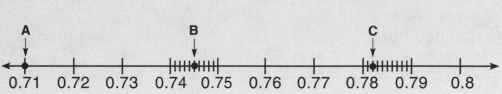

Name the decimal represented by A, B, and C on each number line.

1.

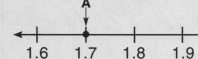

A represents _____

B represents _____

C represents _____

2.

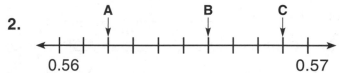

A represents _____

B represents _____

C represents _____

3.

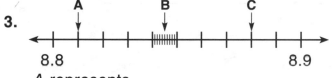

A represents _____

B represents _____

C represents _____

4.

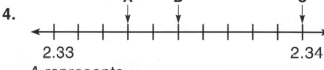

A represents _____

B represents _____

C represents _____

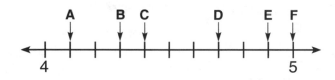

5. *A* _____   **6.** *D* _____

7. *B* _____   **8.** *E* _____

Name the point represented by each decimal.

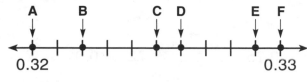

9. 0.329 _____   **10.** 4.41 _____   **11.** 0.326 _____   **12.** 4.415 _____

13. 4.413 _____   **14.** 0.322 _____   **15.** 4.419 _____   **16.** 0.32 _____

Use with Lesson 8-1, pages 268–269 in the Student Book.
Then go to Lessons 8-2, pages 270–271 in the Student Book.

91

Decimals and Place Value

Name _____

Date _____

Standard Form:
321.233

Read:
Three hundred twenty-one and two hundred thirty-three thousandths

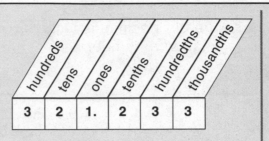

hundreds	tens	ones	tenths	hundredths	thousandths
3	2	1.	2	3	3

Expanded Form:
300 + 20 + 1 + 0.2 + 0.03 + 0.003

Write the short word name for 6,100,000.

6,100,000

$= 6\frac{1}{10}$ million

$= 6.1$ million

Short Word Name:
6.1 million

Write the place of the underlined digit. Then write its value.

1. 2.4<u>1</u>6 _____

2. 4.93<u>9</u> _____

3. 66.3<u>9</u>2 _____

4. 98.<u>7</u>18 _____

Write each number in expanded form.

5. 0.329 _____

6. 2.03 _____

7. 4.007 _____

8. 23.45 _____

Write each in standard form.

9. 8 + 0.2 + 0.02 + 0.004 _____

10. 4 + 0.5 + 0.003 _____

11. 0.8 + 0.03 + 0.001 _____

12. forty-two and nine hundredths _____

13. two and fifty-five thousandths _____

14. ten and thirty-nine hundredths _____

Write the short word name.

15. 3,130,000 _____

16. 7,098,000 _____

17. 6,524,000,000 _____

18. 1,009,000,000 _____

Write as a fraction in simplest form.

19. 0.3 _____

20. 0.45 _____

21. 0.75 _____

22. 0.91 _____

23. 0.012 _____

24. 0.625 _____

25. 0.32 _____

26. 0.86 _____

Use with Lesson 8-2, pages 270–271 in the Student Book.
Then go to Lessons 8-2A and 8-2B, pages 203–206 in this Workbook.

Add Decimals

Name _____

Date _____

Add: 0.49 + 0.7 + 0.28

To add decimals:
- Line up the decimal points.
- Add as with whole numbers.
- Write the decimal point in the sum.

```
  1 1
  0.49
  0.70  ← 0.7 = 0.70
+ 0.28
  1.47
```

Add.

1.	2.	3.	4.	5.
0.04 + 0.23	0.73 + 0.25	0.5 + 0.5	0.72 + 0.2	0.7 + 0.4

6.	7.	8.	9.	10.
0.38 + 0.21	0.5 + 0.68	0.35 + 0.7	0.47 + 0.09	0.13 + 0.08

Find the sum.

11.	12.	13.	14.	15.
0.3 0.68 + 0.97	0.63 0.04 + 0.15	0.7 0.63 + 0.08	0.21 0.14 + 0.07	0.24 0.2 + 0.91

Align and add.

16. 0.04 + 0.64 + 0.13 _____   17. 0.27 + 0.56 + 0.38 _____

18. 0.74 + 0.19 + 0.72 _____   19. 0.47 + 0.6 + 0.09 _____

20. 0.08 + 0.05 + 0.11 _____   21. 0.3 + 0.09 + 0.86 _____

Compare. Write <, =, or >.

22. 0.04 + 0.74 + 0.13 _____ 0.08 + 0.64 + 0.32

23. 0.27 + 0.31 + 0.72 _____ 0.38 + 0.03 + 0.7

24. 0.471 + 0.563 + 0.32 _____ 0.573 + 0.581 + 0.2

Problem Solving

25. A triangle has 3 equal sides. One side has a length of 0.85 cm. What is the perimeter of the triangle?

26. A quadrilateral has 4 equal sides. Two of the sides have a total length of 0.90 m. What is the perimeter?

_____   _____

Ⓒ Use with Lesson 8-3, pages 272–273 in the Student Book.
Ⓒ Then go to Lesson 8-4, pages 274–275 in the Student Book.

Estimate Decimal Sums

Name _____

Date _____

> Estimate: 2.9 + 3.06
>
> | **Front-End** | **Rounding** |
> |---|---|
> | 2.9 | 2.9 ⟶ 3 |
> | + 3.06 | + 3.06 ⟶ + 3 |
> | about 5.00 | about 6 |
>
> So the exact sum is between 5 and 6.

Estimate the sum by rounding.

1.	2.71	2.	6.3	3.	6.5	4.	0.73
	4.12		5.92		1.624		0.9
	+ 6.5		+ 2.37		+ 7.328		+ 3.321

Estimate the sum by front-end estimation.

5.	0.35	6.	5.45	7.	5.34	8.	4.296
	0.21		2.13		1.358		1.683
	+ 0.7		+ 2.97		+ 2.824		+ 9.198

Estimate by both rounding and front-end estimation.
Between what two numbers will the exact sum be?

9.	5.8	10.	7.82	11.	426.82	12.	5.66
	+ 2.63		+ 2.9		+ 254.63		3.628
							+ 6.089

_____   _____   _____   _____

_____   _____   _____   _____

13.	0.38	14.	0.19	15.	0.471	16.	2.369
	+ 0.7		+ 0.136		+ 0.563		+ 1.247

_____   _____   _____   _____

_____   _____   _____   _____

Estimate the sum.

17.	36.134	18.	24.491	19.	1.56	20.	100.09	21.	3.62
	12.1		16.032		8.002		298.9		3.090
	+ 63.08		+ 13.92		+ 1.1		+ 305.321		+ 1.01

Use with Lesson 8-4, pages 274–275 in the Student Book.
Then go to Lesson 8-5, pages 276–277 in the Student Book.

Add More Decimals

Add: 5.72 + 0.009 + 27.8

- Line up the decimal points.
- Add as usual.
- Write the decimal point in the sum.

```
        1 1
     5.720    ←  5.72 = 5.720
     0.009
  + 27.800    ←  27.8 = 27.800
    33.529
```

Use rounding to estimate. Then add.

1.   4.87
   + 6.9

2.   12
   + 8.34

3.   9.7
   + 9.75

4.   0.38
   + 0.8

5.   5.09
   + 4.93

6.   23.1
   + 4.042

7.   7.395
   + 8.46

8.   36.05
   + 6.2

9.   58.912
   + 0.066

10.   2.736
      0.5
    + 3.04

11.   1.17
      8.064
    + 9.106

12.   17.4
      3.909
    + 16.83

13.   0.627
      8.58
    + 2.391

14.   5.298
      0.63
    + 4.04

15.   20.6
      1.379
    + 24.42

16.   0.67
      9.209
    + 1.8

17.   3.841
      0.933
    + 5.5

Align and add.

18. 4.3 + 62.04 + 8.7 = _____

19. 0.008 + 13.6 + 1.775 = _____

20. 1.838 + 2.5 + 3.32 = _____

21. 64.9 + 0.05 + 3.833 = _____

22. 44 + 0.736 + 8.1 = _____

23. 26.05 + 2.514 + 8.8 = _____

Problem Solving

24. Jenelle scored 8.913, 8.099, and 9.2 in three gymnastics events. What was her total score?

_____

25. In a charity relay walk, Mike walks 2.7 km and hands his baton to Kristen. Kristen walks 2.45 km and hands her baton to Tommy, who walks 1.98 km. How much distance do they cover?

_____

Ⓒ Use with Lesson 8-5, pages 276–277 in the Student Book.
Ⓒ Then go to Lesson 8-5A, pages 207–208 in this Workbook.

Subtract Decimals

Name _____

Date _____

Subtract: 0.9 − 0.85

To subtract decimals:

- Line up the decimal points.
- Subtract as with whole numbers.
- Write the decimal point in the difference.

$$
\begin{array}{r}
\overset{8\ 10}{0.\cancel{9}\cancel{0}} \\
-\ 0.85 \\
\hline
0.05
\end{array}
$$

0.9 = 0.90

Find the difference.

1. 0.6
− 0.4

2. 0.8
− 0.3

3. 0.35
− 0.26

4. 0.92
− 0.09

5. 0.77
− 0.54

6. 0.99
− 0.7

7. 0.58
− 0.4

8. 0.72
− 0.1

9. 0.33
− 0.2

10. 0.88
− 0.6

11. 0.9
− 0.65

12. 0.7
− 0.53

13. 0.8
− 0.37

14. 0.5
− 0.29

15. 0.6
− 0.18

Align and subtract.

16. 0.54 − 0.3 = _____

17. 0.8 − 0.46 = _____

18. 0.75 − 0.44 = _____

19. 0.7 − 0.5 = _____

20. 0.4 − 0.39 = _____

21. 0.5 − 0.26 = _____

Write the pattern rule and the next two terms in each set.

22. 0.3, 0.6, 0.9, 1.2, _?_ , _?_

_____

23. 0.71, 0.67, 0.63, 0.59, _?_ , _?_

_____

24. 0.88, 0.8, 0.72, 0.64, _?_ , _?_

_____

25. 0.15, 0.3, 0.45, 0.6, _?_ , _?_

_____

Problem Solving

26. What is the difference between 0.38 and 0.09?

_____

27. How much less than 0.7 is 0.25?

_____

28. Rafael lives 0.6 km from school. Marisa lives 0.67 km from school. Who lives farther from school? how much farther?

_____

96

Estimate Decimal Differences

Name _____

Date _____

Estimate: 4.75 − 2.36

Front-End	Rounding
4.75	4.75 ⟶ 5
− 2.36	− 2.36 ⟶ − 2
about 2.00	about 3

So the exact difference is between 2 and 3.

Estimate the difference by rounding.

1. 0.553
   − 0.274

2. 0.5
   − 0.385

3. 0.58
   − 0.316

4. 4.13
   − 2.98

Estimate the difference. Use front-end estimation.

5. 0.85
   − 0.24

6. 0.517
   − 0.284

7. 5.46
   − 3.65

8. 30.34
   − 12.06

Estimate by both rounding and front-end estimation.
Between what two numbers will the exact difference be?

9. 8.25
   − 3.76

10. 6.34
    − 3.76

11. 69.372
    − 12.53

12. 45.326
    − 23.917

_____   _____   _____   _____

_____   _____   _____   _____

Estimate. Choose a method.

13. 0.29
    −0.14

14. 0.57
    − 0.32

15. 0.34
    − 0.19

16. 42.09
    − 28.245

17. 0.538
    − 0.295

18. 6.89
    − 1.148

19. 52.385
    − 27.06

20. 33.79
    − 18.82

21. 0.89
    − 0.6

22. 0.251
    − 0.075

Problem Solving

23. Susan used 1.75 m of a 3.5-meter length
    of yarn. She needs 1 m of the yarn for
    a project. Does she have enough yarn left?   _____

Use with Lesson 8-7, pages 280–281 in the Student Book.
Then go to Lesson 8-8, pages 282–283 in the Student Book.

Subtract More Decimals

Name _____

Date _____

Subtract: 5.2 − 4.738

- Line up the decimal points.
- Subtract as usual.
- Write the decimal point
  in the difference.

$$\begin{array}{r} \overset{11\ \ 9}{} \\ \overset{4\ \ \cancel{1}\ \cancel{10}\ 10}{5.200} \\ -\ 4.738 \\ \hline 0.462 \end{array}$$

5.2 = 5.200

Use rounding to estimate. Then find the difference.

1.	8.7 − 4.3	**2.**	3.05 − 0.17	**3.**	6.26 − 3.91	**4.**	4.097 − 1.625	**5.**	9.342 − 5.806
6.	7.52 − 5.8	**7.**	12.25 − 8.1	**8.**	6.198 − 4.28	**9.**	9.077 − 8.35	**10.**	3.281 − 1.9
11.	5.5 − 2.37	**12.**	10.91 − 6.358	**13.**	8.2 − 4.019	**14.**	7.7 − 5.05	**15.**	6.04 − 3.549
16.	13.2 − 11.073	**17.**	54.1 − 0.84	**18.**	22.16 − 9.504	**19.**	33.5 − 3.55	**20.**	17 − 15.606

Align and subtract.

21. 45.6 − 3.67 = _____

22. 101.75 − 47.8 = _____

23. 5.51 − 4.936 = _____

24. 55.7 − 18.586 = _____

25. 86.13 − 0.999 = _____

26. 99.9 − 9.123 = _____

Problem Solving

27. The distance from the library to the
school is 2.7 km. The distance from
the library to Town Hall is 2.086 km.
Which is the longer distance?
by how much?

_____

28. Malik has painted 3.75 m of a fence
that is 10.5 m long. How much of the
fence is left for him to paint?

_____

Use with Lesson 8-8, pages 282–283 in the Student Book.
Then go to Lesson 8-9, pages 284–285 in the Student Book.

Problem-Solving Strategy: Use More Than One Step

Name _____

Date _____

Read ▶ Plan ▶ Solve ▶ Check

Maya walks 1.1 mi to school, then 0.85 mi to piano practice, then 0.7 mi back home. If she walks 2.5 miles per hour, does it take her more than hour to walk all those distances?

$$1.1 + 0.85 + 0.7 = \underline{\ ?\ }$$

$$
\begin{array}{r}
1 \\
1.10 \\
0.85 \\
+ 0.70 \\
\hline
2.65
\end{array}
$$

2.65 > 2.5

Yes, it takes Maya more than an hour to walk those distances.

---

1. Yuko is 1.15 m tall. His mother is 0.3 m taller than Yuko. His father is 0.26 m taller than Yuko's mother. How tall are Yuko's parents?

2. Vinnie lives 2.9 mi directly east of the movie theatre. Ellen lives twice as far directly west of the theatre. How far is it from Ellen's house to Vinnie's house?

3. Mr. and Mrs. Ortiz rode their bicycles for half an hour to the post office, for 17 minutes to the grocery store, and then for 3 minutes to the drugstore. Then they took the same route home. How long did they ride their bicycles in all?

4. Brecca noted that the temperature rose from 33.6°F at noon on Monday to 41.2°F at 2:30 P.M. On Tuesday the temperature rose from 30.9°F at noon to 43.6°F at 2:30 P.M. What was the total increase in temperature for both days?

5. Pamela buys two cartons of pineapple juice for $1.99 each. She also buys five cartons of grape juice for $1.86 each. How much money did Pamela spend on juice in all?

6. Perry buys two cans of tomato soup for $0.57 each, 1 can of minestrone for $2.49, and 3 cans of extra-chunky vegetable soup for $1.29 each. How much does Perry pay in all?

Use with Lesson 8-9, pages 284–285 in the Student Book.
Then go to Lesson 8-10, pages 286–287 in the Student Book.

99

Problem-Solving Applications: Mixed Review

Name _____

Date _____

Solve each problem and explain the method you used. If needed, do all your work on a separate sheet of paper.

Strategy File

Use These Strategies
Use More Than One Step
Make an Organized List
Guess and Test
Work Backward
Use a Model/Diagram

1. Chandra has 4 places she wants to visit. She can drive, take a train, or fly to each place. She can either go with her friend Elsa or by herself. How many different ways can Chandra configure her vacation?

_____

2. It takes Alan 2.6 minutes to make a sandwich. It takes him 0.14 minutes to pour a glass of juice. How long does it take him to do both 3 times?

_____

3. Of the 61 people at the recital, 44 could play the violin, 26 could play the cello, and 9 could play both instruments. How many people could play only the cello?

_____

4. Erika wants to buy batteries for $5.39 and a magazine for $3.95, but she is $.59 short. How much money does she have?

_____

5. Bob and Tara together can lift 318.7 lb. Bob can lift 22.1 more lb than Tara. How much can Bob and Tara each lift?

_____

6. Sales at Terri's Tackle went up 1.4% in June, down 4.87% in July, up 3% in August, and down 1.33% in September. Did Terri's sales rise or fall over those four months? by how much?

_____

7. Sasha sold 2 lbs of potato salad at the fair. If she ate 4 oz for lunch and had 8 oz left over, how much potato salad did Sasha start with?

_____

8. Benny has $1.35 in quarters, dimes, and nickels. He has less nickels than dimes, and less dimes than quarters. What coins does Benny have?

_____

9. Juanita runs a mile in 8.7 minutes. If she starts at 3:30 P.M. and runs three miles, will she be done by 4:00 P.M?

_____

Use with Lesson 8-10, pages 286–287 in the Student Book.

Multiply by 10, 100, and 1000

Name _____

Date _____

Multiply:

$10 \times 0.437 = 4.37$ ← | 1 zero. Move 1 place to the right.

$100 \times 0.058 = 5.8$ ← | 2 zeros. Move 2 places to the right.

$1000 \times 0.007 = 7$ ← | 3 zeros. Move 3 places to the right.

$1000 \times 9.600 = 9600$ ← | 3 zeros. Move 3 places to the right. Write 2 zeros as placeholders.

Write the product.

1. $10 \times 0.637 =$ _____
$100 \times 0.637 =$ _____
$1000 \times 0.637 =$ _____

2. $10 \times 0.003 =$ _____
$100 \times 0.003 =$ _____
$1000 \times 0.003 =$ _____

3. $10 \times 1.008 =$ _____
$100 \times 1.008 =$ _____
$1000 \times 1.008 =$ _____

4. $10 \times 0.12 =$ _____
$100 \times 0.12 =$ _____
$1000 \times 0.12 =$ _____

5. $10 \times 6.47 =$ _____
$100 \times 6.47 =$ _____
$1000 \times 6.47 =$ _____

6. $10 \times 0.9 =$ _____
$100 \times 0.9 =$ _____
$1000 \times 0.9 =$ _____

Multiply.

7. $10 \times 0.03 =$ _____

8. $100 \times 0.237 =$ _____

9. $1000 \times 0.036 =$ _____

10. $100 \times 0.004 =$ _____

11. $10 \times 7.5 =$ _____

12. $100 \times 24.8 =$ _____

13. $1000 \times 0.001 =$ _____

14. $10 \times 6.841 =$ _____

15. $1000 \times 4.3 =$ _____

Find the missing factor.

16. $n \times 0.703 = 70.3$

$n =$ _____

17. $n \times 0.084 = 0.84$

$n =$ _____

18. $n \times 0.523 = 523$

$n =$ _____

Find the product.

19. $20 \times 0.7 =$ ___

20. $50 \times 0.3 =$ ___

21. $400 \times 0.4 =$ ___

22. $700 \times 0.7 =$ ___

23. $600 \times 0.2 =$ ___

24. $300 \times 0.8 =$ ___

25. $90 \times 0.6 =$ ___

26. $60 \times 0.1 =$ ___

Problem Solving

27. Grace bought a 10 lb turkey at $1.19 per pound. How much did she spend?

_____

28. If Debbie walked 1.026 mi each day for 100 days, how far did she walk?

_____

Use with Lesson 9-1, pages 294–295 in the Student Book.
Then go to Lesson 9-2, pages 296–297 in the Student Book.

Estimate
Decimal Products

Name _____

Date _____

Estimate: 4.2 × 0.843	Estimate: 56.93 × 0.452	Estimate: 1.03 + 1.2 + 0.9
0.843 ⟶ 0.8 × 4.2 ⟶ × 4 about 3.2	0.452 ⟶ 0.5 × 56.93 ⟶ × 60 about 30.0	1.03 + 1.2 + 0.9 ↓ ↓ ↓ 1 + 1 + 1 Use clustering: 3 × 1 = 3
Both factors are rounded down. The actual product is greater than 3.2.	Both factors are rounded up. The actual product is less than 30.	So the sum is about 3.

**Estimate each product. Then tell whether the actual product
is greater than or *is less than* the estimated product.**

1. 5.21
    × 4.3

2. 0.98
    × 7.61

3. 4.52
    × 3.8

4. 1.208
    × 5.1

5. 2.534
    × 8.63

6. 9.127
    × 6.04

7. 4.008
    × 2.09

8. 5.375
    × 9.25

9. 18.54
    × 0.78

10. 61.203
    × 0.42

11. 72.842
    × 0.63

12. 38.002
    × 0.49

Estimate the sum. Use clustering.

13. 6.13 + 5.9 + 6.008 _____

14. 0.82 + 0.8 + 0.84 + 0.79 + 0.78 _____

15. 42.1 + 39.5 + 41.4 + 40.75 + 39.631 _____

16. 7.004 + 6.75 + 6.891 + 7.2 + 7.5 + 7.4 _____

17. $.25 + $.32 + $.34 + $.28 _____

18. $.07 + $.13 + $.06 + $.13 + $.14 _____

19. $1.05 + $.98 + $.95 + $1.02 _____

20. $.45 + $.51 + $.54 + $.49 + $.48 _____

Problem Solving

21. Pilar packs 6.1 cartons per hour. At this rate, about how
    many cartons can she pack in 2.25 hours?   _____

22. Mark prints 17.5 pages on his printer each hour.
    About how many pages can he print in 7.8 hours?   _____

23. Jane weighs samples of a salt and water solution. The
    samples weigh 3.5 g, 4.01 g, 4.3 g, 3.75 g, and 3.9 g.
    About how much do all the samples weigh together?   _____

Use with Lesson 9-2, pages 296–297 in the Student Book.
Then go to Lesson 9-2A, pages 209–210 in this Workbook.

Multiply Decimals by Whole Numbers

Name _____

Date _____

$7 \times 0.5 = \underline{?}$

$$\begin{array}{r} 0.5 \\ \times\ 7 \\ \hline 3.5 \end{array}$$

1 decimal place

$23 \times 3.12 = \underline{?}$

$$\begin{array}{r} 3.12 \\ \times\ 23 \\ \hline 936 \\ +\ 6240 \\ \hline 71.76 \end{array}$$

2 decimal places

$31 \times \$15.25 = \underline{?}$

$$\begin{array}{r} \$15.25 \\ \times\ 31 \\ \hline 1525 \\ +\ 45750 \\ \hline \$472.75 \end{array}$$

2 decimal places with money

Write the decimal point in each product.

1.
$$\begin{array}{r} 3.7 \\ \times\ 2 \\ \hline 74 \end{array}$$

2.
$$\begin{array}{r} 8.23 \\ \times\ 15 \\ \hline 12345 \end{array}$$

3.
$$\begin{array}{r} 0.31 \\ \times\ 7 \\ \hline 217 \end{array}$$

4.
$$\begin{array}{r} 6.54 \\ \times\ 12 \\ \hline 7848 \end{array}$$

5.
$$\begin{array}{r} 3.264 \\ \times\ 63 \\ \hline 205632 \end{array}$$

Use rounding to estimate. Then find the product.

6.
$$\begin{array}{r} 0.5 \\ \times\ 19 \end{array}$$

7.
$$\begin{array}{r} 0.3 \\ \times\ 42 \end{array}$$

8.
$$\begin{array}{r} 0.76 \\ \times\ 28 \end{array}$$

9.
$$\begin{array}{r} 1.04 \\ \times\ 16 \end{array}$$

10.
$$\begin{array}{r} 0.089 \\ \times\ 47 \end{array}$$

11.
$$\begin{array}{r} 3.059 \\ \times\ 14 \end{array}$$

12.
$$\begin{array}{r} 3.427 \\ \times\ 53 \end{array}$$

13.
$$\begin{array}{r} \$.34 \\ \times\ 12 \end{array}$$

14.
$$\begin{array}{r} \$6.37 \\ \times\ 45 \end{array}$$

15.
$$\begin{array}{r} \$23.82 \\ \times\ 68 \end{array}$$

Find the product.

16. $8 \times 0.4 =$ _____

17. $2 \times 0.315 =$ _____

18. $7 \times 0.86 =$ _____

19. $5 \times 0.236 =$ _____

20. $4 \times 4.9 =$ _____

21. $3 \times 1.064 =$ _____

22. $7 \times 8.703 =$ _____

23. $12 \times 12.8 =$ _____

24. $23 \times 16.5 =$ _____

25. two times eighteen hundredths = _____

26. six times thirty-four thousandths = _____

27. $n \times 7.69$ when $n = 4$ _____

28. $19.2 \times n$ when $n = 5.6$ _____

Problem Solving

29. A can contains 6.5 oz of tuna fish. How many ounces do 15 cans contain?

_____

30. Marilyn bought 6 cans of tuna at $1.29 a can. How much did she spend?

_____

C Use with Lesson 9-3, pages 298–299 in the Student Book.
C Then go to Lesson 9-3A, pages 211–212 in this Workbook.

103

Multiply Decimals by Decimals

Name _____

Date _____

$0.5 \times 0.7 =$ __?__

35 out of 100 squares are marked off.

So $0.5 \times 0.7 = 0.35$.

Multiply: $4.2 \times 3.08 =$ __?__

```
    3.08  ←  [2 decimal places]
  ×  4.2  ←  [1 decimal place]
    6 16
  1232 0
  12.936  ←  [3 decimal places]
```

Use the diagram to complete each statement.

1.

$0.3 \times 0.6 =$ _____

2.

$0.7 \times$ _____ $= 0.42$

3.

_____ $\times$ _____ $= 0.32$

Find the product.

4.	5.	6.	7.	8.
5.9 × 0.6	3.76 × 3.4	7.13 × 0.4	15.2 × 0.03	18.2 × 0.05

9.	10.	11.	12.	13.
3.1 × 0.7	20.5 × 3.4	0.37 × 2.1	36.2 × 0.83	24.6 × 0.3

14. $n \times 3.7$ when $n = 5.3$ _____

15. $n \times 28.9$ when $n = 6.1$ _____

16. $0.8 \times n$ when $n = 4.6$ _____

17. $18.7 \times n$ when $n = 0.15$ _____

Problem Solving

18. A nature trail is 24.8 km long. Lizzie has hiked 0.65 of the length. How many kilometers has Lizzie hiked? _____

19. Jim paid $3.25 per pound for lamb chops. How much did he pay for a 2.2 lb package? _____

Ⓒ Use with Lesson 9-4, pages 300–301 in the Student Book.
Ⓒ Then go to Lesson 9-5, pages 302–303 in the Student Book.

Zeros in the Product

Name _____

Date _____

$0.3 \times 0.02 = \underline{\ ?\ }$

Multiply as with whole numbers.

$$\begin{array}{r} 0.02 \\ \times\ 0.3 \\ \hline 6 \end{array}$$

Write the decimal point in the product.

$$\begin{array}{r} 0.02 \\ \times\ 0.3 \\ \hline 0.006 \end{array}$$

0.02 ← 2 decimal places
× 0.3 ← 1 decimal place
0.006 ← 3 decimal places

Write 2 zeros to the left of 6.

Write the decimal point in the product. Write in zeros where necessary.

1.
$$\begin{array}{r} 0.3 \\ \times\ 0.7 \\ \hline 21 \end{array}$$

2.
$$\begin{array}{r} 0.2 \\ \times\ 0.4 \\ \hline 8 \end{array}$$

3.
$$\begin{array}{r} 0.43 \\ \times\ 0.5 \\ \hline 215 \end{array}$$

4.
$$\begin{array}{r} 0.41 \\ \times\ 0.3 \\ \hline 123 \end{array}$$

5.
$$\begin{array}{r} 0.05 \\ \times\ 0.1 \\ \hline 5 \end{array}$$

Multiply.

6.
$$\begin{array}{r} 0.53 \\ \times\ 0.4 \\ \hline \end{array}$$

7.
$$\begin{array}{r} 0.23 \\ \times\ 0.3 \\ \hline \end{array}$$

8.
$$\begin{array}{r} 0.05 \\ \times\ 0.8 \\ \hline \end{array}$$

9.
$$\begin{array}{r} 0.02 \\ \times\ 0.6 \\ \hline \end{array}$$

10.
$$\begin{array}{r} 0.04 \\ \times\ 0.4 \\ \hline \end{array}$$

11.
$$\begin{array}{r} 0.002 \\ \times\ 0.8 \\ \hline \end{array}$$

12.
$$\begin{array}{r} 0.05 \\ \times\ 0.3 \\ \hline \end{array}$$

13.
$$\begin{array}{r} 6.3 \\ \times\ 0.4 \\ \hline \end{array}$$

14.
$$\begin{array}{r} 9.1 \\ \times\ 0.03 \\ \hline \end{array}$$

15.
$$\begin{array}{r} 2.6 \\ \times\ 0.05 \\ \hline \end{array}$$

Find the product.

16. $1.2 \times 0.02 =$ _____

17. $6.1 \times 0.01 =$ _____

18. $0.02 \times 0.3 =$ _____

19. $4 \times 0.002 =$ _____

20. $4.1 \times 0.02 =$ _____

21. $0.5 \times 0.07 =$ _____

Circle the letter of the correct answer.

22. 6×0.005 **a.** 0.3   **b.** 0.03   **c.** 0.003

23. 7×0.004 **a.** 0.028   **b.** 0.28   **c.** 2.8

24. 0.08×0.5 **a.** 0.4   **b.** 0.04   **c.** 0.004

Problem Solving

25. Don has 6 test tubes each containing 0.01 L of a glucose solution. How much glucose solution does he have?

_____

26. A piece of wire measured 0.03 m. Jane cut off 0.3 of the wire. How long was the piece she cut off?

_____

C Use with Lesson 9-5, pages 302–303 in the Student Book.
C Then go to Lesson 9-6, pages 304–305 in the Student Book.

105

Divide by
10, 100, and 1000

Name _____

Date _____

Divide:

$4.2 \div \mathbf{10} = 0.42$ ← 1 zero. Move 1 place to the left.

$12.5 \div \mathbf{100} = 0.125$ ← 2 zeros. Move 2 places to the left.

$174 \div \mathbf{1000} = 0.174$ ← 3 zeros. Move 3 places to the left.

$07.1 \div \mathbf{100} = 0.071$ ← 2 zeros. Move 2 places to the left. Write 1 zero as a place holder.

Write the quotient.

1. $521.6 \div 10 = $ _____

   $521.6 \div 100 = $ _____

2. $647 \div 10 = $ _____

   $647 \div 100 = $ _____

3. $73.9 \div 10 = $ _____

   $73.9 \div 100 = $ _____

4. $1825 \div 10 = $ _____

   $1825 \div 100 = $ _____

   $1825 \div 1000 = $ _____

5. $88 \div 10 = $ _____

   $88 \div 100 = $ _____

   $88 \div 1000 = $ _____

6. $4 \div 10 = $ _____

   $4 \div 100 = $ _____

   $4 \div 1000 = $ _____

Divide.

7. $0.6 \div 10 = $ _____

8. $0.03 \div 10 = $ _____

9. $7 \div 10 = $ _____

10. $5.32 \div 10 = $ _____

11. $0.9 \div 100 = $ _____

12. $4 \div 100 = $ _____

13. $16.7 \div 100 = $ _____

14. $0.36 \div 10 = $ _____

15. $4781.9 \div 100 = $ _____

Find the missing number.

16. $5.06 \div n = 0.506$

    $n = $ _____

17. $7.3 \div n = 0.073$

    $n = $ _____

18. $78 \div n = 0.078$

    $n = $ _____

19. $n \div 1000 = 4.125$

    $n = $ _____

20. $n \div 100 = 0.68$

    $n = $ _____

21. $n \div 1000 = 0.012$

    $n = $ _____

Problem Solving

22. Howard cut 658.4 cm of rope into 100 equal pieces. How long is each piece? _____

23. A sporting goods store paid $19,950 for 1000 sweatshirts. How much did each sweatshirt cost? _____

C Use with Lesson 9-6, pages 304–305 in the Student Book.
C Then go to Lesson 9-6A, pages 213–214 in this Workbook.

Divide Decimals by Whole Numbers

Name _____

Date _____

Divide: 3.76 ÷ 4

Write the decimal point of the quotient above the decimal point of the dividend.

$$4\overline{)3.76}$$

Divide as you would with whole numbers.

$$\begin{array}{r} 0.94 \\ 4\overline{)3.76} \\ -\,36 \\ \hline 16 \\ -\,16 \\ \hline 0 \end{array}$$

4 > 3 **Not enough** ones
4 < 37 **Enough** tenths
The quotient begins in the tenths place.

Check.
$$\begin{array}{r} 0.94 \\ \times\quad 4 \\ \hline 3.76 \end{array}$$

Divide and check.

1. $4\overline{)1.6}$
2. $7\overline{)3.5}$
3. $9\overline{)8.1}$
4. $7\overline{)6.3}$

5. $5\overline{)0.70}$
6. $2\overline{)0.38}$
7. $3\overline{)0.54}$
8. $6\overline{)0.96}$

9. $6\overline{)\$.78}$
10. $5\overline{)\$9.45}$
11. $6\overline{)\$21.72}$
12. $8\overline{)\$77.36}$

13. $4.2 \div 7 =$ _____
14. $11.8 \div 2 =$ _____
15. $\$.87 \div 3 =$ _____

16. $2.59 \div 7 =$ _____
17. $49.38 \div 6 =$ _____
18. $\$25.35 \div 3 =$ _____

19. $\$58.48 \div 8 =$ _____
20. $\$18.99 \div 9 =$ _____
21. $\$8.12 \div 7 =$ _____

Compare. Write <, =, or >.

22. $1.8 \div 3$ _____ $0.96 \div 8$
23. $6.75 \div 5$ _____ $12.15 \div 9$

24. $0.09 \div 6$ _____ $0.07 \div 1$
25. $\$24.16 \div 8$ _____ $\$49.95 \div 5$

Problem Solving

26. If Carmen paid $32.70 for 5 rolls of film, how much did she pay for each roll? _____

27. If Mrs. Singer has $15.24 and distributes it equally among her 6 grandchildren, how much money do they each get? _____

Use with Lesson 9-7, pages 306–307 in the Student Book.
Then go to Lesson 9-8, pages 308–309 in the Student Book.

107

Zeros in Division

Name _____

Date _____

Divide: $0.215 \div 5 =$ __?__

Write the decimal point in the quotient.

$$5\overline{)0.215}$$

Divide.

$$5\overline{)0.21^15}$$
$$0.043$$

$5 > 2$ **Not enough** tenths
Write 0 in the tenths place.
$5 < 21$ **Enough** hundredths
The quotient begins in the hundredths place.

Check.

$$\begin{array}{r} 0.043 \\ \times 5 \\ \hline 0.215 \end{array}$$

Divide and check.

1. $6\overline{)0.024}$ **2.** $3\overline{)0.006}$ **3.** $7\overline{)7.21}$ **4.** $9\overline{)36.27}$

5. $4\overline{)8.12}$ **6.** $3\overline{)2.118}$ **7.** $4\overline{)4.12}$ **8.** $6\overline{)0.018}$

9. $5\overline{)\$0.80}$ **10.** $8\overline{)\$0.64}$ **11.** $4\overline{)\$4.20}$ **12.** $6\overline{)\$9.60}$

13. $0.510 \div 5 =$ _____ **14.** $\$9.06 \div 3 =$ _____ **15.** $5.76 \div 8 =$ _____

16. $\$24.30 \div 6 =$ _____ **17.** $2.448 \div 6 =$ _____ **18.** $\$86.00 \div 5 =$ _____

Divide. Round the quotient to the nearest thousandth.

19. $3\overline{)8.5}$ **20.** $7\overline{)3.2}$ **21.** $6\overline{)5.3}$ **22.** $3\overline{)9.44}$

23. $9\overline{)0.53}$ **24.** $7\overline{)0.81}$ **25.** $9\overline{)0.93}$ **26.** $6\overline{)0.82}$

Use with Lesson 9-8, pages 308–309 in the Student Book.
Then go to Lessons 9-8A and 9-8B, pages 215–218 in this Workbook.

Estimate Decimal Quotients

Name _____

Date _____

Estimate: $251.72 \div 8$	Estimate: $4.53 \div 6$

$$\overset{30.00}{8\overline{)251.72}}$$

8 > 2 **Not enough** hundreds
8 < 25 **Enough** tens
The quotient begins in the tens place.
About how many 8s in 25? **3**

The quotient is greater than 30.

Use compatible numbers.

$$6\overline{)4.53}$$

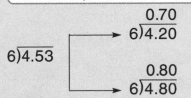

$$\overset{0.70}{6\overline{)4.20}}$$

$$\overset{0.80}{6\overline{)4.80}}$$

The quotient is between 0.70 and 0.80.

Estimate the quotient.

1. $5\overline{)0.156}$ **2.** $8\overline{)0.651}$ **3.** $4\overline{)2.542}$ **4.** $7\overline{)5.125}$

5. $6\overline{)13.025}$ **6.** $5\overline{)45.834}$ **7.** $8\overline{)10.728}$ **8.** $9\overline{)9.381}$

9. $3\overline{)0.71}$ **10.** $2\overline{)7.306}$ **11.** $6\overline{)26.535}$ **12.** $9\overline{)67.733}$

13. $0.576 \div 2 =$ _____   **14.** $9.183 \div 7 =$ _____   **15.** $45.206 \div 6 =$ _____

Estimate the quotient. Use compatible numbers.

16. $6\overline{)4.765}$ **17.** $8\overline{)7.196}$ **18.** $7\overline{)5.528}$ **19.** $4\overline{)29.001}$

20. $52\overline{)3.162}$ **21.** $68\overline{)4.305}$ **22.** $4\overline{)13.25}$ **23.** $6\overline{)3.55}$

24. $1.52 \div 7 =$ _____   **25.** $91 \div 28.13 =$ _____   **26.** $152.68 \div 32 =$ _____

Problem Solving

27. Ms. Yakimoto drove 354.046 km in 4 hours. About how many kilometers did she drive in one hour?   _____

28. There are 589.7 mL of water evenly divided into 222 test tubes. About how much water is in each test tube?   _____

Use with Lesson 9-9, pages 310–311 in the Student Book.
Then go to Lesson 9-10, pages 312–313 in the Student Book.

109

Estimate with Money

Name _____

Date _____

Estimate: $25.56 ÷ 3

Use compatible numbers.

$$3)\overline{\$25.56}$$

$$\begin{array}{r} \$\ 8.00 \\ 3)\overline{\$24.00} \\ \$\ 9.00 \\ 3)\overline{\$27.00} \end{array}$$

The exact quotient is between $8.00 and $9.00.

Divide: $4.34 ÷ 3 = _?_

$$\begin{array}{r} \$1.4\,4\,6 \\ 3)\overline{\$4.^13^14^20} \end{array}$$

6 > 5
Round **up** to $1.45.

Add a zero in the dividend.

**Write what compatible numbers you would use.
Then estimate the quotient.**

1. $4)\overline{\$2.17}$

2. $8)\overline{\$7.25}$

3. $2)\overline{\$1.49}$

4. $5)\overline{\$3.35}$

_____   _____   _____   _____

5. $52)\overline{\$98.35}$

6. $16)\overline{\$74.39}$

7. $33)\overline{\$68.98}$

8. $25)\overline{\$78.16}$

_____   _____   _____   _____

9. $165.27 ÷ 14 = _____

10. $346.64 ÷ 28 = _____

11. $296.50 ÷ 65 = _____

12. $835.12 ÷ 38 = _____

Divide. Round the quotient to the nearest cent.

13. $7)\overline{\$8.85}$

14. $9)\overline{\$8.70}$

15. $6)\overline{\$7.41}$

16. $5)\overline{\$4.92}$

17. $8)\overline{\$42.36}$

18. $4)\overline{\$27.41}$

19. $3)\overline{\$65.51}$

20. $7)\overline{\$22.09}$

Problem Solving

21. Jamal bought 5 lb of onions for $4.98. About how much did 1 lb of onions cost?

_____

22. One dozen fine-point pens cost $15.39 and 5 erasers cost $2.39. To the nearest cent, what is the cost of 1 fine-point pen? What is the cost of 1 eraser?

_____

Use with Lesson 9-10, pages 312–313 in the Student Book.
Then go to Lesson 9-11, pages 314–315 in the Student Book.

Problem-Solving Strategy: Write a Number Sentence

Name _____

Date _____

Frank hiked 0.75 as far as his brother, Joe.
If Joe hiked 4.8 miles, how far did Frank hike?

Let *d* represent the unknown distance.

0.75 × 4.8 mi = *d*

0.75 × 4.8 mi = 3.6 mi; *d* = 3.6 mi

Frank hiked 3.6 miles.

Solve. Do your work on a separate sheet of paper.

1. Harry's cat weighs 8.75 lb, and Maria's cat weighs 3.65 lb more. How much does Maria's cat weigh?

2. Lisa can run 3 miles in 24.12 min. How long will it take her to run 1 mile if she runs each mile at the same speed?

3. Nina bought 4.3 lb of potato salad and 3.65 lb of macaroni salad for a picnic. How much more potato salad than macaroni salad did she buy?

4. The distance from Paul's house to the lake shore is 86.25 m. The distance from the lake shore to the raft is 3.8 m. What is the total distance from Paul's house to the raft?

5. At Oscar's Office Supply Center, one pen costs $1.19. How much do 15 of the same kind of pens cost?

6. Sam earns $5.88 per hour. Last week he worked 9.5 hours. How much did he earn?

7. Judy is half as old as Shawn. If Shawn is 23.5 years old, how old is Judy?

8. Mr. Watanabi drives 224.4 mi in 4 h. What is his rate of speed per hour?

9. Beth lifts weights at the gym. She lifts 5.5 lb on Monday and 7 lb on Tuesday. How much more does she lift on Tuesday than on Monday?

10. Marisol's sister lives 144 miles away. If Marisol drives at a rate of 48 miles per hour, how long should it take her to drive to her sister's house?

Use with Lesson 9-11, pages 314–315 in the Student Book.
Then go to Lesson 9-12, pages 316–317 in the Student Book.

111

Problem-Solving
Applications: Mixed Review

Name _____

Date _____

Solve each problem and explain the method you used. If needed, do all your work on a separate sheet of paper.

Read ▶ Plan ▶ Solve ▶ Check

Strategy File

Use These Strategies
Write a Number Sentence
Use More Than One Step
Logical Reasoning
Use a Model/Diagram

1. Jodi's flower is 3.57 cm tall. Ahmed's flower is three times taller than Jodi's. How tall is Ahmed's flower?

_____

2. It is 5.1 km from Amy's house to Sondra's house. It is 0.6 as far from Amy's house to Gail's house. How far is it from Amy's house to Gail's house?

_____

3. Brandon runs 100 m in 13.4 s. If he runs each 100 m 0.45 s slower than the previous 100 m, how long does it take Brandon to run 400 m?

_____

4. Geri is 33.5 years old. One of her two friends, Sarita and Val, is older than her. Geri and Sarita's combined age is 66.75 years. Who is the oldest member of the group?

_____

5. Ty has 27.63 kg of comic books. He wants to divide them equally among his three brothers. Will he be able to do that?

_____

6. Shawn caught a fish that weighed 5328 g. He cut it into 6 equal parts. How many kg did each part weigh?

_____

7. Saul went on a diet on February 1st. If February has 28 days and Saul loses 0.3 lb a day, will he lose 10 lb by March 1st?

_____

8. Fran has a stack of paper. Each sheet weighs 0.03 g. If she has 38 sheets, how much does the stack of paper weigh?

_____

9. Rachel has 0.09 L of a liquid. Joel has 10 times that much. If Sara has 1 L of that liquid, who has the most? the least?

_____

Use with Lesson 9-12, pages 316–317 in the Student Book.

Measure and Draw Angles

Name _____

Date _____

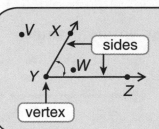

Name: ∠Y or ∠XYZ or ∠ZYX

Sides: $\overrightarrow{YX}$, $\overrightarrow{YZ}$

Vertex: Y

∠Y measures 60°.

V is in the **exterior** of ∠XYZ.

W is in the **interior** of ∠XYZ.

Name the sides and vertex of each angle, and tell whether point X is in the _interior_ or _exterior_ of the angle.

1.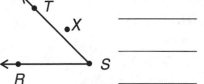
_____
_____
_____

2.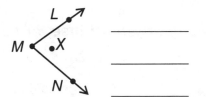
_____
_____
_____

3.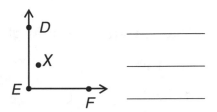
_____
_____
_____

Estimate the measure of each angle. Then use a protractor to find the exact measure of each angle.

4.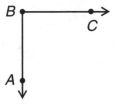
_____
_____

5.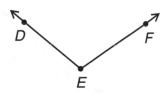
_____
_____

6.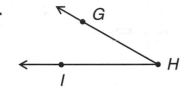
_____
_____

7.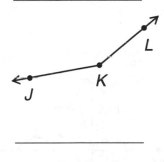
_____
_____

8.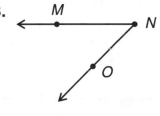
_____
_____

9.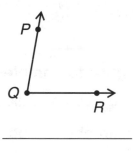
_____
_____

Use a protractor to draw each angle. Then label each angle.

10. 85°

11. 130°

12. 100°

Use with Lesson 10-1, pages 324–325 in the Student Book.
Then go to Lesson 10-2, pages 326–327 in the Student Book.

113

Identify Angles

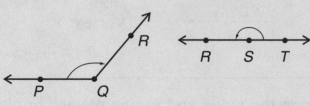

right angle	acute angle	obtuse angle	straight angle
∠ABC = 90°	∠DEF < 90°	∠PQR > 90°	∠RST = 180°

Write whether each angle is *acute, right, obtuse,* or *straight*.

1. 130° _____ **2.** 15° _____ **3.** 88° _____ **4.** 90° _____

5. 7° _____ **6.** 94° _____ **7.** 174° _____ **8.** 180° _____

Find the measure of each angle. Then classify the angle.

9.   10. 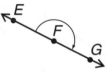 11. 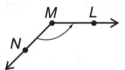 12.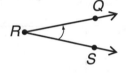

_____ _____ _____ _____

13.  14. 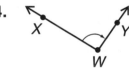 15.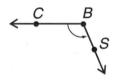

_____ _____ _____

Use the figure to complete exercises 16–18.

16. Name an acute angle. _____

17. Name an obtuse angle. _____

18. Name a right angle. _____

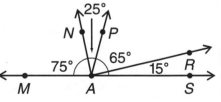

**Are the lines perpendicular? Write *Yes* or *No*.
Use a protractor to check.**

19.  20.  21.   22.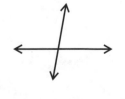

_____ _____ _____ _____

Use with Lesson 10-2, pages 326–327 in the Student Book.
Then go to Lesson 10-3, pages 328–329 in the Student Book.

Polygons

Name _____

Date _____

A polygon is a closed plane figure made up of line segments that meet at vertices but do not cross.

Polygons

   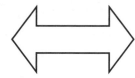

Write the number of sides, vertices, and angles.

1.

   Sides: _____
   Vertices: _____
   Angles: _____

2.

   Sides: _____
   Vertices: _____
   Angles: _____

3.

   Sides: _____
   Vertices: _____
   Angles: _____

4.

   Sides: _____
   Vertices: _____
   Angles: _____

Complete the table. Then answer the question.

	Name of Polygon	Number of Sides	Number of Angles	Drawing of Polygon
5.	Heptagon	7	?	
6.	Octagon	?	?	?
7.	Nonagon	9	?	?
8.	Decagon	?	10	?

9. What can you say about the number of sides and the number of angles

   for each polygon? _____

Draw four different polygons. Write the number of sides and angles.

10. · · · · · · ·
    · · · · · · ·
    · · · · · · ·
    · · · · · · ·
    · · · · · · ·
    · · · · · · ·

    Sides: _____

    Angles: _____

11. · · · · · · ·
    · · · · · · ·
    · · · · · · ·
    · · · · · · ·
    · · · · · · ·
    · · · · · · ·

    Sides: _____

    Angles: _____

12. · · · · · · ·
    · · · · · · ·
    · · · · · · ·
    · · · · · · ·
    · · · · · · ·
    · · · · · · ·

    Sides: _____

    Angles: _____

13. · · · · · · ·
    · · · · · · ·
    · · · · · · ·
    · · · · · · ·
    · · · · · · ·
    · · · · · · ·

    Sides: _____

    Angles: _____

Use with Lesson 10-3, pages 328–329 in the Student Book.
Then go to Lesson 10-4, pages 330–331 in the Student Book.

115

Congruent and Similar Figures

Name _____

Date _____

Congruent Polygons	Similar Polygons

Congruent Polygons

Corresponding Sides:

$\overline{AB} \cong \overline{DE}$
$\overline{AC} \cong \overline{DF}$
$\overline{BC} \cong \overline{EF}$

Corresponding Angles:

$\angle A \cong \angle D$
$\angle B \cong \angle E$
$\angle C \cong \angle F$

$\triangle ABC \cong \triangle DEF$

Similar Polygons

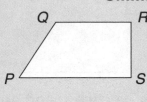

Corresponding Angles:

$\angle P \cong \angle W$
$\angle Q \cong \angle X$
$\angle R \cong \angle Y$
$\angle S \cong \angle Z$

Quadrilateral *PQRS* ~ Quadrilateral *WXYZ*

Do the figures appear to be congruent? Write *Yes* or *No*.

1. _____ **2.** _____ **3.** _____

Find the corresponding sides and the corresponding angles of the given congruent quadrilaterals.

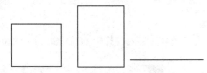

4. $\overline{LK} \cong$ _____ **5.** $\overline{LM} \cong$ _____

6. $\overline{KN} \cong$ _____ **7.** $\overline{MN} \cong$ _____

8. $\angle K \cong$ _____ **9.** $\angle M \cong$ _____

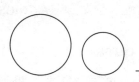

Quadrilateral *KLMN* $\cong$ Quadrilateral *QRST*

Do the figures appear to be similar? Write *Yes* or *No*.

10. _____

11. _____

12. _____

Use the symbol $\cong$ to identify corresponding angles.

13.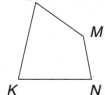

Quadrilateral *WXYZ* ~ Quadrilateral *ABCD*

_____

14.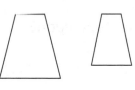

$\triangle MLN \sim \triangle PQR$

_____

Use with Lesson 10-4, pages 330–331 in the Student Book.
Then go to Lesson 10-5, pages 332–333 in the Student Book.

Triangles

Name _____

Date _____

Triangles may be classified by the length of their sides or by the measures of their angles. The sum of the measures of the angles of a triangle is 180°.

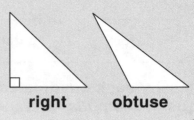 

scalene   **isosceles**   **equilateral** | **acute**   **right**   **obtuse**

Classify each triangle as *scalene*, *isosceles*, or *equilateral*.

1.

2.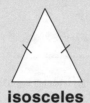

3.

4.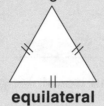

_____   _____   _____   _____

5.

6.

7.

8.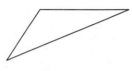

_____   _____   _____   _____

Classify each triangle as *acute*, *right*, or *obtuse*.

9.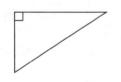

10.

11.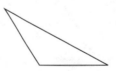

12.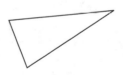

_____   _____   _____   _____

13.

14.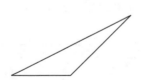

15.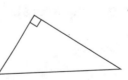

16.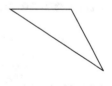

_____   _____   _____   _____

Is it possible for each triangle to have the given angle measures? Write *Yes* or *No*.

17.
60°
60° 55°

18.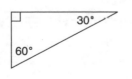
30°
60°

19.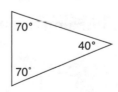
70°
70° 40°

20.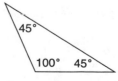
45°
100° 45°

_____   _____   _____   _____

C Use with Lesson 10-5, pages 332–333 in the Student Book.
C Then go to Lesson 10-6, pages 334–335 in the Student Book.

117

Quadrilaterals

Name _____

Date _____

 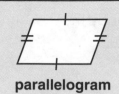 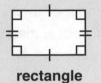 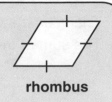

Classify each quadrilateral in as many ways as possible: *parallelogram, rectangle, square, rhombus,* **or** *trapezoid.*

1.

2.

3.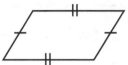

4.

_____ _____ _____ _____

5.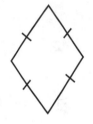

6.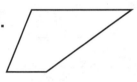

7.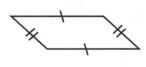

8.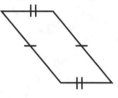

_____ _____ _____ _____

Draw all the diagonals for each figure. Then write the number of diagonals.

9.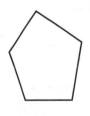

10.

11.

_____ _____ _____

Write the name of each quadrilateral. Use the figure below.

12. figure *ACEH* _____

13. figure *BDJI* _____

14. figure *BDHI* _____

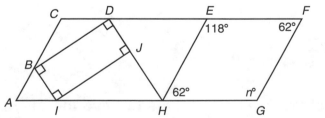

Find the measure of the missing angle in quadrilateral *EFGH*.

15. $n =$ _____

Use with Lesson 10-6, pages 334–335 in the Student Book.
Then go to Lesson 10-6A, pages 219–220 in this Workbook.

Perimeter

Name _____

Date _____

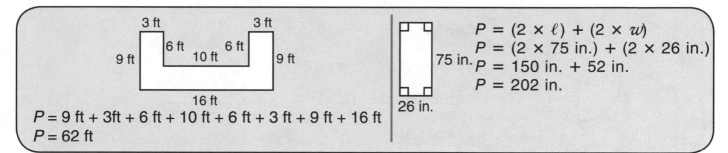

$P = 9\text{ ft} + 3\text{ft} + 6\text{ ft} + 10\text{ ft} + 6\text{ ft} + 3\text{ ft} + 9\text{ ft} + 16\text{ ft}$
$P = 62\text{ ft}$

$P = (2 \times \ell) + (2 \times w)$
$P = (2 \times 75\text{ in.}) + (2 \times 26\text{ in.})$
$P = 150\text{ in.} + 52\text{ in.}$
$P = 202\text{ in.}$

Find the perimeter of each polygon.

1.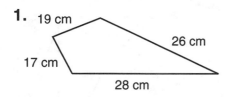

_____

2.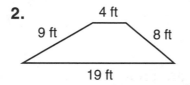

_____

3.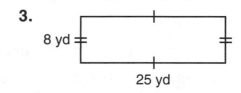

_____

4.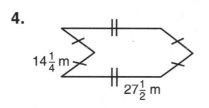

_____

5.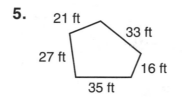

_____

6.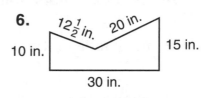

_____

Complete the table.

	Polygon	Length of One Side	Perimeter
7.	square	14 in.	
8.	regular pentagon	6 ft	
9.	equilateral triangle	5 in.	
10.	regular hexagon		18 m
11.	regular octagon	7 cm	
12.	regular decagon		90 yd
13.	square	12 mm	

Problem Solving You may draw a diagram.

14. A rectangular garden is 23 ft wide and 35 ft long. How many feet of fencing are needed to enclose the garden?

_____

15. The sides of a quadrilateral have lengths of 18 in., 24 in., 35 in., and 19 in. Find the perimeter.

_____

16. Each side of a square park measures 160 yd. If Gina walks twice around the outside of the park, how many yards does she walk?

_____

Use with Lesson 10-7, pages 336–337 in the Student Book.
Then go to Lesson 10-8, pages 338–339 in the Student Book.

Circles

Name _____

Date _____

Center: *O*

Diameter: $\overline{AB}$

Radii: $\overline{OA}$, $\overline{OB}$, $\overline{OD}$

Chord: $\overline{BC}$

A circle is named by its center.

Use the circle at the right.

1. Name the circle. _____

2. Name 4 points on the circle. _____

3. How many chords of the circle are shown?
   Name them. _____

4. How many diameters of the circle are shown?
   Name them. _____

5. How many radii of the circle are shown?
   Name them. _____

Complete each table.

	Diameter	Radius
6.		8 in.
7.	58 cm	
8.		$6\frac{1}{4}$ ft

	Diameter	Radius
9.	14 m	
10.		12 in.
11.	136 yd	

Use your compass to construct a circle on a separate sheet of paper. Then do the following:

12. Label the center point, *C*.

13. Draw radius $\overline{CD}$.

14. Draw chord $\overline{AE}$.

15. Draw diameter $\overline{ST}$.

Problem Solving

16. The radius of a circular track is 18 m.
    Find the diameter. _____

17. The diameter of a circular rug is 11 ft.
    What is the radius? _____

18. Jill's bicycle wheel has a radius of $23\frac{3}{5}$ cm.
    What is its diameter? _____

Use with Lesson 10-8, pages 338–339 in the Student Book.
Then go to Lesson 10-9, pages 340–341 in the Student Book.

Circumference

Name _____

Date _____

<table>
<tr>
<td>

Find the circumference of each circle.

Diameter is given. Use 3.14 for π.

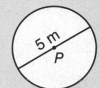

$$C \approx \pi \times d$$
$$\approx 3.14 \times 5 \text{ m}$$
$$\approx 15.7 \text{ m}$$

The circumference of circle P
is about 15.7 m.

</td>
<td>

Radius is given. Use $\frac{22}{7}$ for π.

$$C \approx \pi \times 2 \times r$$
$$C \approx \frac{22}{7} \times 2 \times 3.5$$
$$\approx \frac{22}{7} \times \frac{7}{1}$$
$$\approx 22 \text{ m}$$

The circumference of circle R
is about 22 m.

</td>
</tr>
</table>

Find the circumference of each circle. Use $\pi \approx 3.14$.

1. 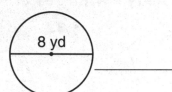 _____

2. 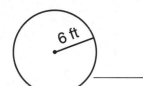 _____

3. 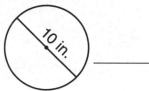 _____

4. 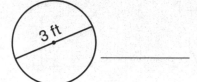 _____

5.  _____

6.  _____

Find the circumference of each circle. Use $\pi \approx \frac{22}{7}$.

7. 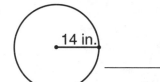 _____

8.  _____

9.  _____

10. 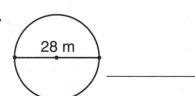 _____

11. 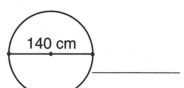 _____

12. 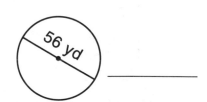 _____

Estimate the circumference of each circle. Circle the letter of the correct answer.

13.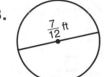
    a. $1\frac{5}{6}$ ft   **b.** $1\frac{5}{12}$ ft
    c. $1\frac{1}{2}$ ft   **d.** 3 ft

14.
    a. $\frac{1}{2}$ in.   **b.** $\frac{3}{8}$ in.
    c. $\frac{11}{14}$ in.   **d.** 1 in.

Use with Lesson 10-9, pages 340–341 in the Student Book.

Then go to Lesson 10-10, pages 342–343 in the Student Book.

Lines of Symmetry

Name _____

Date _____

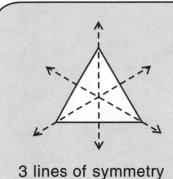 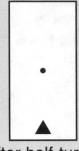 

3 lines of symmetry

A rectangle has half-turn symmetry.

after half-turn

Is the dashed line a line of symmetry? Write _Yes_ or _No_.

1.   2.   3. 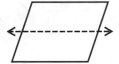   4.

_____   _____   _____   _____

Draw all the lines of symmetry for each figure.

5.   6.   7.   8.

Does the figure have half-turn symmetry? Write _Yes_ or _No_.

9. 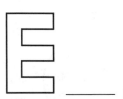   10.   11. 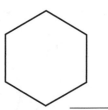   12.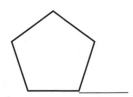

Complete the figure so that the dashed line is the line of symmetry.

13. 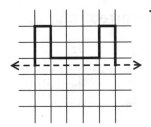   14. 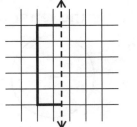   15. 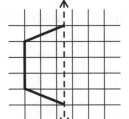   16.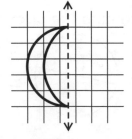

122

Use with Lesson 10-10, pages 342–343 in the Student Book.
Then go to Lessons 10-11 and 10-12, pages 344–347 in the Student Book.

Transformations and Tessellations

Name _____

Date _____

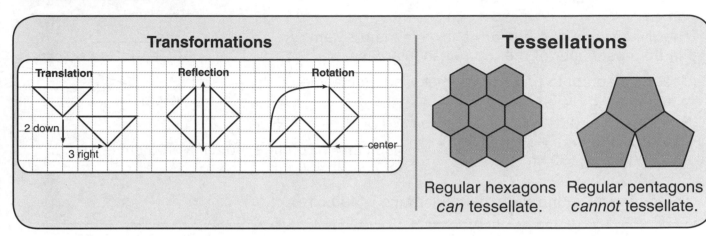

Transformations

Translation
2 down
3 right

Reflection

Rotation
center

Tessellations

Regular hexagons *can* tessellate.

Regular pentagons *cannot* tessellate.

Is figure B a result of moving figure A? Write *Yes* or *No*. If yes, write the movement.

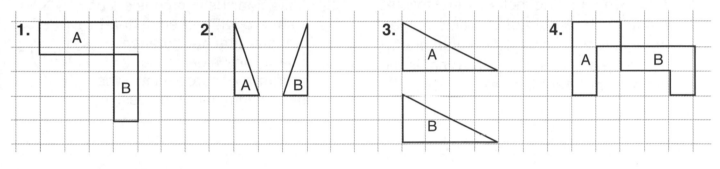

1. A B

2. A B

3. A B

4. A B

_____   _____   _____   _____

Are these figures in a tessellation? Write *Yes* or *No*.

5.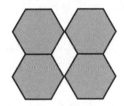

6.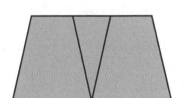

7.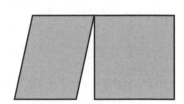

_____   _____   _____

Name the polygons used in each tessellation.

8.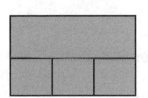

9.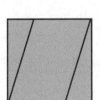

10.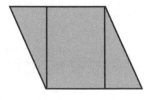

_____   _____   _____

Use with Lessons 10-11 and 10-12, pages 344–347 in the Student Book.
Then go to Lesson 10-13, pages 348–349 in the Student Book.

Problem-Solving Strategy: Use a Diagram/Model

Name _____

Date _____

The dimensions of a box are shown in the diagram.
Find the perimeter of the top rectangular face.

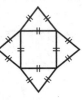

60 cm
150 cm
90 cm

Use the diagram to find the perimeter of a rectangle.

$P = \ell + w + \ell + w$
$P = (2 \times \ell) + (2 \times w)$
$P = (2 \times 150 \text{ cm}) + (2 \times 90 \text{ cm})$
$P = 300 \text{ cm} + 180 \text{ cm}$
$P = 480 \text{ cm}$

Check:
$P = \ell + w + \ell + w$

$480 \text{ cm} = 150 \text{ cm} + 90 \text{ cm} + 150 \text{ cm} + 90 \text{ cm}$
$480 \text{ cm} = 480 \text{ cm}$

The perimeter of the top rectangular face is 480 cm.

Solve. Do your work on a separate sheet of paper.

1. A design on a flag includes an isosceles triangle. The length of one side of the triangle is 2 in. long. The length of each of the other sides is $2\frac{1}{4}$ in. What is the perimeter of the triangle?

2. A tile floor design consists of a square with an equilateral triangle attached to each side. If one side of the square measures 5 cm, what is the perimeter of the design?

_____

3. A garden has the shape of a regular hexagon. If the perimeter of the garden is 138 ft, what is the length of one side of the garden?

4. Two of the angle measures for a triangle are 54° and 35°. What is the measure of the third angle?

_____

5. Parallelogram *PQRS* has two pairs of congruent sides. The perimeter is 190 cm. If the length of $\overline{PQ}$ is 20 cm, what is the length of $\overline{QR}$?

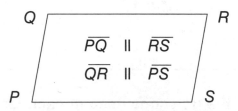

$\overline{PQ}$ ∥ $\overline{RS}$

$\overline{QR}$ ∥ $\overline{PS}$

_____

6. A circular swimming pool has a diameter of 28 ft. Find the circumference.

7. The perimeter of a yard shaped like a regular octagon is 24 ft. What is the length of one side of the yard?

_____

Use with Lesson 10-13, pages 348–349 in the Student Book.
Then go to Lesson 10-14, pages 350–351 in the Student Book.

Problem-Solving
Applications: Mixed Review

Name _____

Date _____

Solve each problem and explain the method you used. If needed, do all your work on a separate sheet of paper.

Read ▷ Plan ▷ Solve ▷ Check ▷

Strategy File

Use These Strategies
Use a Diagram/Model
Logical Reasoning
Work Backward
Guess and Test
Use More Than One Step

1. A room in Shelley's house is a square whose perimeter is 52 ft. She removes a wall, making the room a rectangle that is 24 ft long. What is the perimeter of the room now?

_____

2. Each hexagonal tile on Carrie's floor has a perimeter of 72 in. How long is each side of the tile?

_____

3. Farook puts two triangles together to make a square. Classify the triangles Farook used.

_____

4. In the parallelogram $ABCD$, $\angle D$ is 125°. What are the measures of all the other angles?

_____

5. The radius of Paula's wagon wheel is $10\frac{1}{2}$ in. What is the circumference of Paula's wheel?

_____

6. A rectangular piece of lumber in Greg's yard is four times as long as it is wide. Its perimeter is 40 in. How long is the piece of lumber?

_____

7. If one angle of a triangle is 29° and another angle is twice that, what is the measure of the third angle? Is the angle obtuse or acute?

_____

Use the diagram at left to solve.

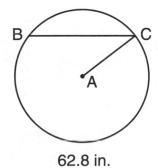

62.8 in.

8. The circumference of a circle is 62.8 in. What is the radius? Use $\pi = 3.14$.

_____

9. Is $\overline{BC}$ a radius? a diameter? Why or why not?

_____

Use with Lesson 10-14, pages 350–351 in the Student Book.

Relate Customary Units of Length

Name _____

Date _____

> **Multiply** to rename larger units as smaller units.
> **Divide** to rename smaller units as larger units.
>
> 3 ft 8 in. = _?_ in.
>
> 3 ft = (3 × 12) in. = 36 in.
> 36 in. + 8 in. = 44 in.
> So 3 ft 8 in. = 44 in.
>
> | Think:
> | 12 in. = 1 ft
>
> 138 in. = _?_ yd _?_ in.
>
> (138 ÷ 36) yd = $3\frac{20}{36}$ yd
> $3\frac{20}{36}$ yd = 3 yd 20 in.
> So 138 in. = 3 yd 20 in.
>
> | Think:
> | 36 in. = 1 yd

List two classroom items that are:

1. longer than 1 inch but shorter than 1 foot.

   _____

2. longer than 1 foot but shorter than 1 yard.

   _____

3. longer than 1 yard.

   _____

Rename each measurement.

4. 7 ft 2 in. = _____ in.   5. 5 ft 5 in. = _____ in.   6. 8 yd 2 ft = _____ ft

7. 253 in. = _____ yd _____ in.   8. 137 ft = _____ yd _____ ft

9. 63 in. = _____ ft _____ in.   10. 99 in. = _____ ft _____ in.

11. 6790 ft = _____ mi _____ ft   12. 29 ft = _____ yd _____ ft

Measure each to the nearest inch, $\frac{1}{2}$ inch, $\frac{1}{4}$ inch, and $\frac{1}{8}$ inch.

13. |———————————————|

    _____

14. |———————————————|

    _____

15. |————————————————————————|

    _____

Problem Solving

16. The height of a doorway is 7 ft 4 in. Randall says it is 88 in. high. Kyoko says it is 2 yd 1 ft 6 in. high. James says it is 2 yd 16 in. high. Can they all be correct? Explain your answer.

    _____

Relate Customary Units of Capacity and Weight

Name _____

Date _____

Multiply to rename larger units as smaller units.
Divide to rename smaller units as larger units.

15 pt = __?__ qt
15 pt = (15 ÷ 2) qt
So 15 pt = $7\frac{1}{2}$ qt.

Think:
2 pt = 1 qt

3 lb 2 oz = __?__ oz
3 lb = (3 × 16) oz = 48 oz
48 oz + 2 oz = 50 oz
So 3 lb 2 oz = 50 oz.

Think:
1 lb = 16 oz

Rename each unit of measure. Do your work on a separate sheet of paper.

1. 4 gal = _____ qt

2. 19 qt = ___ gal ___ qt

3. 2 gal = _____ pt

4. 10 pt = _____ qt

5. 2 qt 1 pt = _____ c

6. $3\frac{1}{2}$ c = _____ fl oz

7. 27 c = ___ pt ___ c

8. 3 gal 1 qt = _____ pt

9. 18 fl oz = ___ c

10. 4 qt 1 c = _____ c

11. 1 gal 1 qt = _____ qt

12. 12 fl oz = ___ c

13. 5 T = _____ lb

14. 24 lb = ___ oz

15. 8000 lb = ___ T

16. 260 oz = ___ lb ___ oz

17. 5000 lb = ___ T ___ lb

18. 3 lb 9 oz = ___ oz

19. 4 T 625 lb = ___ lb

20. 12 lb 5 oz = ___ oz

21. 638 oz = ___ lb

22. 5 T 1908 lb = _____ lb

23. 490 oz = ___ lb ___ oz

24. 7300 lb = ___ T

Compare. Write <, =, or >.

25. 30 fl oz ___ 3 c 5 fl oz

26. 3 qt ___ 5 pt

27. 3 gal 2 qt ___ 16 qt

28. 10 qt ___ 2 gal 3 qt

29. 32 pt ___ 15 qt 1 pt

30. 2 c 7 fl oz ___ 21 fl oz

31. 6000 lb ___ 3 T

32. 3 lb ___ 45 oz

33. 4010 lb ___ 2 T 1 lb

34. 11 lb 5 oz ___ 180 oz

35. 5 lb 17 oz ___ 4 lb 33 oz

36. 111 oz ___ 7 lb 9 oz

Problem Solving

37. A punch recipe calls for $2\frac{1}{2}$ qt orange juice. William needs to make 5 times as much punch for a banquet. Will he have enough orange juice if he buys 4 gallons?

_____

38. Darla is shipping a statue that weighs 120 oz. Can she safely ship the statue in a box that can hold a maximum of 8 pounds?

_____

Use with Lessons 11-2 and 11-3, pages 360–363 in the Student Book.
Then go to Lesson 11-4, pages 364–365 in the Student Book.

Temperature

Name _____

Date _____

Water boils	Water freezes	Starting Temperature: 20°C
Fahrenheit: 212°F	32°F	Change: falls 30°C
Celsius: 100°C	0°C	Final Temperature: –10°C

Circle the most reasonable temperature for each.

1. going swimming   **a.** 32°F   **b.** 60°F   **c.** 92°F
2. building a snowman   **a.** –60°F   **b.** 10°F   **c.** 50°F
3. roasting a chicken   **a.** 15°C   **b.** 150°C   **c.** 32°C
4. body temperature   **a.** 37°C   **b.** 10°C   **c.** 70°C

Write the final temperature.

5. Celsius

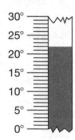

Change: falls 22°

Final Temperature: _____

6. Fahrenheit

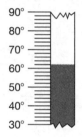

Change: rises 8°

Final Temperature: _____

7. Fahrenheit

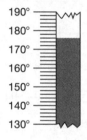

Change: rises 14°

Final Temperature: _____

8. Celsius

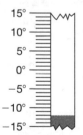

Change: rises 21°

Final temperature: _____

9. Fahrenheit

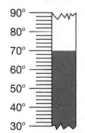

Change: falls 24°

Final temperature: _____

10. Celsius

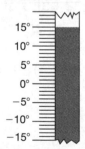

Change: falls 20°

Final temperature: _____

Complete.

11.

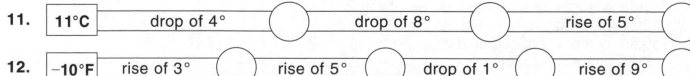

11°C — drop of 4° ◯ drop of 8° ◯ rise of 5° ◯

12.

–10°F — rise of 3° ◯ rise of 5° ◯ drop of 1° ◯ rise of 9° ◯

128

Use with Lesson 11-4, pages 364–365 in the Student Book.
Then go to Lesson 11-5, pages 366–367 in the Student Book.

Units of Time

Name _____

Date _____

> 60 s = 1 min
> 60 min = 1 h
> 24 h = 1 d
> 7 d = 1 wk
> 12 mo = 1 y
> 365 d = 1 y
> 100 y = 1 cent.
>
> **Multiply** to rename larger units as smaller units.
>
> **Divide** to rename smaller units as larger units.

Rename each unit of time.

1. 48 mo = _____ y
2. 10 y = _____ mo
3. 4 h = _____ min
4. 56 d = _____ wk
5. 240 s = _____ min
6. 168 h = _____ d
7. 120 min = _____ h
8. 36 mo = _____ y
9. 2 wk = _____ d
10. 480 s = _____ min
11. 12 d = _____ h
12. 3 h = _____ min
13. 153 min = _____ h _____ min
14. 18 mo = _____ y _____ mo
15. 115 s = _____ min _____ s
16. 130 d = _____ wk _____ d
17. 630 y = _____ cent. _____ y
18. 45 h = _____ d _____ h

Write s, min, h, d, wk, or mo to complete.

19. Summer lasts about 12 _____.
20. The cake baked for 45 _____.
21. Jill opened the can of tomatoes in 10 _____.
22. Paul's test was 1 _____ long.

Find the elapsed time. Use the clock at the right to help.

23. from 1:30 P.M. to 11:45 P.M. _____

24. from 8:20 A.M. to 1:15 P.M. _____

25. from 10:30 P.M. to 12:10 A.M. _____

26. from 6:24 A.M. to 2:13 P.M. _____

Problem Solving

27. One flight time around the world was 63 hours. How many days and hours was this? _____

28. One boat arrived at 1:33 P.M. and a second boat arrived at 3:43 P.M. How much time elapsed between the two arrivals? _____

29. Susan is 1 y 4 mo old. William is 18 mo old. Which child is older? how much older? _____

Use with Lesson 11-5, pages 366–367 in the Student Book.
Then go to Lesson 11-6, pages 368–369 in the Student Book.

129

Time Zones

Name _____

Date _____

West ▪ - → East

| Pacific | Mountain | Central | Eastern |
| 7:56 A.M. | 8:56 A.M. | 9:56 A.M. | 10:56 A.M. |

As you travel from west to east, the time in each zone is one hour later.

Use the given time to complete each row.

	Time Zone			
	Pacific	Mountain	Central	Eastern
1.				8:00 P.M.
2.		11:30 A.M.		
3.			2:43 P.M.	
4.	7:27 A.M.			

	City	Time Zone			
		Pacific	Mountain	Central	Eastern
5.	Portland, OR	6:29 A.M			
6.	Portland, ME				7:14 P.M.
7.	Denver, CO		12:00 noon		
8.	Dallas, TX			12:00 midnight	

Problem Solving

9. Thomas flies from Boston to Seattle in 5 hours. If he leaves at 9:00 A.M. Eastern time, what time will it be in Pacific time when he arrives in Seattle? _____

10. A company schedules a conference call at 11:00 A.M. Central time. At what time does the call take place in Eastern time? in Mountain time? in Pacific time? _____

11. James lives in Los Angeles. He calls his sister at 10:30 A.M. Pacific time. His sister lives in the Central time zone. At what time does she receive the call? _____

12. Alicia lives in Portland, ME. She calls her mother in the Mountain time zone at 9:00 P.M. Eastern time. At what time does her mother receive the call? _____

Use with Lesson 11-6, pages 368–369 in the Student Book.
Then go to Lesson 11-7, pages 370–371 in the Student Book.

Compute with Customary Units

Name _____

Date _____

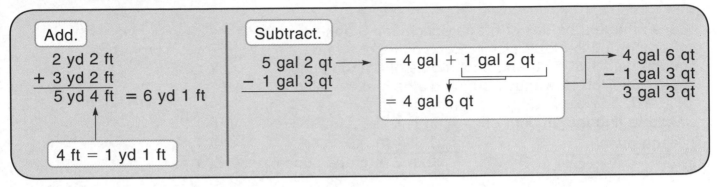

Add.

2 yd 2 ft
+ 3 yd 2 ft
5 yd 4 ft = 6 yd 1 ft

4 ft = 1 yd 1 ft

Subtract.

5 gal 2 qt ⟶
− 1 gal 3 qt

= 4 gal + 1 gal 2 qt

= 4 gal 6 qt

⟶ 4 gal 6 qt
− 1 gal 3 qt
3 gal 3 qt

Add.

1. 9 lb 3 oz
+ 2 lb 7 oz

2. 7 yd 2 ft
+ 3 yd 1 ft

3. 8 qt 1 pt
+ 1 qt 1 pt

4. 2 gal 2 qt
+ 4 gal 2 qt

5. 6 wk 4 d
+ 2 wk 9 d

6. 21 ft 9 in.
+ 9 ft 8 in.

Subtract.

7. 8 d 7 h
− 5 d 3 h

8. 11 gal 3 qt
− 11 gal 1 qt

9. 3 wk 5 d
− 2 wk 5 d

10. 5 yd 12 in.
− 2 yd 22 in.

11. 4 qt
− 2 qt 1 pt

12. 6 T   240 lb
− 2 T   680 lb

Find the sum or difference.

13. 5 pt 1 c + 3 pt 1 c = _____

14. 5 d 8 h − 4 d 20 h = _____

15. 3 h 39 min + 4 h 57 min = _____

16. 9 h 16 min − 3 h 38 min = _____

17. 4 ft 11 in. + 6 ft 8 in. = _____

18. 6 lb 2 oz − 1 lb 7 oz = _____

Problem Solving

19. Elena has a piece of lumber 7 yd long. How much must she cut off to have 2 yd 1 ft of lumber left?

_____

20. Sam watched a music video on television that lasted 17 minutes and a movie that lasted 1 hour and 39 minutes. How long did Sam watch television?

_____

C Use with Lesson 11-7, pages 370–371 in the Student Book.
C Then go to Lesson 11-8, pages 372–373 in the Student Book.

Problem-Solving Strategy: Use More Than One Step

Name _____

Date _____

Lucas made 2 bottles of grape punch and 3 bottles of orange punch for a picnic. Each bottle of grape punch held 1 qt 1 pt, and each bottle of orange punch held 2 qt 1 pt. How much punch did he make in all?

Add to find the amount of each punch.	1 qt 1 pt + 1 qt 1 pt 2 qt 2 pt grape punch	2 qt 1 pt 2 qt 1 pt + 2 qt 1 pt 6 qt 3 pt of orange punch

3 qt grape punch   7 qt 1 pt orange punch

Change the units: 2 pt = 1 qt

Add to find the total amount of punch.	3 qt + 7 qt 1 pt 10 qt 1 pt	Lucas made 10 qt 1 pt of punch.

Solve. Do your work on a separate sheet of paper.

1. Lori used 2 ft 4 in. of ribbon for each dress she made and 1 ft 8 in. for each skirt. She made 3 dresses and 4 skirts. How much ribbon did she use in all?

2. There are 4 dozen blueberry muffins in the display case at Betty's Bakery. There are also 7 trays of bran muffins, with 8 muffins in each tray. How many muffins are there altogether?

3. Peter rented a movie that has a running time of 1 hour 55 minutes. He began watching the movie at 6:30 P.M. He turned it off for 15 minutes and then continued watching the movie to the end. What time did he finish watching the movie?

4. Jacques recorded the noon temperatures every day last week and found the average temperature to be 20°C. This week he recorded the following temperatures: 18°C, 16°C, 13°C, 15°C, 14°C, 16°C, and 13°C. How many degrees did the average temperature decrease?

5. Eleanor bought 5 bags of peanuts and 3 bags of raisins. Each bag of peanuts weighed 1 lb 2 oz, and each bag of raisins weighed 2 lb 9oz. What was the total weight of the peanuts and raisins Eleanor bought?

Use with Lesson 11-8, pages 372–373 in the Student Book.
Then go to Lesson 11-9, pages 374–375 in the Student Book.

Problem-Solving Applications: Mixed Review

Name _____

Date _____

Solve each problem and explain the method you used. If needed, do all your work on a separate sheet of paper.

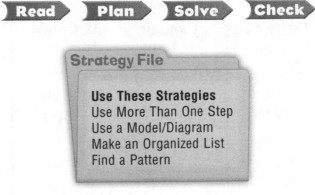

1. Rona is buying a picture frame. The frame she wants comes in large and small, and in 7 colors. How many different frames does Rona have to chose from?

   _____

2. Sonny's best high jump is 5 ft 8 in. If he's improved by 5 in. a year for 4 years, what was his best jump when he started?

   _____

3. Pat's little brother is 4 ft 2 in. tall. Pat is 71 in. How much taller than his little brother is Pat?

   _____

4. Maria walks for half an hour to get from her house to school. After two 45-minute classes it is 10:15 A.M. What time did Maria leave her house?

   _____

5. Carl sees two bottles of juice in the grocery store. One is 3 qt for $3.72. The other is 5 pt for $2.95. Which is the better deal?

   _____

6. The temperature at 4 P.M was 42° F. It then dropped 4° per hour until 10 P.M. What was the temperature at 9 P.M?

   _____

7. Shauna puts five 18 oz cutlets into a bag that can only hold 6 pounds. Will the bag break?

   _____

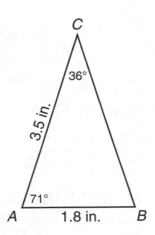

Use the diagram at left to solve.

8. ∠C is 36°. ∠A is 71°. What is ∠B?

   _____

9. If AB is 1.8 in., AC is 3.5 in., and the perimeter of the triangle is 8.8 in., what is the length of BC?

   _____

C Use with Lesson 11-9, pages 374–375 in the Student Book.

Metric Measurement

Name _____

Date _____

Metric Units of Length	(10 × 100) m = 1 kilometer (km)	1 meter (m)	(1 ÷ 10) m = 1 decimeter (dm)	(1 ÷ 100) m = 1 centimeter (cm)	(1 ÷ 1000) m = 1 millimeter (mm)
Metric Units of Capacity	(10 × 100) L = 1 kiloliter (kL)	1 liter (L)	(1 ÷ 10) L = 1 deciliter (dL)	(1 ÷ 100) L = 1 centiliter (cL)	(1 ÷ 1000) L = 1 milliliter (mL)
Metric Units of Mass	(10 × 100) g = 1 kilogram (kg)	1 gram (g)	(1 ÷ 10) g = 1 decigram (dg)	(1 ÷ 100) g = 1 centigram (cg)	(1 ÷ 1000) g = 1 milligram (mg)

Which metric unit is used to measure each? Write *m*, *L*, or *g*.

1. distance of a race _____
2. mass of a banana _____
3. capacity of a fish tank _____
4. height of a fence _____
5. length of a car _____
6. mass of a barrel _____
7. water in a pool _____
8. perimeter of a house _____
9. mass of a grape _____
10. milk in a bottle _____

Write the letter of the larger unit of measure.

11. _____ a. kiloliter   b. deciliter
12. _____ a. milligram   b. gram
13. _____ a. decimeter   b. centimeter
14. _____ a. liter   b. milliliter
15. _____ a. meter   b. kilometer
16. _____ a. decigram   b. kilogram

Write the letter of the smaller unit of measure.

17. _____ a. centigram   b. gram
18. _____ a. centimeter   b. millimeter
19. _____ a. centiliter   b. liter
20. _____ a. kilometer   b. decimeter
21. _____ a. kilogram   b. gram
22. _____ a. liter   b. kiloliter

Rename each unit of measure.

23. 8.29 m = _____ cm
24. 91.9 dm = _____ m
25. 12.02 g = _____ cg
26. 0.46 L = _____ mL
27. 3003 g = _____ kg
28. 1.79 km = _____ m
29. 2.083 kg = _____ g
30. 5.8 dL = _____ L
31. 2.02 kL = _____ L
32. 11.1 m = _____ km
33. 80.4 L = _____ cL
34. 21.03 g = _____ dg

Ⓒ Use with Lesson 12-1, pages 382–283 in the Student Book.
Ⓒ Then go to Lesson 12-2, pages 384–385 in the Student Book.

Relate Metric Units of Length

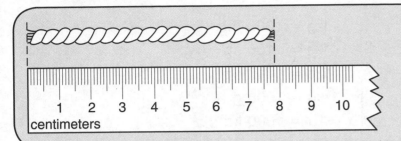

The length of the piece of yarn is
- 1 dm to the nearest decimeter.
- 8 cm to the nearest centimeter.
- 79 mm to the nearest millimeter.

Circle the letter of the unit you would use to measure each.

		a.		b.		c.	
1.	width of a calculator	a.	kilometer	b.	decimeter	c.	centimeter
2.	height of a wall	a.	kilometer	b.	meter	c.	decimeter
3.	thickness of a quarter	a.	decimeter	b.	centimeter	c.	millimeter
4.	height of a person	a.	meter	b.	decimeter	c.	millimeter
5.	distance to Mars	a.	kilometer	b.	meter	c.	decimeter

Write the name of an item you would measure in:

6. millimeters _____   7. centimeters _____

8. decimeters _____   9. meters _____

10. kilometers _____

Measure each to the nearest millimeter, nearest centimeter, and nearest decimeter.

11. |————————————————————|———— _____ mm _____ cm _____ dm

12. |————————————————|———— _____ mm _____ cm _____ dm

13. |——————————————————————————|

_____ mm _____ cm _____ dm

14. |————————————————————————————————|

_____ mm _____ cm _____ dm

![Problem Solving]

15. Suppose you are describing the size of your math workbook. What unit would you use? Why?

_____

_____

Use with Lesson 12-2, pages 384–385 in the Student Book.
Then go to Lessons 12-3 and 12-4, pages 386–389 in the Student Book.

135

Relate Metric Units of Capacity and Mass

Name _____

Date _____

1 L = 1000 mL	1 g = 1000 mg
1 L = 100 cL	1 g = 100 cg
1 L = 10 dL	1 g = 10 dg
1 kL = 1000 L	1 kg = 1000 g
	1 t = 1000 kg

Circle the letter of the unit you would use to measure the capacity of each.

1. swimming pool   **a.** kiloliter   **b.** liter   **c.** deciliter
2. aquarium   **a.** liter   **b.** centiliter   **c.** milliliter
3. soup bowl   **a.** kiloliter   **b.** liter   **c.** milliliter
4. bucket   **a.** liter   **b.** deciliter   **c.** milliliter

Circle the letter of the unit you would use to measure the mass of each.

5. baseball card   **a.** kilogram   **b.** gram   **c.** milligram
6. human being   **a.** metric ton   **b.** kilogram   **c.** milligram
7. computer   **a.** kilogram   **b.** gram   **c.** decigram
8. Earth   **a.** metric ton   **b.** kilogram   **c.** gram
9. crayon   **a.** kilogram   **b.** gram   **c.** milligram

Compare. Write <, =, or >.

10. 3 L ____ 300 mL
11. 16 L ____ 15 000 mL
12. 500 cL ____ 6 L
13. 4 kL ____ 4000 L
14. 670 dL ____ 68 L
15. 4000 L ____ 40 000 kL
16. 460 mL ____ 4.6 L
17. 5000 L ____ 5 kL
18. 2 L ____ 20 dL
19. 182 L ____ 18 200 cL
20. 0.8 L ____ 9 dL
21. 0.7 L ____ 650 mL
22. 42 cL ____ 4 L
23. 18 000 mL ____ 18 L
24. 8.9 L ____ 88 dL
25. 2 kg ____ 1500 g
26. 3 kg ____ 30 000 g
27. 2300 kg ____ 2.5 g
28. 7000 g ____ 70 kg
29. 1000 cg ____ 11 g
30. 6000 dg ____ 60 g
31. 8 g ____ 80 kg
32. 3000 kg ____ 3 t
33. 16 000 g ____ 15 kg
34. 300 mg ____ 3 dg
35. 5 g ____ 500 mg
36. 1 t ____ 1010 kg

Problem Solving

37. Rose has 3 kg of turkey slices from which to make 20 sandwiches. If she divides the slices equally, how many grams of turkey will be in each sandwich? _____

Copyright © by William H. Sadlier, Inc. All rights reserved.

Use with Lessons 12-3 and 12-4, pages 386–389 in the Student Book.
Then go to Lesson 12-5, pages 390–391 in the Student Book.

Square Measure

Name _____

Date _____

Count the squares to find the area.

1 m² ▸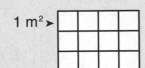

Each square = 1 m²
Area = 12 m²

1 mi² ▸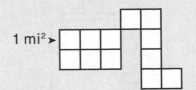

Each square = 1 mi²
Area = 12 mi²

Find the area of each figure.

1. 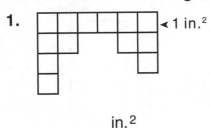 ◂ 1 in.²

_____ in.²

2. ◂ 1 yd²

_____ yd²

3. 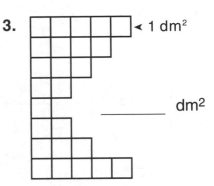 ◂ 1 dm²

_____ dm²

4. ◂ 1 km²

_____ km²

5. 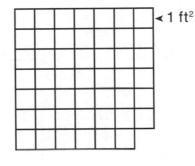 ◂ 1 ft²

_____ ft²

6. 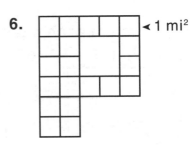 ◂ 1 mi²

_____ mi²

Estimate the area of each shaded figure.

7. km²
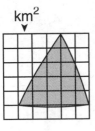

_____ km²

8. yd²
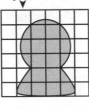

_____ yd²

9. dm²

_____ dm²

10. in.²
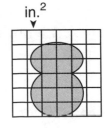

_____ in.²

137

Use with Lesson 12-5, pages 390–391 in the Student Book.
Then go to Lesson 12-5A, pages 221–222 in this Workbook.

Areas of Rectangles and Squares

Name _____

Date _____

Rectangles	Squares
$A = \ell \times w$	$A = s \times s = s^2$
$A = 17 \text{ ft} \times 10 \text{ ft}$	$A = 12.3 \text{ m} \times 12.3 \text{ m}$
$A = 170 \text{ ft}^2$	$A = 151.29 \text{ m}^2$

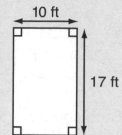

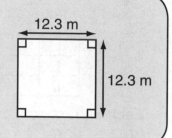

Find the area of each rectangle.

1. $2\frac{1}{2}$ ft $\quad$ $8\frac{1}{5}$ ft

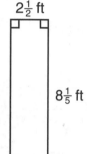

_____

2. 6.4 km $\quad$ 4.9 km

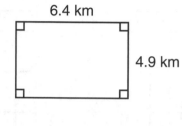

_____

3. 6 cm $\quad$ $7\frac{1}{2}$ cm

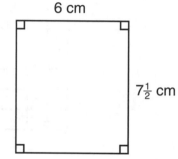

_____

4. 15.6 mm $\quad$ 25.4 mm

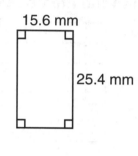

_____

Find the area of each square.

5. 13 in.

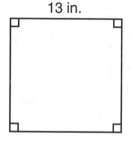

_____

6. 8.8 yd

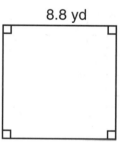

_____

7. $2\frac{1}{5}$ m

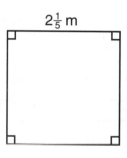

_____

8. 6.1 mi

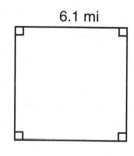

_____

Find the area of each square or rectangle.

9. 7.3 dm long
3.9 dm wide

_____

10. $s = 6\frac{1}{8}$ in.

_____

11. 22 mm long
18 mm wide

_____

12. $s = 4.9$ cm

_____

13. 29 yd long
$9\frac{3}{4}$ yd wide

_____

14. $s = 9.6$ m

_____

15. 2 km long
0.5 km wide

_____

16. $s = 8\frac{1}{2}$ ft

_____

Use with Lesson 12-6, pages 392–393 in the Student Book.
Then go to Lesson 12-7, pages 394–395 in the Student Book.

Areas of Parallelograms and Triangles

Name _____

Date _____

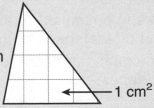
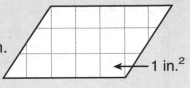

$A = \frac{1}{2} \times b \times h$

$A = \frac{1}{2} \times \overset{2}{\cancel{4}} \text{ cm} \times 4 \text{ cm}$

$A = \overset{1}{\cancel{8}} \text{ cm}^2$ ←— 1 cm²

$A = b \times h$

$A = 5 \text{ in.} \times 3 \text{ in.}$

$A = 15 \text{ in.}^2$ ←— 1 in.²

Find the area.

1.
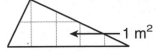
←— 1 m²

_____

2.
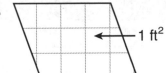
←— 1 ft²

_____

3.

←— 1 yd²

_____

4.
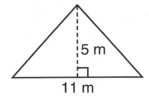
5 m
11 m

_____

5.

9 in.
27 in.

_____

6.
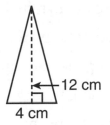
12 cm
4 cm

_____

7.
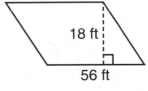
18 ft
56 ft

_____

8.
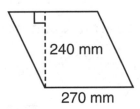
240 mm
270 mm

_____

9.
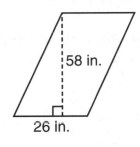
58 in.
26 in.

_____

Problem Solving

10. A square measures 14 in. along one side. A parallelogram has a base of 18 in. and a height of 10 in. Which figure has the greater area?

_____

11. A parallelogram has a base of 32 cm and a height of 25 cm. A triangle has a base of 66 cm and a height of 25 cm. Which figure has the greater area? by how much?

_____

Use with Lesson 12-7, pages 394–395 in the Student Book.
Then go to Lesson 12-8, pages 396–397 in the Student Book.

Solid Figures

Name _____

Date _____

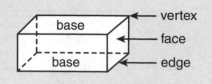

Pyramids and prisms other than cubes are named by the shape of their bases.

Cylinders, cones, and spheres have curved surfaces.

Complete the table.

	Solid Figure	Number of		
		Faces	Vertices	Edges
1.	square pyramid			
2.	rectangular pyramid			
3.	pentagonal prism			
4.	triangular pyramid			
5.	rectangular prism			
6.	pentagonal pyramid			
7.	hexagonal prism			
8.	triangular prism			
9.	hexagonal pyramid			

Write the solid figure that can be made from each net.

10.

_____

11.

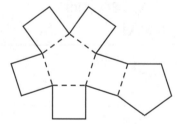

_____

12.

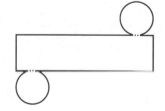

_____

Write *True* or *False* for each statement.

13. A square pyramid and a rectangular pyramid have the same number of faces and edges. _____

14. Three of the faces of a triangular prism are rectangles. _____

15. A hexagonal prism has 8 hexagonal faces. _____

16. A triangular pyramid has 4 triangular faces. _____

17. The base of a cube is a square. _____

18. The number of edges on a cube is triple the number of its faces. _____

Use with Lesson 12-8, pages 396–397 in the Student Book.
Then go to Lesson 12-9, pages 398–399 in the Student Book.

Surface Area

Name _____

Date _____

The surface area (S) of a solid figure is the sum of the area of all its faces.

Cube

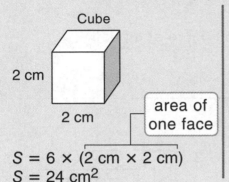

2 cm

2 cm

area of one face

$S = 6 \times (2\ cm \times 2\ cm)$
$S = 24\ cm^2$

Rectangular Prism

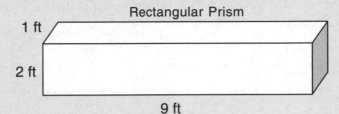

1 ft

2 ft

9 ft

$S = 2 \times (1\ ft \times 2\ ft) + 2 \times (2\ ft \times 9\ ft) + 2 \times (1\ ft \times 9\ ft)$
$S = 4\ ft^2 + 36\ ft^2 + 18\ ft^2$
$S = 58\ ft^2$

Find the surface area of each cube.

1.

1.6 yd

1.6 yd

1.6 yd

_____

2.

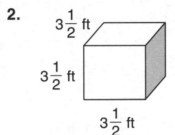

$3\frac{1}{2}$ ft

$3\frac{1}{2}$ ft

$3\frac{1}{2}$ ft

_____

3.

5.9 cm

5.9 cm

5.9 cm

_____

4.

$8\frac{3}{4}$ m

$8\frac{3}{4}$ m

$8\frac{3}{4}$ m

_____

Find the surface area of each rectangular prism.

5.

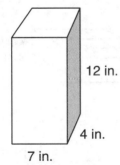

12 in.

4 in.

7 in.

_____

6.

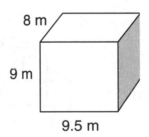

2 ft

5 ft

11 ft

_____

7.

8 m

9 m

9.5 m

_____

8.

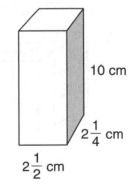

10 cm

$2\frac{1}{4}$ cm

$2\frac{1}{2}$ cm

_____

Problem Solving

9. What is the surface area of a toolbox that is 8 in. tall, 7 in. wide, and 1 ft 1 in. long?

_____

10. What is the surface area of a cube that is 1.7 cm tall?

_____

Use with Lesson 12-9, pages 398–399 in the Student Book.
Then go to Lesson 12-10, pages 400–401 in the Student Book.

141

Cubic Measure

Name _____

Date _____

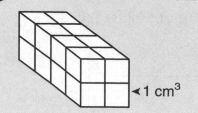
◄1 cm³

Count cubes to find the cubic measure of a solid figure.

The cubic measure of the figure at the left is 16 cm³.

Find the cubic measure in cubic units.

1.

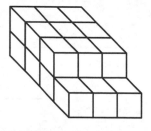

_____

2.

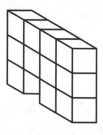

_____

3.

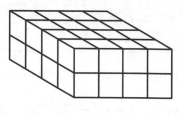

_____

Find the cubic measure of each.

4.

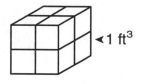 ◄1 ft³

_____ ft³

5.

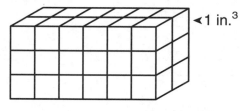 ◄1 in.³

_____ in.³

6.

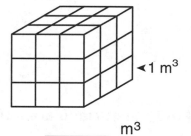 ◄1 m³

_____ m³

7.

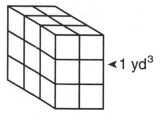 ◄1 yd³

_____ yd³

8.

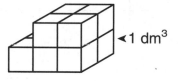 ◄1 dm³

_____ dm³

9.

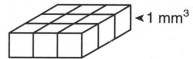 ◄1 mm³

_____ mm³

Find the equivalent measure to complete the table.

	Cubic Measure	Capacity of Water	Mass of Water
10.	2 cm³	2 mL	
11.	4 dm³		4 kg
12.		6 mL	6 g
13.	8 dm³		
14.	10 cm³		

142

C Use with Lesson 12-10, pages 400–401 in the Student Book.
C Then go to Lesson 12-11, pages 402–403 in the Student Book.

Volume

Name _____

Date _____

Find the volume of the solid figure.

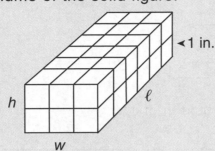

◄ 1 in.

h ℓ

w

Use the formula.

$V = \ell \times w \times h$

$V = 6 \text{ in.} \times 3 \text{ in.} \times 2 \text{ in.}$

$V = 36 \text{ in.}^3$

Find the volume in cubic units.

1.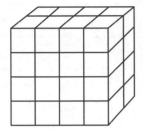

2.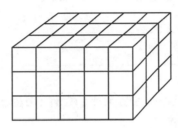

3.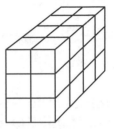

_____ _____ _____

Find the volume of each rectangular prism.

4.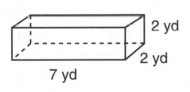

2 yd

2 yd

7 yd

5.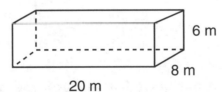

6 m

8 m

20 m

6.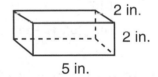

2 in.

2 in.

5 in.

_____ _____ _____

Complete the table.

	ℓ	w	h	$V = \ell \times w \times h$
7.	$21\frac{1}{2}$ ft	$3\frac{1}{3}$ ft	$2\frac{1}{2}$ ft	
8.	2.8 cm	2.4 cm	2.2 cm	
9.	8.3 dm	3.9 dm	4.8 dm	
10.	$29\frac{3}{4}$ in.	$10\frac{1}{2}$ in.	3 in.	
11.	6.4 m	5.2 m	12 m	

Ⅽ Use with Lesson 12-11, pages 402–403 in the Student Book.
Ⅽ Then go to Lessons 12-11A and 12-11B, pages 223–226 in this Workbook.

143

Estimate Volume

Name _____

Date _____

Net of a centimeter cube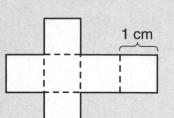

centimeter cube ($V = 1\ cm^3$)

The shell would fit inside a centimeter cube.

Name 3 objects that would fit inside a cube with a volume of:

1. $1\ cm^3$ _____

2. $1\ dm^3$ _____

3. $1\ in.^3$ _____

Which size is the most reasonable to hold each object?
Circle the letter of the best answer.

4. mug   a. m^3 b. dm^3 c. cm^3 d. $in.^3$

5. pearl   a. m^3 b. dm^3 c. cm^3 d. ft^3

6. pitcher   a. $in.^3$ b. dm^3 c. cm^3 d. ft^3

7. thimble   a. m^3 b. $in.^3$ c. ft^3 d. dm^3

8. television set   a. m^3 b. dm^3 c. cm^3 d. ft^3

Circle the letter of the best estimate for the volume of each.

9. box for index cards   a. $60\ yd^3$ b. $60\ ft^3$ c. $60\ in.^3$

10. cereal box   a. $3500\ m^3$ b. $3500\ cm^3$ c. $3500\ mm^3$

11. board game box   a. $288\ yd^3$ b. $288\ ft^3$ c. $288\ in.^3$

12. videocassette box   a. $660\ dm^3$ b. $660\ cm^3$ c. $660\ mm^3$

13. refrigerator   a. $22\ yd^3$ b. $22\ ft^3$ c. $22\ in.^3$

14. box for a computer monitor   a. $8505\ dm^3$ b. $8505\ cm^3$ c. $8505\ mm^3$

Problem Solving

15. How many centimeter cubes fit into a decimeter cube? _____

16. How many inch cubes fit into a 1-foot cube? _____

Use with Lesson 12-12, pages 404–405 in the Student Book.
Then go to Lesson 12-12A, pages 227–228 in this Workbook.

Problem-Solving Strategy: Draw a Picture

Jane covered five faces of a box with colored paper, leaving the top open. The box is 4 cm high, 5.8 cm wide, and 6.5 cm long. How much paper did she use?

Draw a picture of the box.

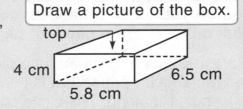

Find the area of each of the faces she covered.

Area = $\ell \times w$

Front: 4 cm × 5.8 cm = 23.2 cm^2 Right Side: 4 cm × 6.5 cm = 26 cm^2

Back: 4 cm × 5.8 cm = 23.2 cm^2 Left Side: 4 cm × 6.5 cm = 26 cm^2

Bottom: 5.8 cm × 6.5 cm = 37.7 cm^2

Add the areas: 23.2 cm^2 + 23.2 cm^2 + 26 cm^2 + 26 cm^2 + 37.7 cm^2 = 136.1 cm^2

Jane used 136.1 cm^2 of paper.

Solve. Do your work on a separate sheet of paper.

1. Laura pastes a blue right triangle in each corner of a red rectangle that is 8 cm wide and 12 cm long. The sides of the triangles are lined up with the sides of the rectangle, and none of the triangles overlap. Each triangle has a base of 4 cm and a height of 6 cm. How much red area is still showing?

2. Leona places a cube with a volume of 512 cm^3 into a rectangular fish tank that has two square faces, each with sides measuring 20 cm, and three rectangular faces each that are 40 cm long and 20 cm wide. How much of the total volume of the fish tank is left to be filled with water?

3. What is the least perimeter you can make by joining 4 rectangles side to side if each length is 6 cm and each width is 3.5 cm? What is the greatest perimeter?

4. A rectangle has a perimeter of 20 m and an area of 9 m^2. What are the length and width of the rectangle?

5. A rectangle has an area of 24 m^2. What are the possible pairs of lengths and widths? Which measurements give the greatest perimeter? Which measurements give the least perimeter?

6. Les made a rectangular path around his garden. The garden has a length of 18 ft and a width of 12 ft. If the outer edge of the path has a length of 22 ft and a width of 16 ft, how much area does the path cover?

Problem-Solving
Application: Mixed Review

Name _____

Date _____

Solve each problem and explain the
method you used. If needed, do all your
work on a separate sheet of paper.

Read ▶ Plan ▶ Solve ▶ Check

Strategy File

Use These Strategies
Guess and Test
Use a Model/Diagram
Draw a Picture
Use More Than One Step
Logical Reasoning

1. Katie cuts a circle out of a piece of
   rectangular paper that is 8 in. wide
   and 11 in. long. The circle covers the
   full width of the paper. How much does
   Katie need to cut off the length?

   _____

2. The surface area of a cube is 96 cm^2.
   What is the length of one side of the
   cube?

   _____

3. Carl has a pan that is 14.2 in. long,
   7.8 in. wide. If its volume is 221.52 in.^{3},
   how deep is the pan?

   _____

4. Sam, Bill, and Sonia have a thimble, a
   glass, and a barrel. Sonia measured
   the capacity of her container in dL. Bill
   measured the capacity of his container
   in mL. Which container did Sam have?

   _____

5. Desiree cuts a rectangle into two
   matching right triangles. The triangles
   have height of 9 cm and an area of
   27 cm^2. What is the area of the rectangle?

   _____

6. Maura has 1.3 kg of cheese. She wants
   to give 220 g each to 6 people. Does
   she have enough?

   _____

7. The area of Ron's rectangular driveway
   was 147 ft^2. It is three times as long as
   it is wide. What is the length and width
   of Ron's driveway?

   _____

Use the diagram for problems 8–9.

8. What is the area of Talia's garden?

   _____

9. What is the area of Talia's backyard,
   not including the garden?

   _____

Talia's Backyard

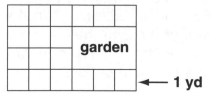

garden

← 1 yd

Use with Lesson 12-14, pages 408–409 in the Student Book.

Ratios as Fractions

Name _____

Date _____

The ratio of bees to butterflies is
2 to 3 or 2 : 3 or $\frac{2}{3}$.

The ratio of butterflies to bees is
3 to 2 or 3 : 2 or $\frac{3}{2}$.

Equivalent Ratios

$\frac{4}{6} = n$

$\frac{4}{6} = \frac{4 \times 2}{6 \times 2} = \frac{8}{12}$

or

$\frac{4}{6} = \frac{4 \div 2}{6 \div 2} = \frac{2}{3}$

So $\frac{4}{6} = \frac{8}{12} = \frac{2}{3}$ are equivalent ratios.

**There are 5 dogs, 6 cats, 7 birds, 11 mice, and 2 snakes in the pet store.
Write each ratio in three ways.**

1. dogs to cats _____

2. cats to birds _____

3. birds to mice _____

4. mice to snakes _____

5. snakes to dogs _____

6. birds to dogs _____

7. mice to cats _____

8. snakes to birds _____

9. dogs to mice _____

10. cats to mice _____

Write each ratio in simplest form.

11. 4 to 8 _____

12. 4 : 12 _____

13. $\frac{14}{7}$ _____

14. 16 to 32 _____

15. 24 to 6 _____

16. 7 : 18 _____

17. 16 : 24 _____

18. $\frac{15}{36}$ _____

19. $\frac{84}{16}$ _____

20. 6 to 36 _____

21. 13 : 100 _____

22. $\frac{16}{40}$ _____

Find the missing value to show equivalent ratios.

23. $\frac{1}{3} = \frac{}{15}$

24. $\frac{2}{3} = \frac{}{9}$

25. $\frac{4}{5} = \frac{}{20}$

26. $\frac{3}{4} = \frac{}{24}$

27. $\frac{12}{16} = \frac{}{4}$

28. $\frac{4}{36} = \frac{}{9}$

29. $\frac{8}{32} = \frac{}{4}$

30. $\frac{9}{12} = \frac{}{4}$

31. $\frac{3}{5} = \frac{}{25}$

32. $\frac{21}{7} = \frac{}{1}$

33. $\frac{110}{120} = \frac{}{12}$

34. $\frac{3}{7} = \frac{}{28}$

Problem Solving

35. There are 18 girls and 12 boys in Ms. Lorenzo's class.
What is the ratio in simplest form of boys to girls? _____

36. Tammy has 64 baseball cards and Ricardo has 100. What
is the ratio in simplest form of the number of cards that
Tammy has to the number of cards that Ricardo has? _____

Use with Lesson 13-1, pages 416–417 in the Student Book.
Then go to Lesson 13-2, pages 418–419 in the Student Book.

147

Proportions

Name _____

Date _____

Do the two given ratios form a proportion? Write *Yes* or *No*.

1. $\frac{5}{6}, \frac{15}{18}$ _____

2. $\frac{3}{4}, \frac{9}{16}$ _____

3. $\frac{2}{5}, \frac{5}{2}$ _____

4. $\frac{3}{7}, \frac{6}{14}$ _____

5. $\frac{1}{4}, \frac{3}{12}$ _____

6. $\frac{28}{21}, \frac{4}{3}$ _____

7. $\frac{18}{9}, \frac{9}{3}$ _____

8. $\frac{15}{20}, \frac{3}{4}$ _____

Use the cross-products rule to find out which of these are proportions. Write *Yes* or *No*.

9. $\frac{4}{10} = \frac{12}{30}$ _____

10. $\frac{1}{2} = \frac{8}{16}$ _____

11. $\frac{2}{3} = \frac{4}{9}$ _____

12. $\frac{3}{5} = \frac{9}{15}$ _____

13. $\frac{6}{12} = \frac{18}{36}$ _____

14. $\frac{18}{24} = \frac{6}{12}$ _____

15. $\frac{16}{20} = \frac{4}{5}$ _____

16. $\frac{6}{10} = \frac{18}{30}$ _____

Find the missing number in the proportion.

17. $\frac{2}{7} = \frac{4}{n}$ _____

18. $\frac{5}{6} = \frac{n}{18}$ _____

19. $\frac{3}{5} = \frac{n}{45}$ _____

20. $\frac{4}{n} = \frac{12}{60}$ _____

21. $\frac{1}{3} = \frac{1\frac{1}{3}}{n}$ _____

22. $\frac{1}{7} = \frac{1\frac{2}{7}}{n}$ _____

23. $\frac{n}{8} = \frac{1}{3}$ _____

24. $\frac{n}{7} = \frac{1}{5}$ _____

25. $\frac{1 \text{ case}}{4 \text{ cases}} = \frac{12 \text{ bottles}}{n \text{ bottles}}$ _____

26. $\frac{3 \text{ goldfish}}{9 \text{ goldfish}} = \frac{2 \text{ guppies}}{n \text{ guppies}}$ _____

Problem Solving

27. Three goldfish cost $2.00. How many goldfish will $10.00 buy? _____

28. If 2 plums cost $.28, how much do 12 plums cost? _____

29. If oranges cost $2.40 a dozen, how much do 2 oranges cost? _____

30. If 2 cups of rice serve 5 people, how many cups of rice do you need to serve 60 people? _____

Use with Lesson 13-2, pages 418–419 in the Student Book.
Then go to Lesson 13-3, pages 420–421 in the Student Book.

Scale and Maps

Name _____

Date _____

Measure the scale distance on the map to the nearest $\frac{1}{8}$ inch.
Then find the actual distance.

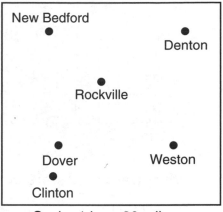

Scale: 1 in. = 80 miles

0   40   80

$\frac{1}{8}$ in.   1 in.

	Between Cities	Scale Distance (in.)	Actual Distance (mi)
1.	New Bedford-Rockville	$\frac{3}{4}$	
2.	New Bedford-Denton		
3.	Dover-Clinton		
4.	Dover-Weston		
5.	Rockville-Weston		

Use the scale 1 in. = 2 mi to find the actual distance.

	To go from:	Scale Distance	Actual Distance
6.	Troy to Dixmont	2 in.	
7.	Monroe to Swanville	$3\frac{1}{4}$ in.	
8.	Prospect Ferry to Sandy Point	$2\frac{1}{8}$ in.	

	To go from:	Scale Distance	Actual Distance
9.	Carmel to Etna	$1\frac{5}{8}$ in.	
10.	Carmel to Winterport	$7\frac{7}{8}$ in.	
11.	Dixmont to Brooks	$4\frac{1}{2}$ in.	

Measure the scale distance to the nearest centimeter. Then estimate each distance.

12. From Center City to Parville _____

13. From Center City to Sikes Ave. _____

14. The length of Long Ave. _____

15. From road marker 12 to road marker 16 _____

16. From road marker 9 to road marker 12 _____

17. From Center City to road marker 16 _____

18. From Center City to road marker 4 _____

19. The shortest distance along a road from road marker 5 to road marker 4 _____

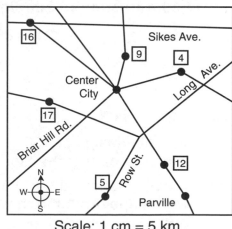

Scale: 1 cm = 5 km

0   15 km

0 cm 1 cm 2 cm 3 cm

Use with Lesson 13-3, pages 420–421 in the Student Book.
Then go to Lesson 13-4, pages 422–423 in the Student Book.

149

Relate Fractions to Percents

Name _____

Date _____

Tell what fractional part of the grid is shaded. Then write the fraction as a percent.

1.

$\overline{100} = $ _____ %

2.

$\overline{100} = $ _____ %

3.

$\overline{100} = $ _____ %

4.

$\overline{100} = $ _____ %

Write as a percent.

5. $\frac{4}{5} = $ _____

6. $\frac{19}{25} = $ _____

7. $\frac{1}{4} = $ _____

8. $\frac{6}{10} = $ _____

9. 4 out of 20 = _____

10. 7 out of 50 = _____

11. 8 out of 25 = _____

Write as a fraction with a denominator of 100.

12. 87% _____

13. 25% _____

14. 2% _____

15. 17% _____

16. 33% _____

17. 56% _____

18. 66% _____

19. 1% _____

Write as a fraction in simplest form.

20. 25% _____

21. 8% _____

22. 20% _____

23. 60% _____

24. 10% _____

25. 15% _____

26. 75% _____

27. 17% _____

Problem Solving

28. In a tile design of 100 tiles, 39 of the tiles are red. What percent of the tiles are red? _____

29. A survey showed that 85 out of 100 people questioned were happy with the mayor of the town. What percent of the people questioned were happy with the mayor? _____

30. In a group of 100 children, 48 had brown hair. What percent of the children had brown hair? _____

Use with Lesson 13-4, pages 422–423 in the Student Book.
Then go to Lesson 13-5, pages 424–425 in the Student Book.

Relate Percents to Decimals

Name _____

Date _____

Percent	Fraction	Decimal		Decimal	Fraction	Percent		Write 7 dimes as a percent of a dollar.
37% →	$\frac{37}{100}$ →	0.37		0.43 →	$\frac{43}{100}$ →	43%		$7 \times \$0.10 = \$0.70$
2% →	$\frac{2}{100}$ →	0.02		0.07 →	$\frac{7}{100}$ →	7%		$0.70 = 70\%$

So 7 dimes is 70% of a dollar.

Write as a fraction and a decimal.

1. 43% _____ **2.** 16% _____ **3.** 10% _____ **4.** 33% _____

5. 1% _____ **6.** 72% _____ **7.** 18% _____ **8.** 68% _____

9. 14% _____ **10.** 25% _____ **11.** 52% _____ **12.** 77% _____

Write as a fraction and a percent.

13. 0.47 _____ **14.** 0.05 _____ **15.** 0.71 _____ **16.** 0.99 _____

17. 0.08 _____ **18.** 0.17 _____ **19.** 0.54 _____ **20.** 0.09 _____

21. 0.64 _____ **22.** 0.59 _____ **23.** 0.36 _____ **24.** 0.85 _____

Write each as a percent of a dollar.

25. 8 dimes _____ **26.** 7 nickels _____ **27.** 4 pennies _____

28. 3 quarters _____ **29.** 73 pennies _____ **30.** 1 quarter _____

31. 5 dimes _____ **32.** 3 nickels _____ **33.** 18 pennies _____

34. 1 quarter, 7 nickels _____ **35.** 3 dimes, 7 pennies _____

36. 11 nickels, 4 pennies _____ **37.** 1 half dollar, 3 nickels _____

Problem Solving

38. Ron spent 43¢. What percent of a dollar did he spend?

_____

39. Luis added 0.38 liters of water to a solution he was mixing in chemistry class. What percent of a liter of water did he use?

_____

40. Wynton sprinted 0.65 the length of a 100-meter long soccer field. What percent of the length of the field did he sprint?

_____

Use with Lesson 13-5, pages 424–425 in the Student Book.
Then go to Lesson 13-6, pages 426–427 in the Student Book.

151

Find the Percent of a Number

Name _____

Date _____

45% of 80 = *n*

Use Decimals or **Use Fractions**

45% = 0.45

0.45 × 80 = 36

So 45% of 80 is 36.

45% = $\frac{45}{100}$ = $\frac{9}{20}$

$\frac{9}{\underset{1}{\cancel{20}}}$ × $\overset{4}{\cancel{80}}$ = 36

Estimate: 26% of 397

25% of 400 = 25% × 400

= $\frac{1}{4}$ × $\frac{400}{1}$

= 100

So 26% of 397 is about 100.

Find the percent of the number.

1. 45% of 40 _____
2. 15% of 60 _____
3. 60% of 40 _____

4. 20% of 90 _____
5. 7% of 300 _____
6. 8% of 350 _____

7. 50% of 86 _____
8. 25% of 44 _____
9. 10% of 70 _____

10. 15% of 480 _____
11. 45% of 200 _____
12. 90% of 450 _____

Estimate the percent of the number.

13. 73% of 380 _____
14. 27% of 600 _____
15. 81% of 230 _____

16. 32% of 150 _____
17. 32% of 550 _____
18. 65% of 260 _____

19. 78% of 310 _____
20. 16% of 125 _____
21. 9% of 295 _____

Compare. Use <, =, or >.

22. 20% of 50 _____ 25% of 100
23. 40% of 60 _____ 60% of 40

24. 80% of 20 _____ 75% of 20
25. 20% of 20 _____ 50% of 40

26. 35% of 500 _____ 45% of 500
27. 60% of 60 _____ 90% of 40

Problem Solving

28. Don had 280 baseball cards. He gave 15% of them to his sister. How many cards did Don give to his sister? _____

29. There were 600 tickets sold for the dance recital. Trixie sold 5% of all tickets sold. How many tickets did Trixie sell? _____

Use with Lesson 13-6, pages 426–427 in the Student Book.
Then go to Lesson 13-7, pages 428–429 in the Student Book.

Use Percent

Name _____

Date _____

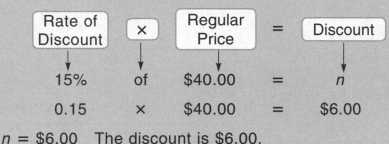

A sale on sweaters offers a discount of 15% off the regular price of $40.00. How much is the discount?

Rate of Discount	×	Regular Price	=	Discount
↓	↓	↓		↓
15%	of	$40.00	=	n
0.15	×	$40.00	=	$6.00

$n = 6.00 The discount is $6.00.

**Use the circle graph at right to complete the table.
Entertainment Plus rented 480 videotapes last week.**

Weekly Rental

	Videotape	Percent	Number of Tapes Rented
1.	Adventure		
2.	Mystery		
3.	Romance		
4.	Comedy		
5.	Science Fiction		

**Jaclyn earns $2000 a month.
How much does she spend on each?**

Monthly Expenses

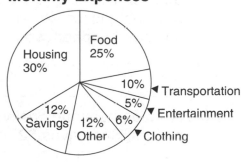

6. Housing _____   7. Food _____

8. Savings _____   9. Transportation _____

10. Entertainment _____ 11. Clothing _____

Find the discount for each item.

	Item	Regular Price	Rate of Discount	Discount
12.	sweater	$64	15%	
13.	jacket	$250	35%	
14.	sweat suit	$50	8%	
15.	jump suit	$125	20%	

Problem Solving

16. Computers with a regular price of $1980 are offered at a 12% discount. What is the discount? _____

17. Printers with a regular price of $320 are offered at a 7% discount. What is the discount? _____

Use with Lesson 13-7, pages 428–429 in the Student Book.
Then go to Lesson 13-8, pages 430–431 in the Student Book.

153

Problem-Solving Strategy: Combine Strategies

Name _____

Date _____

Palvik saves $1 the first week, $3 the second week, and $5 the third week. If he continues to save this way, how much will he have saved after 6 weeks?

First, *find a pattern* to tell how much he saves in the fourth, fifth, and sixth weeks. Each week, he saves $2 more than he did the preceding week.
Then, *use a table* to find the total amount he saved.

Palvik saved a total of $36.

+$2	+$2	+$2	+$2	+$2
$1	$3	$5	$7	$9	$11

Week	1	2	3	4	5	6
Amount	$1	$3	$5	$7	$9	$11
Total	$1	$4	$9	$16	$25	$36

Solve. Do your work on a separate sheet of paper.

1. Cathy bought a bag of wheat chips. Alan took 4 chips, and Paula took 3. She gave 4 to her mother and ate 3 herself. There were 6 chips left in the bag. What percent of the chips originally in the bag does Cathy have left?

2. Willis is making omelets for himself and 6 friends. He has 2 dozen eggs. He uses 2 eggs to make each omelet, and each person gets 1 omelet. How many eggs are left over?

3. Sharess has 100 rare coins. Twelve of the coins are silver dollars, 9 are silver quarters, 18 are silver dimes, 6 are buffalo nickels, and the rest are copper two-cent pieces. What percent of the coins are copper two-cent pieces?

4. Ramon uses 20 shells to make one necklace. Twenty-five percent of the shells are large shells and the rest are small shells. If Ramon wants to make 14 necklaces, how many large shells and how many small shells will he need?

5. Jane earns money delivering newspapers. She saves $2 the first week, $3 the second week, and $4 the third week. If she continues saving this way, how much money will she have saved by the end of the sixth week?

6. Donna's mother gives her money for a savings account. She gives $1 the first week, $5 the second week, and $9 the third week. If she continues saving this way, how many weeks will it take to save $45?

7. Emilio has 189 books to put onto 9 shelves. Some shelves hold 15 books and others hold two dozen. How many of each size shelf will Emilio use?

8. Four out of every 9 people surveyed said they would vote for Smith. If 80 people said they would vote for Smith, how many people were surveyed?

Use with Lesson 13-8, pages 430–431 in the Student Book.
Then go to Lesson 13-9, pages 432–433 in the Student Book.

Problem-Solving Applications: Mixed Review

Name _____

Date _____

Solve each problem and explain the method you used. If needed, do all your work on a separate sheet of paper.

Read ▶ Plan ▶ Solve ▶ Check

Strategy File

Use These Strategies
Use a Model/Diagram
More Than One Solution
Use More Than One Step
Guess and Test
Make a Table
Use a Graph

1. At Campus Books, the price of calendars is reduced by 25¢ each week of the new year. If the calendars cost $12.99 on January 1st, how much do they cost after 6 weeks?

_____

2. Wally bought a t-shirt listed at $7.75 for 20% off. If he was charged $1.19 in sales tax, how much did Wally spend in all?

_____

3. When making fruit salad, Julio uses three grapes for every two cherries. If he uses a total 45 grapes and cherries, how many did he use of each?

_____

4. Lois spends $\frac{7}{20}$ of her salary on rent. She spends $\frac{3}{10}$ of her salary on food. What percent of her money does Lois spend on rent and food together?

_____

5. Jin told his parents he spent 60% of his free time on Saturday gardening. If he had 5 free hours and spent 3 gardening, did Jin tell the truth?

_____

6. After drinking a glass of juice, Barry has 1.6 L of his 2 L bottle left. What percent of the bottle did Barry drink?

_____

7. Blaine has 41% of a dollar. She has four coins. What coins does she have?

_____

Sales at Burns' Butcher Shop

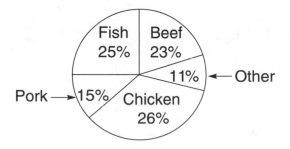

Use the graph at left to solve.

8. Which two meats combined represent $\frac{2}{5}$ of the sales?

_____

9. If sales totaled $694, was more than $150 worth of beef sold?

_____

Algebraic Expressions and Equations

Name _____

Date _____

Algebraic Expressions	Equations
$2a + 3x$	$3n = 24$
$10 - y$	$f + 7 = 19$

Write whether each is an *expression* or an *equation*.

1. $z + 17$ **2.** $r - 8 = 25$ **3.** $10q = 90$ **4.** $5n + 3$ **5.** $a + b = c$

_____   _____   _____   _____   _____

6. $6t - 4$ **7.** $2x = 20$ **8.** $7p + 3s$ **9.** $10 + m$ **10.** $9g + 1 = 10$

_____   _____   _____   _____   _____

Write each word phrase as an algebraic expression or an equation.

11. the sum of 12 and a number y

_____

12. a number added to 16 is equal to 23

_____

13. the quotient of a number x and 9

_____

14. a number subtracted from 41 is equal to 19

_____

15. 23 less than the product of 4 times a number is equal to 37

_____

16. seven times a number z, increased by 12

_____

Find a value of n that will make each a true equation. Let $x = 2$, $y = 5$, and $z = 4$.

17. $x + y - z = n$

$n = $ _____

18. $\frac{(zy)}{x} = n$

$n = $ _____

19. $6y - 3x = n$

$n = $ _____

20. $5(y + z) = n$

$n = $ _____

21. $\frac{(4x)}{z} = n$

$n = $ _____

22. $\frac{6(x + z)}{z} = n$

$n = $ _____

Evaluate each algebraic expression.

23. $t - 0$, when $t = 8$ _____

24. $311 + b$, when $b = 145$ _____

25. $r - 7\frac{1}{2}$, when $r = 9$ _____

26. $p - 17$ when $p = 34$ _____

27. $g + h - i$, when $g = 2$, $h = 5$, and $i = 7$ _____

28. $a + b + c$, when $a = 0.5$, $b = 3$, and $c = 1.6$ _____

29. $m - n + p$, when $m = 459$, $n = 32$, and $p = 199$ _____

Use with Lesson 14-1, pages 440–441 in the Student Book.
Then go to Lesson 14-2, pages 442–443 in the Student Book.

Properties of Equality

Use the Addition, Subtraction, Multiplication, and Division Properties of Equality to isolate the variables.

$x - 7 = 9$	$x + 9 = 15$	$\frac{x}{5} = 4$	$3x = 21$
add 7	subtract 9	multiply by 5	divide by 3
$x - 7 + 7 = 9 + 7$	$x + 9 - 9 = 15 - 9$	$\frac{x}{5} \cdot 5 = 4 \cdot 5$	$3x \div 3 = 21 \div 3$
$x = 16$	$x = 6$	$x = 20$	$x = 7$

Name the property of equality used.

1. $13 - 5 = 8$

$(13 - 5) + 6 = 8 + 6$

_____

2. $\frac{1}{5} = \frac{3}{15}$

$\frac{1}{5} \cdot 3 = \frac{3}{15} \cdot 3$

_____

Write the inverse operation that would isolate the variable.

3. $n + 12 = 19$

_____

4. $r \div 7 = 4$

_____

5. $8s = 48$

_____

6. $b - 3.8 = 6.5$

_____

7. $\frac{x}{4.3} = 9.1$

_____

8. $m - \frac{1}{2} = 4\frac{1}{4}$

_____

9. $t + 3.01 = 4$

_____

10. $6.4q = 57.6$

_____

11. $b \cdot 7.6 = 38$

_____

12. $33\frac{2}{3}g = 101$

_____

13. $l - 6.9 = 15$

_____

14. $3k = 24 \div 4$

_____

Write the number, variable, or operation that makes each equation true.

15. $(17 - 9) + \rule{1.5cm}{0.4pt} = 17$

16. $(r + 7) - \rule{1.5cm}{0.4pt} = r$

17. $(2 \times 7) \div \rule{1.5cm}{0.4pt} = 2$

18. $\left(\frac{n}{5}\right) \cdot \rule{1.5cm}{0.4pt} = n$

19. $(d + 7) \rule{1.5cm}{0.4pt} 7 = d$

20. $15c \div \rule{1.5cm}{0.4pt} = 15$

21. $(y - 13) \rule{1.5cm}{0.4pt} 13 = y$

22. $(m + h) - \rule{1.5cm}{0.4pt} = m$

23. $(6 \div s) \rule{1.5cm}{0.4pt} s = 6$

Use with Lesson 14-2, pages 442–443 in the Student Book.
Then go to Lesson 14-3, pages 444–445 in the Student Book.

157

Addition and Subtraction Equations

Name _____

Date _____

$$
\begin{array}{l}
n + 16 = 30 \\
n = 30 - 16 \quad \longleftarrow \boxed{\text{Subtract 16 from both sides.}} \\
n = 14
\end{array}
\qquad
\begin{array}{l}
x - 29 = 57 \\
x = 57 + 29 \quad \longleftarrow \boxed{\text{Add 29 to both sides.}} \\
x = 86
\end{array}
$$

Solve and check each addition equation.

1. $34 + x = 69$ _____

2. $e + 5 = 19$ _____

3. $n = 9 + 8$ _____

4. $c + 21 = 21$ _____

5. $43 = r + 7.3$ _____

6. $28.08 + 8 = f$ _____

7. $11 = 10 + y$ _____

8. $14.31 + w = 70$ _____

9. $a + 19 = 28$ _____

10. $b = 12 + 8$ _____

11. $p + 62.56 = 90.31$ _____

12. $76.94 = 14.72 + s$ _____

13. $0.8 = t + 0.2$ _____

14. $1.5 + d = 2$ _____

Solve and check each subtraction equation.

15. $a - 12 = 9$ _____

16. $40 - w = 24$ _____

17. $8.56 - h = 4.55$ _____

18. $77 - m = 60$ _____

19. $q - 1.75 = 5.75$ _____

20. $101 - e = 39$ _____

21. $t - 0.75 = 0.5$ _____

22. $2.7 = u - 7.1$ _____

23. $74.3 - f = 17.5$ _____

24. $7.023 - k = 4.15$ _____

25. $5.04 - j = 3.91$ _____

26. $3.5 - p = 1.25$ _____

27. $13 - r = 6.303$ _____

28. $d - 4.001 = 5.999$ _____

Problem Solving

29. Rodney had his 6th birthday 7 years ago. How old is Rodney now?

_____

30. If Rosa were 6 inches taller she would be the same height as her mother. Her mother is 5 feet 7 inches. How tall is Rosa?

_____

Use with Lesson 14-3, pages 444–445 in the Student Book.
Then go to Lesson 14-4, pages 446–447 in the Student Book.

Multiplication and Division Equations

Name _____

Date _____

$15x = 780$		$\frac{y}{14} = 38$	
$\frac{15x}{15} = \frac{780}{15}$	Divide both sides by 15.	$\frac{y}{14} \cdot 14 = 38 \cdot 14$	Multiply both sides by 14.
$x = 52$		$y = 532$	

Solve and check each multiplication equation.

1. $12c = 144$ _____

2. $60 = 4(e)$ _____

3. $9 \cdot r = 117$ _____

4. $49 = 7t$ _____

5. $3u = 90$ _____

6. $69 = w \times 23$ _____

7. $n(29.06) = 0$ _____

8. $280.7 = 7g$ _____

9. $y \times 5 = 7.505$ _____

10. $10.4i = 124.8$ _____

11. $47.92(v) = 47.92$ _____

12. $12.35m = 6.175$ _____

Solve and check each division equation.

13. $\frac{p}{7} = 4$ _____

14. $\frac{y}{3} = 9$ _____

15. $\frac{n}{2} = 13$ _____

16. $\frac{r}{5} = 9$ _____

17. $\frac{h}{7} = 6$ _____

18. $\frac{c}{16} = 18$ _____

19. $\frac{u}{12} = 11$ _____

20. $\frac{g}{320} = 8$ _____

21. $\frac{a}{45} = 12$ _____

22. $\frac{w}{1} = 25$ _____

23. $\frac{j}{73} = 0$ _____

24. $\frac{v}{8} = 1.01$ _____

Problem Solving

25. Georgia has $\frac{1}{3}$ of money she needs to buy a dress. If the dress costs $66.27, how much money does Georgia have?

_____

26. Roy averaged half as many points per game as Carl. If Roy averaged 9.4 points a game, how many did Carl average?

_____

Use with Lesson 14-4, pages 446–447 in the Student Book.
Then go to Lesson 14-5, pages 448–449 in the Student Book.

159

Equations with Fractions

Name _____

Date _____

Equation	Property	Solution
$x + \frac{3}{7} = \frac{3}{7}$	Identity Property of Addition	$x = 0$
$\frac{1}{5} + \frac{3}{5} = \frac{3}{5} + x$	Commutative Property of Addition	$x = \frac{1}{5}$
$\frac{3}{4} \cdot x = \frac{3}{4}$	Identity Property of Multiplication	$x = 1$
$(4 \cdot \frac{1}{3}) \cdot x = 4 \cdot (\frac{1}{3} \cdot \frac{1}{4})$	Associative Property of Multiplication	$x = \frac{1}{4}$
$x \cdot \frac{4}{7} = 0$	Zero Property of Multiplication	$x = 0$

Solve for *m*. Use the property shown to help you.

Identity Property of Addition

1. $\frac{5}{6} + m = \frac{5}{6}$ _____

2. $m + 0 = \frac{3}{8}$ _____

Commutative Property of Addition

3. $m + \frac{1}{3} = \frac{1}{3} + \frac{4}{5}$ _____

4. $\frac{2}{3} + m = \frac{1}{4} + \frac{2}{3}$ _____

Zero Property of Multiplication

5. $m \times \frac{1}{7} = 0$ _____

6. $\frac{7}{11} \cdot m = 0$ _____

Identity Property of Multiplication

7. $1 \cdot m = \frac{5}{12}$ _____

8. $m \cdot \frac{15}{16} = \frac{15}{16}$ _____

Associative Property of Multiplication

9. $(5 \cdot \frac{1}{3}) \cdot m = 5 \cdot (\frac{1}{3} \cdot 3)$ _____

10. $(3 \cdot \frac{1}{9}) \cdot m = 3 \cdot (\frac{1}{9} \cdot \frac{1}{3})$ _____

Solve the equation.

11. $\frac{4}{7} \cdot p = \frac{4}{7}$ _____

12. $\frac{7}{8} = r + \frac{3}{8}$ _____

13. $(\frac{2}{3} + \frac{1}{4}) + 4 = \frac{2}{3} + (\frac{1}{4} + b)$ _____

14. $\frac{1}{3} = e + \frac{1}{12}$ _____

15. $\frac{1}{12} = \frac{1}{6} \cdot x$ _____

16. $\frac{7}{11} \cdot \frac{4}{5} = \frac{4}{5} \cdot w$ _____

17. $\frac{1}{6} \cdot (\frac{1}{3} \cdot m) = (\frac{1}{6} \cdot \frac{1}{3}) \cdot \frac{1}{5}$ _____

18. $a \cdot \frac{13}{19} = 0$ _____

19. $\frac{9}{13} = f + \frac{6}{13}$ _____

20. $\frac{2}{9} \cdot t = \frac{2}{9}$ _____

21. $c + \frac{5}{7} = \frac{5}{7} + \frac{3}{8}$ _____

22. $b + 0 = \frac{7}{10}$ _____

23. $\frac{5}{12} + u = \frac{5}{12}$ _____

24. $\frac{6}{7} \cdot j = \frac{3}{5} \cdot \frac{6}{7}$ _____

25. $\frac{3}{4} = d \cdot \frac{3}{4}$ _____

26. $d \cdot \frac{7}{8} = 0$ _____

Use with Lesson 14-5, pages 448–449 in the Student Book.
Then go to Lesson 14-6, pages 450–451 in the Student Book.

Introduction to Integers

Name _____

Date _____

The temperature dropped 10° and
then rose 6°.

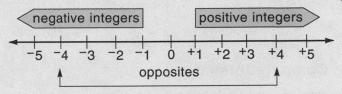

dropped 10° ——————→ ⁻10 degrees
rose 6° ——————→ ⁺6 degrees

Positive (+) integers: *right* of 0; *greater than* 0

Negative (−) integers: *left* of 0; *less than* 0

Zero: neither + nor −.

Opposites: ⁺4 and ⁻4; 0 and 0; ⁺1 and ⁻1

Write each as an integer.

1. 7 pounds gained _____

2. $5 profit _____

3. loss of 6 yards _____

Name the integer that matches each letter on the number line.

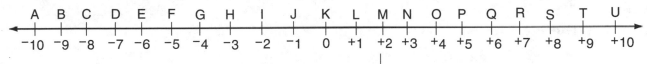

4. *K* _____

5. *A* _____

6. *P* _____

7. *S* _____

8. *M* _____

9. *E* _____

10. *D* _____

11. *G* _____

12. *U* _____

13. *I* _____

14. *N* _____

15. *Q* _____

**For each integer, name the integer that is just *before* and
just *after* it on a number line.**

16. ⁺8 _____

17. ⁻7 _____

18. ⁻12 _____

19. ⁺2 _____

20. 0 _____

21. ⁻23 _____

Write the opposite of each integer.

22. ⁺1 _____

23. ⁻8 _____

24. ⁺13 _____

25. 0 _____

26. ⁻13 _____

27. ⁺92 _____

Problem Solving

28. If you record a loss of one hundred
dollars as ⁻$100, how would you
record a profit of one hundred
dollars?

_____

29. On a map if you label the ground floor
of an office building 0, how would you
label the third level of the garage below
the ground floor?

_____

Use with Lesson 14-6, pages 450–451 in the Student Book.
Then go to Lesson 14-7, pages 452–453 in the Student Book.

161

Compare and Order Integers

Name _____

Date _____

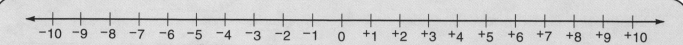

-10 -9 -8 -7 -6 -5 -4 -3 -2 -1 0 +1 +2 +3 +4 +5 +6 +7 +8 +9 +10

Compare Integers

Any integer *is greater than* an integer to its *left*.

$^+6 > {}^+1$ since $^+1$ is to the left of $^+6$. Also $^+1 < {}^+6$.

$^-8 < {}^+2$ since $^+2$ is to the right of $^-8$. Also $^+2 > {}^-8$.

Order Integers

Least to greatest:
Begin with integer farthest to the *left*.
$^-5, {}^-3, 0$

Greatest to least:
Begin with integer farthest to the *right*.
$0, {}^-3, {}^-5$

Choose the greater integer.

1. $^+1, {}^+8$ _____
2. $^-2, {}^+2$ _____
3. $^-5, {}^-4$ _____
4. $^-10, {}^-11$ _____

Compare. Write < or >.

5. $^-6$ _____ $^+3$
6. $^+9$ _____ $^-1$
7. 0 _____ $^-3$
8. $^-10$ _____ $^-15$

Arrange in order from least to greatest.

9. $^+5, 0, {}^-7$ _____
10. $^-9, {}^-1, {}^+4$ _____
11. $^-10, {}^+2, {}^-13$ _____

Arrange in order from greatest to least.

12. $^+10, {}^+6, {}^-6$ _____
13. $^-8, {}^-12, 0$ _____
14. $^+6, 0, {}^+16$ _____

Write *always, sometimes,* or *never* to make true statements.

15. A negative integer is _____ greater than a positive integer.

16. A negative integer is _____ greater than another negative integer.

17. Zero is _____ greater than a negative integer.

Problem Solving

18. In her checkbook register Brenda records deposits as positive integers and withdrawals as negative integers. For the following entries: $^+\$100, {}^-\$18, {}^+\$50, {}^-\$55,$ and $^-\$45,$ which withdrawal is between $40 and $50? _____

Use with Lesson 14-7, pages 452–453 in the Student Book.
Then go to Lesson 14-8, pages 454–455 in the Student Book.

Add Integers with Like Signs

Name _____

Date _____

<table>
<tr>
<td>
To model adding integers on a number line:
Add: $^-4 + \,^-1 = n$

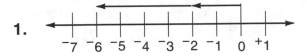

-6   -5   -4   -3   -2   -1   0   +1   +2

• Start at 0.
• Move <i>left</i> for negative integers.
• Move <i>right</i> for positive integers.
• Zero means <i>no</i> movement. $^-4 + \,^-1 = \,^-5$
</td>
<td>
To add integers with like signs:
Add: $^-4 + \,^-1 = n$

• Add the integers.
• Use the sign of the addends.

  $4 + \,1 = 5$

  $^-4 + \,^-1 = \,^-5$
</td>
</tr>
</table>

Write an addition sentence for each number line.

1.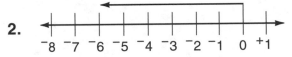

    -7   -6   -5   -4   -3   -2   -1   0   +1

_____

2.

    -8   -7   -6   -5   -4   -3   -2   -1   0   +1

_____

Add. Use a number line to help you.

3. $^-6 + \,^-3$ _____

4. $^+9 + \,^+6$ _____

5. $0 + \,^-3$ _____

6. $^-10 + \,^-15$ _____

7. $(^+3 + \,^+3) + \,^+6$

    _____ $+ \,^+6 =$ _____

8. $^-4 + (^-6 + \,^-1)$

    $4 +$ _____ $=$ _____

9. $^-4 + (^-3 + \,^-8) =$ ____

10. $(^-7 + \,^-9) + 0 =$ ____

11. $(^-8 + 0) + \,^-9 =$ ____

Complete each table.

12.

n = integer	$n + \,^+3$
$^+8$	
0	
$^+4$	

13.

n = integer	$n + \,^-3$
$^-5$	
$^-3$	
$^-7$	

Problem Solving

Write the answer in words and as an integer.

14. A golfer shot three strokes above par on the first hole and then one stroke above par on the next hole. How many strokes above par is her score on the two holes? _____

Use with Lesson 14-8, pages 454–455 in the Student Book.
Then go to Lesson 14-9, pages 456–457 in the Student Book.

163

Add Integers with Unlike Signs

To model adding integers on the number line:

Add: $^+4 + {}^-1 = n$

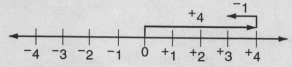

- Start at 0.
- Move *left* for negative integers.
- Move *right* for positive integers.
  $^+4 + {}^-1 = {}^+3$

To add integers with *unlike* signs:

Add: $^+4 + {}^-1 = n$

- Find the difference. (Drop the signs and subtract the numbers.) $4 - 1 = 3$

- Use the sign of the addend farther from zero.
  $^+4 + {}^-1 = {}^+3$

Think:
$^+4$ is farther from zero. The sign is +.

Complete the addition sentence for each number line.

1.

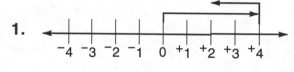

$^+4 + {}^-2 =$ _____

2.

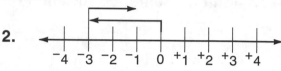

$^-3 + {}^+2 =$ _____

Write the addition sentence for each number line.

3.

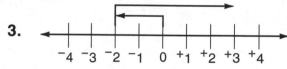

_____

4.

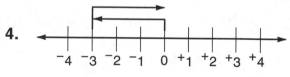

_____

Find the sum. Use a number line to help you.

5. $^-6 + {}^+3$ _____   **6.** $^-9 + {}^+6$ _____   **7.** $^-10 + {}^+3$ _____   **8.** $^-10 + {}^+15$ _____

9. $^+11 + {}^-5$ _____   **10.** $^+7 + {}^-7$ _____   **11.** $^+9 + {}^-6$ _____   **12.** $^+10 + {}^-4$ _____

Problem Solving

Write each answer in words and as an integer.

13. A newborn baby lost 7 ounces in the hospital and gained 5 ounces his first week at home. What is his net gain or loss?

_____

14. Flora climbed 45 feet up the side of a cliff. Then she slipped 10 feet down. Where is she located now?

_____

Use with Lesson 14-9, pages 456–457 in the Student Book.
Then go to Lesson 14-10, pages 458–459 in the Student Book.

Subtract Integers

Subtracting an integer is the same as *adding the opposite* of that integer.

Subtract: $^-3 - {}^-5 = n$

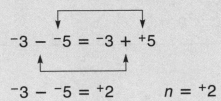

$^-3 - {}^-5 = {}^-3 + {}^+5$

$^-3 - {}^-5 = {}^+2 \qquad n = {}^+2$

Key

$1\,\bigcirc = {}^+1$

$1\,\bullet = {}^-1$

Integer Mat

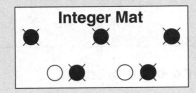

$^+1 + {}^-1 = 0$

zero pair: $\bigcirc\,\bullet$

Rewrite each as an addition expression. Then add.

1. $^-7 - {}^+2$ _____

2. $^+6 - {}^-2$ _____

3. $^-9 - {}^-7$ _____

4. $^-12 - {}^-14$ _____

5. $^+18 - {}^-5$ _____

6. $^-10 - {}^-10$ _____

7. $^-5 - {}^+4$ _____

8. $^+8 - {}^-11$ _____

9. $^+7 - {}^+8$ _____

Subtract. Use counters to help you.

10. $^+6 - {}^-8$ _____

11. $^-9 - {}^-2$ _____

12. $^-6 - {}^-11$ _____

13. $^-4 - {}^-6$ _____

14. $^+6 - {}^+2$ _____

15. $^-1 - {}^-5$ _____

Circle the letter of the correct answer.

16. $^-12 - {}^-1$ **a.** $^-13$ **b.** $^-11$ **c.** $^+13$ **d.** $^-11$

17. $0 - {}^-13$ **a.** $^-13$ **b.** $^+13$ **c.** 0 **d.** $^-1$

18. $^-7 - {}^-7$ **a.** 0 **b.** $^-14$ **c.** $^+14$ **d.** $^+1$

Problem Solving

19. On a winter day, the temperature dropped from $^-3°C$ to $^-11°C$. Find the change in temperature.

_____

20. Kay lives 4 blocks north of school. Joe lives 7 blocks south of school. What is the distance between Kay's house and Joe's house?

_____

Use with Lesson 14-10, pages 458–459 in the Student Book.
Then go to Lesson 14-11, pages 460–461 in the Student Book.

165

Multiply Integers

> **The product of two integers:**
>
> | is *positive* if they have the same sign. | is *negative* if they have *different* signs | is *zero* if one or both is *zero*. |
> |---|---|---|
> | $^+5 \times {}^+2 = {}^+10$ | $^-5 \times {}^+2 = {}^-10$ | $0 \times {}^-2 = 0$ |
> | $^-4 \times {}^-3 = {}^+12$ | $^+4 \times {}^-3 = {}^-12$ | $0 \times {}^+2 = 0$ |
> | | | $0 \times 0 = 0$ |

Use the rules above to find each product.

1. $^-6 \times {}^+3$ _____   **2.** $^-9 \times 0$ _____   **3.** $^+10 \times {}^-3$ _____   **4.** $^-10 \times {}^-5$ _____

5. $^-3 \times {}^+3$ _____   **6.** $^+3 \times {}^+3$ _____   **7.** $^-3 \times {}^-3$ _____   **8.** $0 \times {}^+3$ _____

9. $^-9 \times {}^-3$ _____   **10.** $^+6 \times {}^+3$ _____   **11.** $^-4 \times {}^+5$ _____   **12.** $^+8 \times {}^+3$ _____

**Let p = positive integer and n = negative integer.
Choose a. positive, b. negative, or c. zero to
complete each statement. Explain each answer.**

13. $n \times p =$ _____

14. $(n \times p) \times p =$ _____

15. $(0 \times n) \times p =$ _____

_____

_____

_____

16. $n \times 0 =$ _____

17. $(p \times p) \times p =$ _____

18. $n \times (n \times n) =$ _____

_____

_____

_____

Compute. Use the order of operations.

19. $^-5({}^+7 + {}^+2)$ _____   **20.** $^+3({}^-1 + {}^-2)$ _____   **21.** $^-8({}^-9 + {}^+3)$ _____

22. $^-4({}^+6 + {}^-3)$ _____   **23.** $^+2({}^-5 + {}^+1)$ _____   **24.** $^+3({}^-2 + {}^-7)$ _____

Problem Solving

25. A healthcare stock gains 2 points each day for five days. What is the net gain over the five days?

26. A pipe was leaking water at a rate of 5 gallons an hour. What was the net loss of water over a four-hour period?

_____

_____

Use with Lesson 14-11, pages 460–461 in the Student Book.
Then go to Lesson 14-12, pages 462–463 in the Student Book.

Divide Integers

Name _____

Date _____

Multiplication Sentence	Related Division Sentences
$^-5 \times ^+3 = ^-15$	$^-15 \div ^+3 = ^-5$ $^-15 \div ^-5 = ^+3$
$^+4 \times ^-5 = ^-20$	$^-20 \div ^-5 = ^+4$ $^-20 \div ^+4 = ^-5$
$^-5 \times ^-6 = ^+30$	$^+30 \div ^-6 = ^-5$ $^+30 \div ^-5 = ^-6$

The quotient of two integers:

• is *positive* if they have the *same* sign

$^+10 \div ^+2 = ^+5$

$^-9 \div ^-3 = ^+3$

• is *negative* if they have *different* signs.

$^-10 \div ^+2 = ^-5$

$^+9 \div ^-3 = ^-3$

Complete each related division sentence.

1. $^-9 \times ^+3 = ^-27$

$^-27 \div ^+3 =$ _____

$^-27 \div ^-9 =$ _____

2. $^-8 \times ^-6 = ^+48$

$^+48 \div ^-6 =$ _____

$^+48 \div ^-8 =$ _____

3. $^+4 \times ^+6 = ^+24$

$^+24 \div ^+6 =$ _____

$^+24 \div ^+4 =$ _____

Write two related division sentences.

4. $^-7 \times ^+2 = ^-14$

_____

_____

5. $^+6 \times ^-2 = ^-12$

_____

_____

6. $^-9 \times ^-7 = ^+63$

_____

_____

7. $^+8 \times ^+9 = ^+72$

_____

_____

8. $^-7 \times ^-6 = ^+42$

_____

_____

9. $^+5 \times ^-9 = ^-45$

_____

_____

Divide.

10. $^+64 \div ^-8$ _____

11. $^-90 \div ^-2$ _____

12. $^+24 \div ^-8$ _____

13. $^-56 \div ^-4$ _____

14. $^-42 \div ^+6$ _____

15. $^-12 \div ^-1$ _____

16. $0 \div ^-11$ _____

17. $^-66 \div ^-11$ _____

18. $^-72 \div ^-8$ _____

19. $^+81 \div ^+9$ _____

20. $^-39 \div ^-3$ _____

21. $^-24 \div ^-4$ _____

Problem Solving

22. A scuba diver dives to a depth of 150 feet in 25 minutes. What is the average rate of the dive per minute, written as an integer?

_____

23. A water pump pumps out a basement filled with 45,000 gallons of water in 9 hours. What is the average amount per hour, written as an integer?

_____

Use with Lesson 14-12, pages 462–463 in the Student Book.
Then go to Lesson 14-13, pages 464–465 in the Student Book.

The Coordinate Plane

Name _____

Date _____

Point A is located at (⁻3, 2).
Point B is located at (1, 3).
Point C is located at (⁻1, ⁻2).
Point D is located at (0, 3).

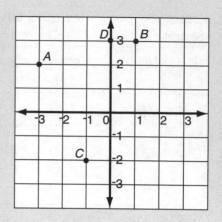

**Use the grid on the right for exercises 1–12.
Name the point for each set of coordinates.**

1. (⁻4, 4) _____   2. (2, 1) _____

3. (⁻4, ⁻3) _____   4. (3, ⁻3) _____

5. (1, 3) _____   6. (2, 2) _____

7. (⁻1, 3) _____   8. (5, 0) _____

9. (4, ⁻4) _____   10. (⁻2, 5) _____

11. (⁻5, 1) _____   12. (2, ⁻5) _____

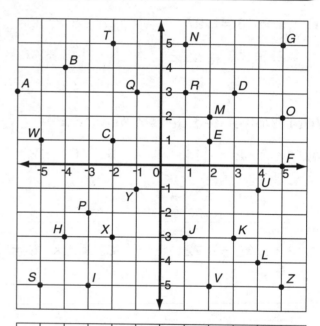

**Use the grid on the right for exercises 13–21.
Name the point to complete the chart.**

	Point	Coordinates
13.		(⁻4, 2)
14.		(⁻3, 4)
15.		(⁻1, 4)
16.		(0, ⁻1)
17.		(⁻3, ⁻3)
18.		(⁻4, ⁻1)
19.		(3, 5)
20.		(5, 2)
21.		(1, 2)

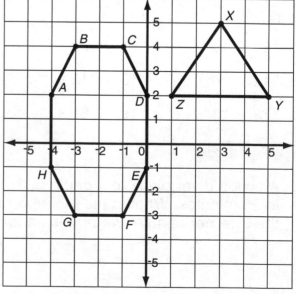

Ⓒ Use with Lesson 14-13, pages 464–465 in the Student Book.
Ⓒ Then go to Lessons 14-13A, 14-13B, and 14-13C, pages 229–234 in this Workbook.

Function Tables

Name _____

Date _____

Let m = 1 month. Let $\frac{m}{12}$ = number of years.

m	5	11	12	36	60
$\frac{m}{12}$	$\frac{5}{12}$	$\frac{11}{12}$	$\frac{12}{12} = 1$	$\frac{36}{12} = 3$	$\frac{60}{12} = 5$

Use the rule to complete each function table.

1. Let s = weight of fruit in pounds. Let $s + 4$ = weight of fruit plus weight of box.

s	12	29	35	51	68
$s + 4$					

2. Let z = number of books. Let $\$7z$ = total cost.

z	1	3	5	7	9
$\$7z$					

3. Let b = perimeter of garden. Let $\frac{b}{4}$ = length of one side of garden.

b	16	40	52	64	100
$\frac{b}{4}$					

Write the rule for each function table.

4.

a	?
3	12
5	20
8	32
12	48

5.

r	?
2	15
4	17
7	20
9	22

6.

f	?
75	15
40	8
15	3
5	1

_____   _____   _____

Use with Lesson 14-14, pages 466–467 in the Student Book.
Then go to Lesson 14-15, pages 468–469 in the Student Book.

Function and Coordinate Graphs

Name _____

Date _____

Graph the function $y = x + {}^-2$ on a coordinate plane.

• Make a function table.

x	$y = x + {}^-2$	y	(x, y)
$^-1$	$y = {}^-1 + {}^-2$	$^-3$	$(^-1, {}^-3)$
0	$y = 0 + {}^-2$	$^-2$	$(0, {}^-2)$
$^+1$	$y = {}^+1 + {}^-2$	$^-1$	$(^+1, {}^-1)$

• Graph each ordered pair. Connect the points.

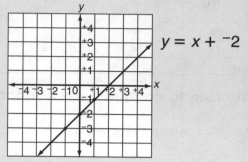

$y = x + {}^-2$

1. **Complete the function table. Then graph on the coordinate plane.**

x	$y = x + {}^-1$	y	(x, y)
$^-1$			
0			
$^+2$			

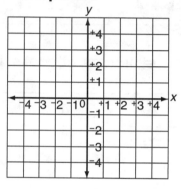

Use the given graph of $y = x + {}^-4$.

2. When $x = 0$, what is the value of y? _____

3. When $x = {}^+2$, what is the value of y? _____

4. For what value of x is $y = {}^-1$? _____

5. For what value of x is $y = 0$? _____

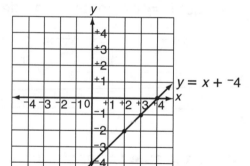

$y = x + {}^-4$

Problem Solving

6. A meteorologist discovered that a storm is following a path on her map made by the equation $y = x + {}^-3$. Will the storm pass through the point $(^+2, 0)$? Make a function table. Then graph on a coordinate plane to answer.

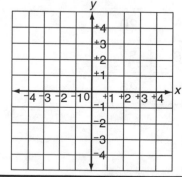

Ⓒ Use with Lesson 14-15, pages 468–469 in the Student Book.
Then go to Lesson 14-16, pages 470–471 in the Student Book.

Problem-Solving Strategy: Write an Equation

Name _____

Date _____

Lionel is 3 years older than his sister Luella.
If the sum of their ages is 27, how old is each?

Write a word equation. Use the word equation to write a number equation with variables.

Let y represent Luella's age.
Then $y + 3$ represents Lionel's age.

Luella's age plus Lionel's age is 27
$y + (y + 3) = 27$

Use Guess and Test to solve.

Luella is 12, and Lionel is 15.

Try 10: $10 + 13 = 23 \longrightarrow 23 \neq 27$
Try 15: $15 + 18 = 33 \longrightarrow 33 \neq 27$
Try 12: $12 + 15 = 27 \longrightarrow 27 = 27$

Solve. Do your work on a separate sheet of paper.

1. Chuck spent 20 minutes longer doing his homework than Stacy took doing hers. Together they spent 2 hours and 30 minutes on their homework. How much time did each spend on homework?

2. Hank, Carlos, and Mindy formed a country music trio. They practiced $1\frac{1}{2}$ hours on Friday and $1\frac{3}{4}$ longer than that on Saturday. How long in all did they practice on Friday and Saturday?

3. Andrea makes decorated baskets at craft shows. She adds $4.50 to the cost of the materials for each basket and then sells the basket for $9.95. How much do the materials for each basket cost?

4. Ginny and Gerald each have one coin. The value of Ginny's coin is 15¢ more than the value of Gerald's coin. The total value of both coins is 35¢. What coin does each person have?

5. There are 18 people in the Computer Club. There are 2 more girls than there are boys. How many girls and how many boys are in the club?

6. If you double Kari's age and add 2, you will get Ted's age. The sum of their ages is 20. How old is Kari? how old is Ted?

7. There are 9 more violinists than cellists in the orchestra. There are 15 violinists and cellists in all. How many violinists are there? how many cellists?

8. Juwon has 250 baseball cards of National League players and $\frac{1}{2}$ that number of American League players. How many baseball cards does he have in all?

Use with Lesson 14-16, pages 470–471 in the Student Book.
Then go to Lesson 14-17, pages 472–473 in the Student Book.

171

Problem-Solving Applications: Mixed Review

Name _____

Date _____

Solve each problem and explain the method you used. If needed, do all your work on a separate sheet of paper.

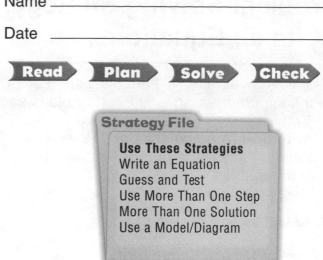

Read Plan Solve Check

Strategy File

Use These Strategies
Write an Equation
Guess and Test
Use More Than One Step
More Than One Solution
Use a Model/Diagram

1. Adam collects plant samples for his science project. Each day he collects 6 more samples than on the previous day. If he collects 132 samples over 4 days, how many samples did Adam collect each day?

_____

2. Julio rode his bike 11 mi. His sister Jenna rode her bike 4 mi more than 3 times that far. How far did Jenna ride?

_____

3. Ray measures a cube that has a surface area of 384 cm². What is the volume of the cube?

_____

4. The product of two integers is 14. What are all the possible combinations of integers?

_____

5. If the temperature drops 32° in 4 hours, what is the average rate of change written as an integer?

_____

6. On a coordinate plane, point A is located at (–1, 3). Point B is three spaces to the left and two spaces up. Where is point B located?

_____

7. Sheri sold $156 worth of picture frames. If she sold 12 frames and made $60 profit, how much did each frame cost to make?

_____

8. In the javelin throw, Toshiro threw a javelin $2\frac{1}{4}$ ft past Cal, but $3\frac{1}{2}$ ft short of Todd. If Cal threw the javelin 28 ft, how far did Todd throw it?

_____

9. Sally did yard work for 20 min longer than Kyle. Together they worked for $2\frac{1}{2}$ hours. How long did Sally and Kyle each work in the yard?

_____

Use with Lesson 14-17, pages 472–473 in the Student Book.

Copyright © by William H. Sadlier, Inc. All rights reserved.

Additional CCSS Lessons

Pages 175–234 of this workbook have additional lessons with content based on the Common Core State Standards (CCSS). Each lesson has teaching and practice exercises. These lessons can also be found online at progressinmathematics.com. The bottom of the second page of every lesson directs you to another workbook page of more practice of the math taught in the lesson and also to the next *Progress in Mathematics* lesson.

Practice for Additional CCSS Lessons

Pages 236–265 have more practice of the math taught in the additional CCSS lessons. Doing these practice exercises will help you master the work of each additional CCSS lesson more quickly. The bottom of every practice page identifies the lesson that is being reviewed by the workbook exercises, and also identifies the next *Progress in Mathematics* lesson. Before starting a workbook page, read the title. If you need to review the work in that lesson, turn to the page in your workbook where it is taught.

Additional CCSS Lessons

Name _____

Powers of Ten
Chapter 1, Lesson 3A

Objective: To use exponents to represent powers of ten

▶ Numbers that are multiples of ten can be written in standard form or by using exponents with the base 10. These numbers are called **powers of ten**. The **exponent** tells how many times to use the **base** 10 as a factor.

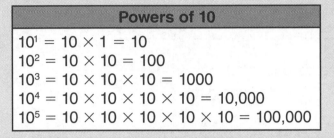

Powers of 10
$10^1 = 10 \times 1 = 10$
$10^2 = 10 \times 10 = 100$
$10^3 = 10 \times 10 \times 10 = 1000$
$10^4 = 10 \times 10 \times 10 \times 10 = 10,000$
$10^5 = 10 \times 10 \times 10 \times 10 \times 10 = 100,000$

10^5 ◀——— **exponent**

——— **base**

Look for a pattern in the number of zeros.
Each place is ten times the value of the place to its right.

What is $(4 \times 10^3) + (2 \times 10^2) + (1 \times 10^1) + (5 \times 1)$ written in standard form?

.....**Think**.....
4×10^3 means
$4 \times (10 \times 10 \times 10)$,
which is 4000

$(4 \times 10^3) + (2 \times 10^2) + (1 \times 10^1) + (5 \times 1)$
$(4 \times 1000) + (2 \times 100) + (1 \times 10) + (5 \times 1)$
$\quad 4000 \quad + \quad 200 \quad + \quad 10 \quad + \quad 5 \quad = 4215$

So, $(4 \times 10^3) + (2 \times 10^2) + (1 \times 10^1) + (5 \times 1) = 4215$.

What is 32,014 written in expanded form using powers of 10?

$32{,}014 = \quad 30{,}000 \quad + \quad 2000 \quad + \quad 10 \quad + \quad 4$
$\quad\quad\quad = (3 \times 10{,}000) + (2 \times 1000) + (1 \times 10) + (4 \times 1)$
$\quad\quad\quad = (3 \times 10^4) \quad + (2 \times 10^3) \quad + (1 \times 10^1) + (4 \times 1)$

So, $32{,}014 = (3 \times 10^4) + (2 \times 10^3) + (1 \times 10^1) + (4 \times 1)$.

Practice

Write each power of ten in standard form.

1. 10^2 _____　　**2.** 10^5 _____　　**3.** 10^1 _____　　**4.** 10^6 _____

Write each as a power of ten.

5. $10 \times 10 \times 10$ _____　　**6.** $10 \times 10 \times 10 \times 10 \times 10$ _____

Discuss and Write

7. Look at the powers of ten in the chart. What do you notice about the number of zeros and the exponent for each number?

Practice

Write each number in standard form.

8. $(5 \times 10^5) + (7 \times 10^3) + (4 \times 10^1)$

_____

9. $(9 \times 10^5) + (2 \times 10^4) + (1 \times 10^3)$

_____

10. $(3 \times 10^3) + (2 \times 10^2) + (3 \times 10^1) + (2 \times 1)$

_____

11. $(1 \times 10^6) + (9 \times 10^2) + (1 \times 10^1)$

_____

Write each number in expanded form using powers of 10.

12. 4702

_____

13. 805,040

_____

14. 14,757

_____

15. 102,529

_____

Problem Solving

Solve. Use a strategy that works best for you. Show your work.

16. Graham lives 1938 miles from his grandparents. Graham's uncle lives just over (2×10^2) miles away. Which relatives are closer? Explain.

_____

17. Lucia's swimming pool holds 60 cubic meters. If one cubic meter is 10^3 liters, how many liters of water does it hold? Explain.

_____

18. A mountain has an elevation of about (3×10^4) feet. Could this mountain be 295,364 feet tall? Explain.

_____

19. An elephant weighs about (9×10^3) pounds. Is this greater or less than 5 tons? Explain. $(1 \text{ T} = 2000 \text{ lb})$

_____

Critical Thinking

20. Amelia's school has $(1 \times 10^3) + (2 \times 10^1) + (5 \times 1)$ students.
Luke's school has $(9 \times 10^2) + (6 \times 10^1) + (4 \times 1)$ students.
Without computing, how could you decide which school has more students?

For additional Practice, go to page 236 in this Workbook.
Then go to Lesson 1-4, pages 36–37 in the Student Book.

Name _____

Objective: To understand and use place value with multi-digit decimal numbers

The decimal 8.888 is greater than one.

Each digit in 8.888 is $\frac{1}{10}$ the value of the digit to its left.

Each digit is 10 times the value of the digit to its right.

$$8 = 0.8 \times 10$$
$$0.8 = 0.08 \times 10$$
$$0.08 = 0.008 \times 10$$

Decimal	Fraction
0.1	$\frac{1}{10}$
0.01	$\frac{1}{100}$
0.001	$\frac{1}{1000}$

Write 0.789 in expanded form using fractions for the decimal part.

▶ Break apart the number using the place value of each digit.

$$0.789 = 0.7 + 0.08 + 0.009$$
$$= (7 \times \tfrac{1}{10}) + (8 \times \tfrac{1}{100}) + (9 \times \tfrac{1}{1000})$$

So, $0.789 = (7 \times \tfrac{1}{10}) + (8 \times \tfrac{1}{100}) + (9 \times \tfrac{1}{1000})$.

Think
$0.7 = \frac{7}{10} = 7 \times \frac{1}{10}$

Write $(7 \times 1) + (3 \times \tfrac{1}{10}) + (5 \times \tfrac{1}{1000})$ as a decimal in standard form.

▶ Simplify each term. Then add the products.

$$(7 \times 1) + (3 \times \tfrac{1}{10}) + (5 \times \tfrac{1}{1000})$$
$$7 \quad + \quad 0.3 \quad + \quad 0.005 \quad = 7.305$$

So, the decimal form of $(7 \times 1) + (3 \times \tfrac{1}{10}) + (5 \times \tfrac{1}{1000})$ is 7.305.

Practice

Write each decimal in fraction form.

1. 0.5 _____

2. 0.08 _____

3. 0.2 _____

4. 0.009 _____

Write each as a decimal.

5. $6 \times \frac{1}{100}$ _____

6. $2 \times \frac{1}{1000}$ _____

7. $1 \times \frac{1}{10}$ _____

8. $4 \times \frac{1}{100}$ _____

Discuss and Write

9. Compare and contrast multiplying by a power of ten and dividing by a power of ten. Explain what happens to the value of the digits.

Name _____

Practice

Write in expanded form.

10. 1.801

_____

11. 2.034

_____

12. 2.292

_____

13. 7.573

_____

14. 3.567

_____

15. 5.951

_____

Write in decimal form.

16. $(2 \times 1) + (8 \times \frac{1}{10}) + (8 \times \frac{1}{1000})$ _____

17. $(3 \times 1) + (1 \times \frac{1}{100}) + (4 \times \frac{1}{1000})$ _____

18. $(4 \times 1) + (1 \times \frac{1}{10}) + (6 \times \frac{1}{100}) + (3 \times \frac{1}{1000})$ _____

19. $(7 \times 1) + (8 \times \frac{1}{10}) + (5 \times \frac{1}{1000})$ _____

20. $(5 \times 1) + (2 \times \frac{1}{10}) + (7 \times \frac{1}{100}) + (1 \times \frac{1}{1000})$ _____

21. $(6 \times 1) + (3 \times \frac{1}{10}) + (1 \times \frac{1}{100}) + (5 \times \frac{1}{1000})$ _____

Problem Solving

Solve. Use a strategy that works best for you. Show your work.

22. In the number 2334, how does the value of the digit in the tens place compare to the value of the digit in the hundreds place?

_____

23. In the number 2334, how does the value of the digit in the hundreds place compare to the value of the digit in the tens place?

_____

Critical Thinking

24. Write a number in which the value of the digit in the hundredths place is exactly $\frac{1}{10}$ the value of the digit in the tenths place. Explain how you found your answer.

C For additional Practice, go to page 237 in this Workbook.
C Then go to Lesson 1-5, pages 38–39 in the Student Book.

Name _____

Objective: To use arrays and area models to divide

You can model division with arrays or area models. An array is an arrangement of objects in rows and columns. An area model shows steps in the division process using rectangles to find parts of the quotient.

▶ Find the quotient $156 \div 13$.
First use compatible numbers to estimate: $150 \div 15 = 10$. | $156 \div 13$ is about 10.

Method 1: Use an array.

Use tens and ones to show 156.

❶ Start by modeling 13.

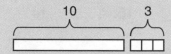

❷ Make rows of 13 to model 156.

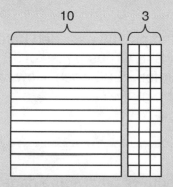

❸ Count how many rows there are. There are 12 rows of 13.

So, $156 \div 13 = 12$.

Note that 12 is close to your estimate, 10.

Method 2: Use an area model.

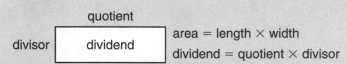

area = length × width
dividend = quotient × divisor

❶ Write the dividend, 156, and the divisor, 13, in the rectangular area model.

```
     10    ← Estimate: 156 ÷ 13 is about 10.
    156
13 −130    ← Multiply 10 × 13 and subtract.
     26
```

❷ Write the difference, 26, in a new rectangle.

```
    10  +  2    ← 26 ÷ 13 = 2
    156    26
13 −130   −26   ← Multiply 2 × 13 and
     26     0      subtract.
```

❸ Add 10 + 2 to find the quotient.

$10 + 2 = 12$

So, $156 \div 13 = 12$.

Practice

1. Use an array to find the quotient.

    $224 \div 16 =$ _____

    _____ rows of 16 model 224.

2. Use an area model to find the quotient.

    $323 \div 17 =$ _____

```
         10  +
        323    153
17     −170   −
        153
```

Discuss and Write

3. Explain how the area model in the teaching display shows $156 \div 13 = 12$.

Practice

Use an array or area model to find the quotient.

4. 330 ÷ 15 = _____   **5.** 612 ÷ 18 = _____   **6.** 492 ÷ 12 = _____

7. 325 ÷ 13 = _____   **8.** 816 ÷ 17 = _____   **9.** 624 ÷ 16 = _____

10. 896 ÷ 28 = _____   **11.** 918 ÷ 34 = _____   **12.** 713 ÷ 31 = _____

13. 1680 ÷ 15 = _____   **14.** 2343 ÷ 11 = _____   **15.** 4802 ÷ 14 = _____

Problem Solving

Solve. Use a strategy that works best for you. Show your work.

16. A machine makes one batch of 624 ball bearings every 5 minutes. They are packed in boxes of 12. How many boxes does one batch make?

17. Kate stamps 288 assorted note cards in 4 days. She wraps packs of 18 to sell at a craft fair for $5.00 each. How many packs does she make?

18. Payton's troop places large flags at the beginning and end of a 1-mile parade route. They place small flags every 66 feet between them. How many small flags do they need? Hint: 1 mi = 5280 ft

19. Mrs. Andrews buys some panes of 20 postage stamps for $79.20. The price of 1 stamp is 44¢. How many panes of stamps does Mrs. Andrews buy? Hint: $79.20 = 7920¢.

Test Preparation

20. Carl is using an area model to divide. He starts but forgets what to do next.

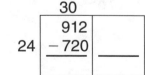

    a. What is the division?

    b. Explain what Carl should do next.

    c. Use the area model to complete the division.

    d. Write a problem that can be solved with this division.

For additional Practice, go to page 238 in this Workbook.
Then go to Lesson 3-10, pages 114–115 in the Student Book.

Name _____

Objective: To use the relationship between multiplication and division to find quotients

Taft School has 481 students who ride the bus. The school has 13 buses. The same number of students rides each bus. How many students ride each bus?

$481 \div 13 = n$

Method 1: Use Multiplication

$$n \times 13 = 481$$

❶ Estimate. Use compatible numbers.

$$n \times 12 = 480$$
$$40 \times 12 = 480$$

So, n is about 40.

❷ Multiply. Use the estimate.

$$40 \times 13 = 520$$

$520 > 481$. Try a factor < 40.

$$39 \times 13 = 507$$
$$38 \times 13 = 494$$ Too much
$$37 \times 13 = 481$$

37 is close to the estimate 40.

So, $481 \div 13 = 37$.

Method 2: Break Apart the Dividend

$$481 \div 13 = n$$

❶ Use an area model.
Show the dividend and the divisor.

❷ Multiply and subtract to break apart the dividend.

$$20 \times 13 = 260 \longleftarrow \text{Not enough}$$
$$30 \times 13 = 390$$
$$40 \times 13 = 520 \longleftarrow \text{Too much}$$

	30 +	7
13	**481** − 390	91 − 91
	91	0

❸ Check your work.
Use the Distributive Property.

$$481 = 13 \times (30 + 7)$$
$$481 = 13 \times 37$$

Practice

1. Use multiplication. Find the quotient.

$1967 \div 7 =$ _____

2. Break apart the dividend. Find the quotient.

$5052 \div 12 =$ _____

Discuss and Write

3. Explain why using multiplication can help you to find a quotient.

Name _____

Practice

Find the quotient. Use a strategy.

4. 4986 ÷ 18 = _____

5. 1188 ÷ 12 = _____

6. 4288 ÷ 16 = _____

7. 1856 ÷ 64 = _____

8. 1960 ÷ 56 = _____

9. 2556 ÷ 36 = _____

10. 1649 ÷ 97 = _____

11. 5022 ÷ 81 = _____

12. 2303 ÷ 47 = _____

13. 2419 ÷ 41 = _____

14. 3850 ÷ 35 = _____

15. 1679 ÷ 23 = _____

Problem Solving

Solve. Use a strategy that works best for you. Show your work.

16. At the Baker's Dozen, all rolls are packed in bags of 13. Today, 585 rolls are made. How many bags of rolls are packed?

_____

17. Ms. Taylor buys 17 yards of fabric and cuts it into strips that are 12 inches wide. How many strips does she make? Hint: 1 yd = 36 in.

_____

18. Tony makes coasters using 40 blue and 24 green tiles each. He has 920 blue tiles and 552 green tiles. How many coasters can he make with the tiles he has?

_____

19. At a charity carnival, 2805 tickets for rides are sold. A strip of 15 ride tickets costs $25.00. A strip of 10 tickets for food costs $27.00. How much money is raised by the sale of ride tickets?

_____

Critical Thinking

20. What number is missing in the division problem shown? Explain your reasoning.

	30 +	9
42		378
	− 1260	− 378
	378	0

For additional Practice, go to page 239 in this Workbook.
Then go to Lesson 3-11, pages 116–117 in the Student Book.

Objective: To write, evaluate, and compare numerical expressions

Nat has three $5-bills and three $10-bills. Jake has three $5-bills and two $10-bills. Write and evaluate an expression to find how much more money Nat has than Jake.

▶ To write the expression, first use parentheses to show how much each person has. Then you can use brackets to show the difference between the two amounts.

| Grouping symbols include: |
| Parentheses ( ) |
| Brackets [ ] |

Nat: $(3 \times 5) + (3 \times 10)$ Jake: $(3 \times 5) + (2 \times 10)$

$[(3 \times 5) + (3 \times 10)]$ $-$ $[(3 \times 5) + (2 \times 10)]$

▶ To evaluate the expression, simplify step by step. Start computing inside the parentheses and work out to the brackets.

$[(3 \times 5) + (3 \times 10)] - [(3 \times 5) + (2 \times 10)]$

$[15 \quad + \quad 30] \quad - \quad [15 \quad + \quad 20]$

$45 \quad - \quad 35 = 10$

So, Nat has $10 more than Jake.

Frank has $2 \times (4 + 8)$ books. Claire has $(4 + 8)$ books. How do the expressions compare?

▶ You can compare the expressions without evaluating them.

• Notice that both expressions contain $(4 + 8)$. In one expression, $(4 + 8)$ is multiplied by 2.

• The value of $2 \times (4 + 8)$ is 2 times the value of $(4 + 8)$.

So, Frank has 2 times as many books as Claire.

Practice

Simplify each expression.

1. $[3 \times (4 + 5)] + 9$

_____

2. $[(4 \times 9) - (2 + 8)] - [2 \times (6 + 7)]$

_____

3. Every day for 4 days Julie makes 3 pencil drawings and 2 chalk drawings. Then she gives away 6 drawings. How many drawings does she have left?

$[4 \times (3 + \text{_____})] - \text{_____}$

$[4 \times \text{_____}] - \text{_____}$

$\text{_____} - \text{_____} = \text{_____}$

_____

Discuss and Write

4. What are some strategies you can use to compare two expressions?

Practice

Simplify each expression.

5. $9 \times [(16 + 2) \div 6]$

_____

6. $[56 \div (2 \times 2)] \div [32 - (6 \times 5)]$

_____

7. $[(3 \times 4) \div (1 + 5)] + 2 \times 8$

_____

8. $[(8 - 2) \times (2 + 8)] \div (5 \times 3)$

_____

9. $[7 - (24 \div 4)] + 9 \times (18 \div 6)$

_____

10. $2 + [(60 - 5) \div (8 - 3)]$

_____

Write an expression for each situation. Do not simplify.

11. Aziza has 1 ten-dollar bill, 2 five-dollar bills, and 3 one-dollar bills. How much money does she have in all?

_____

12. Carlton had 2 ten-dollar bills and 4 five-dollar bills. Then he spent $9. How much money does he have left?

_____

13. Kenny has 3 boxes of pens. Each box has 6 blue and 2 red pens. If he gives 4 pens away, how many pens will he have left?

_____

14. A bag of apples contains 3 red and 4 yellow apples. A box of apples contains 6 red and 8 green apples. Al buys 3 bags and 2 boxes of apples. How many apples does she buy?

_____

Compare the two expressions without evaluating. Explain.

15. $(2 \times 8) - 4$ and $(2 \times 8) + 4$

_____

16. $(13 + 2) \div 3$ and $(13 + 2)$

_____

17. $(14 + 7) \times 3$ and $3 \times (7 + 14)$

_____

18. $(7 - 2) \times 2$ and $(7 - 2) \div 2$

_____

What's the Error?

19. Joella says that $[7 - (3 + 2)] \times 2$ is twice as great as $[7 + (3 - 2)]$. What is her error?

For additional Practice, go to page 240 in this Workbook. Then go to Lesson 3-15, pages 124–125 in the Student Book.

Objective: To use a model to add two fractions with unlike denominators

Laura needs $\frac{1}{2}$ quart blueberries and $\frac{1}{3}$ quart raspberries for a fruit salad. How many quarts of berries does she need in all?

$$\frac{1}{2} + \frac{1}{3} = ?$$

▶ Use models to add $\frac{1}{2} + \frac{1}{3}$.

❶ Model the problem under the strip for 1 whole.

1

$\frac{1}{2}$	$\frac{1}{3}$

$$\frac{1}{2} + \frac{1}{3}$$

❷ Rename the fractions with a common denominator.

❸ Find the total.

$\frac{1}{6}$	$\frac{1}{6}$	$\frac{1}{6}$	$\frac{1}{6}$	$\frac{1}{6}$

$$\frac{3}{6} + \frac{2}{6} = \frac{5}{6}$$

Laura needs $\frac{5}{6}$ quart of berries in all.

At the end of a bake sale, a club has $\frac{2}{3}$ loaf of pumpkin bread and $\frac{5}{6}$ loaf of cranberry bread left. How much bread is left in all?

$$\frac{2}{3} + \frac{5}{6} = ?$$

▶ Rename the fractions to add.

❶ Model the problem under the strip for 1 whole.

1

$\frac{2}{3}$	$\frac{5}{6}$

$$\frac{2}{3} + \frac{5}{6}$$

❷ Rename the fractions with a common denominator.

❸ Find the total.

$\frac{1}{6}$	$\frac{1}{6}$	$\frac{1}{6}$	$\frac{1}{6}$	$\frac{1}{6}$	$\frac{1}{6}$	$\frac{1}{6}$	$\frac{1}{6}$	$\frac{1}{6}$

$$\frac{4}{6} + \frac{5}{6} = \frac{9}{6} = 1\frac{3}{6}$$

Write the sum in simplest form. $1\frac{3}{6} = 1\frac{1}{2}$

In all, $1\frac{1}{2}$ loaves of bread are left.

Practice

Add. Write the answer in simplest form.

1. $\frac{5}{8} + \frac{1}{4} =$ _____

1

$\frac{5}{8}$	$\frac{1}{4}$

$\frac{1}{8}$	$\frac{1}{8}$	$\frac{1}{8}$	$\frac{1}{8}$	$\frac{1}{8}$		

2. $\frac{7}{10} + \frac{4}{5} =$ _____

1

$\frac{7}{10}$	$\frac{4}{5}$

$\frac{1}{10}$	$\frac{1}{10}$	$\frac{1}{10}$	$\frac{1}{10}$	$\frac{1}{10}$	$\frac{1}{10}$	$\frac{1}{10}$						

Discuss and Write

3. How do you decide which size fraction strip to use to model the renaming of two fractions with unlike denominators?

Name _____

Practice

Add. Write the answer in simplest form.

4. $\frac{1}{2} + \frac{1}{5} =$ _____

$\frac{1}{2}$	$\frac{1}{5}$

$\frac{1}{10}$				

5. $\frac{3}{8} + \frac{1}{4} =$ _____

$\frac{3}{8}$	$\frac{1}{4}$

$\frac{1}{8}$			

6. $\frac{5}{9} + \frac{1}{3} =$ _____

$\frac{5}{9}$	$\frac{1}{3}$

$\frac{1}{9}$					

7. $\frac{1}{6} + \frac{2}{3} =$ _____

$\frac{1}{6}$	$\frac{2}{3}$

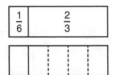

8. $\frac{1}{2} + \frac{3}{10} =$ _____

$\frac{1}{2}$	$\frac{3}{10}$

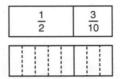

9. $\frac{1}{6} + \frac{1}{2} =$ _____

$\frac{1}{6}$	$\frac{1}{2}$

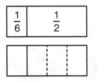

10. $\frac{5}{8} + \frac{1}{2} =$ _____

$\frac{5}{8}$	$\frac{1}{2}$

11. $\frac{7}{10} + \frac{1}{2} =$ _____

$\frac{7}{10}$	$\frac{1}{2}$

12. $\frac{7}{12} + \frac{2}{3} =$ _____

$\frac{7}{12}$	$\frac{2}{3}$

Problem Solving

Solve. Use a strategy that works best for you. Show your work.

13. Frankie has $\frac{3}{4}$ gallon of orange juice, $\frac{1}{4}$ gallon of cranberry juice, and $\frac{3}{8}$ gallon of pineapple juice. If he pours them all into a large container that holds 2 gallons, how much ginger ale could he add?

_____

14. Eli bought $\frac{3}{8}$ pound of peppers, $\frac{1}{2}$ pound of spinach and $\frac{3}{4}$ pound of potatoes. How much less than 2 pounds of vegetables did he buy?

_____

What's the Error?

15. Ann used models to add. Find and correct her error.

$$\frac{1}{2} + \frac{3}{4} = \frac{5}{8}$$

$\frac{1}{2}$	$\frac{3}{4}$

$$\frac{1}{2} + \frac{3}{4}$$

$\frac{1}{8}$	$\frac{1}{8}$	$\frac{1}{8}$	$\frac{1}{8}$	$\frac{1}{8}$

$$\frac{2}{8} + \frac{3}{8} = \frac{5}{8}$$

For additional Practice, go to page 241 in this Workbook.
Then go to Lesson 5-2, pages 166–167 in the Student Book.

Name _____

Objective: To use a model to subtract fractions with unlike denominators

Brice's club volunteers to clean $\frac{5}{8}$ mile of a local highway. They clean $\frac{1}{4}$ mile before lunch. How much is left to clean after lunch?

$$\frac{5}{8} - \frac{1}{4} = ?$$

▶ Subtract $\frac{5}{8} - \frac{1}{4}$ using models.

① Model the problem under a strip for 1 whole

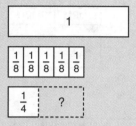

② Rename the fractions with a common denominator.

$\frac{1}{8}$	$\frac{1}{8}$	$\frac{1}{8}$	$\frac{1}{8}$	$\frac{1}{8}$

$\frac{1}{8}$	$\frac{1}{8}$	?

$\frac{1}{8}$	$\frac{1}{8}$	$\frac{1}{8}$

③ Find the difference.

The club has $\frac{3}{8}$ mile left to clean.

Zelda wants to plant $\frac{2}{3}$ of her garden with vegetables. If she uses $\frac{1}{2}$ of her garden for green beans, how much is left for other vegetables?

$$\frac{2}{3} - \frac{1}{2} = ?$$

▶ Subtract $\frac{2}{3} - \frac{1}{2}$ using models.

① Model the problem under a strip for 1 whole

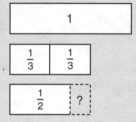

② Rename the fractions with a common denominator.

$\frac{1}{6}$	$\frac{1}{6}$	$\frac{1}{6}$	$\frac{1}{6}$

$\frac{1}{6}$	$\frac{1}{6}$	$\frac{1}{6}$	?

$\frac{1}{6}$

③ Find the difference.

Zelda has $\frac{1}{6}$ of her garden for other vegetables.

Practice

Subtract. Write the answer in simplest form.

1. $\frac{9}{10} - \frac{3}{5} =$ _____

1

$\frac{1}{10}$	$\frac{1}{10}$	$\frac{1}{10}$	$\frac{1}{10}$	$\frac{1}{10}$	$\frac{1}{10}$	$\frac{1}{10}$	$\frac{1}{10}$	$\frac{1}{10}$

$\frac{1}{5}$	$\frac{1}{5}$	$\frac{1}{5}$	?

2. $\frac{5}{6} - \frac{1}{3} =$ _____

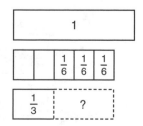

Discuss and Write

3. What similarities and differences do you notice in the teaching display?

Practice

Subtract. Write the answer in simplest form.

4. $\frac{3}{4} - \frac{1}{2} =$ _____

| $\frac{1}{4}$ | $\frac{1}{4}$ | $\frac{1}{4}$ |

| $\frac{1}{2}$ | ? |

5. $\frac{7}{10} - \frac{1}{5} =$ _____

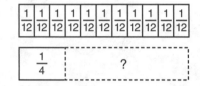

6. $\frac{7}{9} - \frac{1}{3} =$ _____

7. $\frac{5}{6} - \frac{1}{3} =$ _____

| $\frac{1}{6}$ | $\frac{1}{6}$ | $\frac{1}{6}$ | $\frac{1}{6}$ | $\frac{1}{6}$ |

| $\frac{1}{3}$ | ? |

8. $\frac{11}{12} - \frac{1}{4} =$ _____

9. $\frac{7}{12} - \frac{1}{3} =$ _____

10. $\begin{array}{r} \frac{3}{5} \\ -\frac{1}{2} \\ \hline \end{array}$

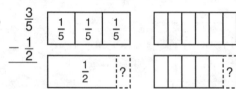

11. $\begin{array}{r} \frac{1}{2} \\ -\frac{3}{10} \\ \hline \end{array}$

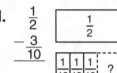

Problem Solving

Solve. Use a strategy that works best for you. Show your work.

12. Joey lives $\frac{4}{5}$ mile from school. Hugh lives $\frac{3}{4}$ mile from school. Who lives closer? _____

How much closer? _____

13. Tyra has $\frac{3}{4}$ feet of ribbon. She uses $\frac{2}{3}$ feet for a hair tie. How much does she have left?

_____

Explain Your Reasoning

14. The assignment is to use models to show $\frac{1}{2} - \frac{1}{4}$. Tom and Melissa use different models. Which model is correct? Explain your thinking.

Tom's Model

$\begin{array}{r} \frac{4}{8} \\ -\frac{2}{8} \\ \hline \frac{2}{8} = \frac{1}{4} \end{array}$

| $\frac{1}{8}$ | $\frac{1}{8}$ | $\frac{1}{8}$ | $\frac{1}{8}$ |

| $\frac{1}{8}$ | $\frac{1}{8}$ | ? |

Melissa's Model

$\begin{array}{r} \frac{2}{4} \\ -\frac{1}{4} \\ \hline \frac{1}{4} \end{array}$

| $\frac{1}{4}$ | $\frac{1}{4}$ |

| $\frac{1}{4}$ | ? |

For additional Practice, go to page 242 in this Workbook.
Then go to Lesson 5-7, pages 176–177 in the Student Book.

Name _____

Objective: To use visual models to subtract fractions or whole numbers from mixed numbers

Justin uses $3\frac{3}{4}$ feet of ribbon to wrap a large package.
He uses 2 feet of ribbon to wrap a smaller package.
How much more ribbon does Justin use for the larger package?

▶ To find how much more ribbon Justin uses, subtract $3\frac{3}{4} - 2$.

❶ Model $3\frac{3}{4}$ and 2.

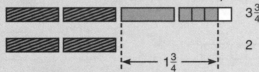

$3\frac{3}{4}$

2

$1\frac{3}{4}$

❷ Use the models to find the difference.
$$3\frac{3}{4} - 2 = 1\frac{3}{4}$$

Justin uses $1\frac{3}{4}$ feet more ribbon for the larger package.

Jim lives $1\frac{2}{3}$ miles from the mall. Cara lives $\frac{1}{2}$ mile from the mall.
How much closer does Cara live to the mall than Jim?

▶ To find how much closer Cara lives to the mall, subtract $1\frac{2}{3} - \frac{1}{2}$.
You can use a model to help you subtract.

❶ Find the LCD of the fractions and write equivalent fractions.

The LCD of $\frac{2}{3}$ and $\frac{1}{2}$ is 6.

$$\frac{2}{3} = \frac{2 \times 2}{3 \times 2} = \frac{4}{6}$$
$$\frac{1}{2} = \frac{1 \times 3}{2 \times 3} = \frac{3}{6}$$

❷ Model the numbers.

$1\frac{4}{6}$

$\frac{3}{6}$

$\frac{1}{6}$

1

❸ Use the models to find the difference.

$$1\frac{4}{6} - \frac{3}{6} = 1\frac{1}{6}$$

So $1\frac{2}{3} - \frac{1}{2} = 1\frac{1}{6}$.

Cara lives $1\frac{1}{6}$ miles closer to the mall than Jim.

Practice

Subtract. Use the model to help.

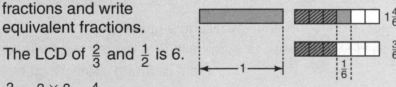

$2\frac{6}{8}$

$\frac{3}{8}$

1. $2\frac{3}{4} - \frac{3}{8}$ _____

Discuss and Write

2. When subtracting a whole number from a mixed number, do you need to find an equivalent fraction before modeling the mixed number? Why or why not?

Name _____

Practice

Subtract. Use models to help.

3. $2\frac{1}{5} - 1$ _____

$2\frac{1}{5}$

1

4. $2\frac{5}{8} - 1$ _____

$2\frac{5}{8}$

1

5. $1\frac{1}{2} - \frac{3}{8}$ _____

$1\frac{4}{8}$

$\frac{3}{8}$

6. $2\frac{3}{4} - \frac{2}{3}$ _____

$2\frac{9}{12}$

$\frac{8}{12}$

Problem Solving

Solve. Use a strategy that works best for you. Show your work.

7. A recipe calls for $1\frac{1}{3}$ cups of water and 1 cup of broth. How much more water than broth is needed for the recipe?

_____

8. Julie buys $5\frac{1}{2}$ gallons of lemonade for her party and two $1\frac{1}{2}$ gallon bottles of juice. How much more lemonade than juice does she buy?

_____

9. Marcus lives $2\frac{3}{4}$ miles away from school. Bruce lives $\frac{1}{3}$ mile closer. How far does Bruce live from school?

_____

10. Maggie uses $3\frac{1}{5}$ yards of fabric to make a quilt. She makes 2 pillows, each using 1 yard of fabric. How much more fabric does Maggie use to make the quilt than to make the pillows?

_____

11. It snows $\frac{5}{6}$ foot, $\frac{2}{3}$ foot, and $1\frac{1}{2}$ feet on three days. What is the greatest difference in snowfall between two of the days?

_____

12. Dave swims $\frac{5}{12}$ mile on Monday. On Tuesday, he swims $\frac{1}{3}$ mile. How far should Dave swim on Wednesday to swim $1\frac{1}{6}$ miles total for the three days?

_____

Explain Your Reasoning

13. Why is it important to rewrite fractions with a common denominator before you compare them with models?

For additional Practice, go to page 243 in this Workbook.
Then go to Lesson 5-9, pages 180–181 in the Student Book.

Objective: To use benchmark fractions to assess the reasonableness of answers

Julian adds $\frac{1}{3} + \frac{5}{8}$. He finds the sum $\frac{23}{24}$. He wonders if his answer is reasonable. How can he tell?

> An answer that is possible and makes sense is a reasonable answer. It may or may not be exactly correct.

▶ To check whether his answer is reasonable, compare each addend to $\frac{1}{2}$. Then estimate to see if the answer makes sense.

Compare: $\frac{1}{3} < \frac{1}{2}$ and $\frac{5}{8} > \frac{1}{2}$.

Since $\frac{1}{3} < \frac{1}{2}$ and $\frac{5}{8} > \frac{1}{2}$, $\frac{1}{3} + \frac{5}{8}$ is about 1.

The sum $\frac{23}{24}$ is about 1. $\boxed{\frac{24}{24} = 1}$

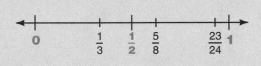

Julian's answer is reasonable.

Kami says that $\frac{3}{8} - \frac{1}{4} = \frac{5}{8}$. Is her answer reasonable? How do you know?

▶ To check whether her answer is reasonable, compare each fraction to $\frac{1}{2}$. Then estimate to see if the answer makes sense.

Compare: $\frac{3}{8} < \frac{1}{2}$ and $\frac{5}{8} > \frac{1}{2}$.

It is not possible to subtract $\frac{1}{4}$ from a number less than $\frac{1}{2}$ and have a difference greater than $\frac{1}{2}$.

Kami's answer is not reasonable.

Practice

Decide whether the answer is reasonable.

1. $\frac{3}{4} - \frac{1}{3} = \frac{5}{12}$ _____

   Compare: $\frac{3}{4}$ _____ $\frac{1}{2}$

   $\frac{1}{3}$ _____ $\frac{1}{2}$

   $\frac{5}{12}$ _____ $\frac{1}{2}$

2. $\frac{1}{8} + \frac{1}{3} = 1\frac{1}{4}$ _____

   Compare: $\frac{1}{8}$ _____ $\frac{1}{2}$

   $\frac{1}{3}$ _____ $\frac{1}{2}$

   $1\frac{1}{4}$ _____ 1

Discuss and Write

3. You want to add two fractions that are each less than $\frac{1}{2}$. Can you tell by estimating whether the sum will be greater than or less than 1? Explain your reasoning.

Practice

Decide whether the answer is reasonable.

4. $\frac{2}{3} - \frac{1}{5} = \frac{13}{15}$ _____

5. $\frac{2}{5} + \frac{1}{4} = \frac{13}{20}$ _____

6. $\frac{2}{3} + \frac{3}{8} = 1$ _____

7. $\frac{4}{7} - \frac{1}{3} = \frac{5}{21}$ _____

8. $\frac{1}{6} + \frac{4}{5} = \frac{5}{11}$ _____

9. $\frac{4}{5} - \frac{3}{10} = \frac{1}{2}$ _____

Give a reasonable estimate.

10. $\frac{3}{8} + \frac{1}{2}$

11. $\frac{5}{6} - \frac{3}{4}$

12. $\frac{1}{2} + \frac{4}{5}$

13. $\frac{2}{3} + \frac{4}{9}$

_____ _____ _____ _____

Problem Solving

Solve. Use a strategy that works best for you. Show your work.

14. Nancy needs 1 gallon of juice. She has $\frac{2}{3}$ gallon of grape juice and $\frac{1}{2}$ gallon of apple juice. How can she estimate to see if she has enough?

15. Alden and his friends eat $\frac{5}{8}$ of a cheese pizza and $\frac{1}{2}$ of a tomato pizza. He asks for more. His mom says they have already eaten more than a full pizza. He said they have eaten less than one. Explain who was right.

_____

_____

16. A class is cleaning up a school park that is $\frac{9}{10}$ acre. They clean $\frac{5}{8}$ acre before lunch. Are they more than half done? How do you know?

17. Kristoff needs 1 gallon of lemonade. He already has $\frac{1}{6}$ gallon. How many $\frac{1}{2}$-gallon bottles should he buy to make sure he has enough? How do you know?

_____

_____

Critical Thinking

18. Elisa explains her way of comparing a fraction to $\frac{1}{2}$. "I double the numerator. If the result is less than the denominator, the fraction is less than $\frac{1}{2}$. If the result is greater than the denominator, the fraction is greater than $\frac{1}{2}$." Does Elisa's method work? Why or why not?

C For additional Practice, go to page 244 in this Workbook.
C Then go to Lesson 5-10, pages 182–183 in the Student Book.

Objective: To use visual models to multiply with fractions

▶ What is $\frac{3}{4} \times 5$?

You can think of $\frac{3}{4} \times 5$ as $\frac{3}{4}$ of 5.

❶ Model 5.

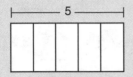

5 wholes

$\frac{3}{4} \times 5 = \frac{15}{4}$

❷ Separate 5 into 4 equal parts.

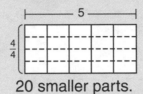

20 smaller parts.

❸ Find 3 of the 4 equal parts.

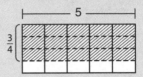

15 of the smaller parts $= \frac{15}{4}$.

So, $\frac{3}{4} \times 5$ is the same as multiplying 3×5 and dividing by 4.

▶ What is $\frac{3}{4} \times \frac{5}{6}$?

You can think of $\frac{3}{4} \times \frac{5}{6}$ as $\frac{3}{4}$ of $\frac{5}{6}$.

❶ Model $\frac{5}{6}$.

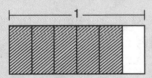

Each part is $\frac{1}{6}$ of the whole.

$\frac{3}{4} \times \frac{5}{6} = \frac{15}{24}$

❷ Separate $\frac{5}{6}$ into 4 equal parts.

24 smaller parts. Each part is $\frac{1}{24}$ of the whole.

❸ Find 3 of the 4 equal parts.

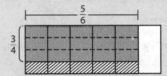

15 of the smaller parts $= \frac{15}{24}$.

So, $\frac{3}{4} \times \frac{5}{6}$ is the same as multiplying 3×5 and dividing by 4×6.

Practice

Use a model to multiply.

1. $\frac{2}{3} \times 4 =$ _____

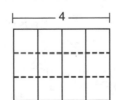

2. $\frac{2}{3} \times \frac{4}{5} =$ _____

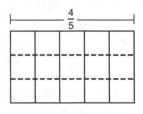

Discuss and Write

3. Write a real-world problem that you would solve by multiplying fractions.

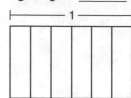
Practice

Use a model to multiply.

4. $\frac{3}{8} \times 2 =$ _____

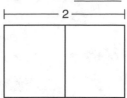

5. $\frac{4}{7} \times \frac{3}{4} =$ _____

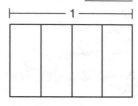

6. $\frac{2}{3} \times \frac{5}{6} =$ _____

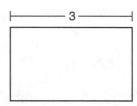

7. $\frac{8}{9} \times 3 =$ _____

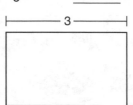

8. $\frac{3}{4} \times \frac{4}{5} =$ _____

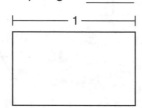

9. $\frac{4}{6} \times 3 =$ _____

10. $\frac{4}{9} \times \frac{3}{8} =$ _____

11. $\frac{5}{8} \times 3 =$ _____

12. $\frac{2}{3} \times \frac{1}{4} =$ _____

Problem Solving

Solve. Use a strategy that works best for you. Show your work.

13. Elsie has 4 pounds of birdseed. She uses $\frac{2}{3}$ of it to fill her bird feeders. How many pounds does she use?

14. A recipe calls for $\frac{3}{4}$ cup of chili sauce. Bianca wants to use $\frac{2}{3}$ as much. How much does she use?

15. David buys $\frac{7}{8}$ pound of cherries. He eats $\frac{2}{5}$ of them. Does he eat more or less than $\frac{1}{2}$ pound of cherries? Explain.

16. There is $\frac{3}{4}$ of a pizza left. Paolo and Peter eat $\frac{5}{9}$ of what is left. Do they eat more or less than $\frac{1}{2}$ of a full pizza? Explain.

Test Preparation

17. Jenny has $\frac{2}{3}$ dozen paint brushes. She uses $\frac{3}{8}$ of her brushes for oil paints and the rest for watercolors.

a. What fact do you need to know to understand this situation?
b. How many paint brushes does Jenny have?
c. Show one way to find the number of paint brushes Jenny uses for watercolors.

For additional Practice, go to page 245 in this Workbook.
Then go to Lesson 6-2B, pages 195–196 in this Workbook.

Objective: To understand how the value of one factor affects the size of the product

When you multiply two fractions, the product will be less than, equal to, or greater than the first factor.

▶ Multiply $\frac{4}{5} \times \frac{3}{3}$

<u>When one factor is equal to 1</u>, use the Identity Property of Multiplication.

$$\frac{3}{3} = 1 \qquad \frac{4}{5} \times 1 = \frac{4}{5}$$

So, the product of $\frac{4}{5} \times \frac{3}{3} = \frac{4}{5}$.

The product is equal to the other factor.

▶ Multiply $\frac{4}{5} \times \frac{2}{3}$

<u>When both factors are less than 1</u>, the product is less than either factor.

$$\frac{4}{5} < 1 \text{ and } \frac{2}{3} < \frac{4}{5}$$

So, the product of $\frac{4}{5} \times \frac{2}{3} < \frac{4}{5}$.

The product is less than the first factor.

▶ Multiply $\frac{4}{5} \times \frac{4}{3}$

<u>When one factor is greater than 1</u>, the product is greater than the other factor.

$$\frac{4}{3} = 4 \times \frac{1}{3}, \text{ so } \frac{4}{3} > 1.$$

So, the product of $\frac{4}{5} \times \frac{4}{3} > 1$.

The product is greater than the other factor.

Practice

Decide if each product will be less than, equal to, or greater than the first factor.
Write $<$, $=$, or $>$.

1. $\frac{3}{8} \times \frac{5}{5}$

$\frac{5}{5} = 1$

So, the product ____ $\frac{3}{8}$

2. $\frac{6}{7} \times \frac{8}{3}$

$\frac{8}{3}$ ____ 1

So, the product ____ $\frac{6}{7}$

3. $\frac{3}{5} \times \frac{3}{7}$

$\frac{3}{7}$ ____ 1

So, the product ____ $\frac{3}{5}$

4. $\frac{3}{4} \times \frac{1}{3}$

$\frac{1}{3}$ ____ 1

So, $\frac{3}{4} \times \frac{1}{3}$ ____ $\frac{3}{4}$.

5. $\frac{3}{2} \times \frac{1}{6}$

$\frac{3}{2}$ ____ 1

So, $\frac{3}{2} \times \frac{1}{6}$ ____ $\frac{1}{6}$.

6. $\frac{8}{8} \times \frac{2}{5}$

$\frac{8}{8}$ ____ 1

So, $\frac{8}{8} \times \frac{2}{5}$ ____ $\frac{2}{5}$.

Discuss and Write

7. How can you determine the size of the product without calculating?

Name _____

Practice

Decide if each product will be less than, equal to, or greater than the first factor.

8. $\frac{4}{9} \times \frac{5}{9}$

_____

9. $\frac{1}{2} \times \frac{8}{5}$

_____

10. $\frac{3}{8} \times \frac{6}{6}$

_____

11. $\frac{8}{9} \times \frac{8}{3}$

_____

12. $\frac{5}{4} \times \frac{7}{7}$

_____

13. $\frac{3}{1} \times \frac{3}{2}$

_____

14. $\frac{7}{8} \times \frac{2}{3}$

_____

15. $\frac{7}{4} \times \frac{1}{8}$

_____

16. Choose one problem from Exercises 8 through 15 and explain how you decided on your answer.

_____

Write a fraction that makes a true statement.

17. $\frac{2}{3} \times$ _____ $> \frac{2}{3}$

18. $\frac{9}{2} \times$ _____ $= \frac{9}{2}$

19. $\frac{5}{5} \times$ _____ $< \frac{5}{5}$

20. $\frac{2}{11} \times$ _____ $= \frac{2}{11}$

21. $\frac{1}{6} \times$ _____ $< \frac{1}{6}$

22. $\frac{4}{3} \times$ _____ $> \frac{4}{3}$

Problem Solving

Solve. Use a strategy that works best for you. Show your work.

23. A recipe makes enough soup for 6 people. Martha multiplies the amount of each ingredient used by $\frac{3}{2}$. Will she have less than 6 servings or more than 6 servings of soup? How do you know?

_____

24. Fred offers to give Uri $\frac{3}{8}$ of a pizza. Alex says he will give Uri $\frac{4}{4}$ times what Fred offers. Who offers Uri the most pizza? How do you know?

_____

Critical Thinking

25. Alice studies the problem $\frac{9}{5} \times \frac{1}{8}$. She concludes that the product is less than $\frac{9}{5}$ but greater than $\frac{1}{8}$. How does she know this?

For additional Practice, go to page 246 in this Workbook.
Then go to Lesson 6-3, pages 202–203 in the Student Book.

Name _____

Objective: To interpret a fraction as a division and to interpret a remainder written as a fraction

Four friends found $3. They want to share it equally.
What part of a dollar is each friend's share?

▶ To find each share, use a model to divide $3 by 4.

1 Start by drawing 3 wholes to represent $3.

2 Divide each whole into 4 equal parts to represent an equal share for each of the 4 friends.

3 Share the parts equally among the 4 friends.

Each friend will receive $\frac{3}{4}$ of a dollar.

The model shows that $3 \div 4 = \frac{3}{4}$
and that $\frac{3}{4} = 3 \div 4$.

Friend 1   **Friend 2**   Friend 3   Friend 4

Think
$\frac{numerator}{denominator} = $ numerator $\div$ denominator

4 Check your work.

number of groups × number in each group = whole

$4 \times \frac{3}{4}$ = 3

▶ For real-world problems, sometimes you need to round a quotient down or up so your answer makes sense.

Round Down

Tom has to put 9 roses in each vase. He has 43 roses. How many vases can he fill?

Divide: $43 \div 9 = 4$ R7

You can write the remainder as a fraction. Use the remainder as the numerator and the divisor as the denominator.

$43 \div 9 = 4\frac{7}{9}$

The answer $4\frac{7}{9}$ vases is not realistic. Tom cannot use part of a vase, so he can only fill 4 vases.

Round Up

Sasha's book has 102 pages. She reads 7 pages a day. In how many days will she finish the book?

Divide: $102 \div 7 = 14$ R4 or $14\frac{4}{7}$

Interpret the remainder. Be sure that your answer makes sense.

$14\frac{4}{7}$ days does not make sense.
After 14 days Sasha still has 4 pages to read, so she will finish the book in 15 days.

Discuss and Write

1. How do you interpret a remainder so that your answer makes sense?

Problem Solving

Solve each problem. Interpret the remainder so that the answer makes sense.

2. Josh has 9 small wheels. He uses 4 wheels each time he makes a toy car. How many cars can he make?

   _____

3. Andrea has a piece of ribbon that is 9 feet long. She wants to cut it into 4 equal pieces. How long will each piece be?

   _____

4. Eleven friends are in line for a roller coaster. Only 3 people fit in each roller coaster car. How many cars will they need?

   _____

5. Brian bakes 11 muffins. He divides them evenly among his 3 nieces and nephews. How many muffins does each child get?

   _____

6. Kathleen wants to bake 30 muffins. Each muffin pan holds 12 muffins. How many muffins pans will she use?

   _____

7. Lori bakes 30 muffins. She sells packages of 12 to a diner. How many packages can she sell?

   _____

8. Lorenzo wants to send 85 jars of jelly to a store. He can put 8 jars in a box. The boxes come in packs of 5. How many packs of boxes should he buy?

   _____

9. Jamie has 62 popcorn balls. She puts 3 balls in a package. She puts 8 packages in a box. How many full boxes can she fill?

   _____

10. A school is going to buy one ice cream bar for each of 62 fifth-graders. Brand A comes in boxes of 8. Brand B is sold in boxes of 9. Brand C has 10 bars in each box. Which brand do they buy to have the fewest ice cream bars left over? How many boxes of that brand do they need?

    _____

11. To deliver a load of crates, a truck must go under a bridge that is 11 feet high. The bed of the truck is 4 feet above the ground. Each crate is 3 feet high. How many layers of crates can be loaded and still allow the truck to pass under the bridge?

    _____

What's the Error?

12. A basketball league accepts 51 players and says that no more than 8 players will be on each team. The coach decides that they need 6 teams. What is his error? How many teams are needed?

For additional Practice, go to page 247 in this Workbook.
Then go to Lesson 6-8, pages 212–213 in the Student Book.

Objective: To solve and write problems that involve dividing with unit fractions

Al makes paper planes using $\frac{1}{2}$ sheet of paper for each plane. How many planes does he make using 4 sheets of paper?

▶ To find the number of planes, divide: $4 \div \frac{1}{2}$.

Method 1: Use a model.

❶ Show 4 ones.

❷ Divide each one into halves.

$\frac{1}{2}$	$\frac{1}{2}$	$\frac{1}{2}$	$\frac{1}{2}$
$\frac{1}{2}$	$\frac{1}{2}$	$\frac{1}{2}$	$\frac{1}{2}$

There are 8 halves. $4 \div \frac{1}{2} = 8$

Method 2: Use inverse operations.

❶ Write a division sentence.

$$4 \div \frac{1}{2} = n$$

❷ Multiply to undo the division.

$$4 - \frac{1}{2} \times n$$

.**Think**..............
$\frac{1}{2}$ of what number equals 4?
....

$$\frac{1}{2} \times 8 = 4$$
So, $n = 8$.

Al can make 8 planes.

Four friends share a half loaf of bread equally. What fraction of the whole loaf does each friend have?

▶ To find the part of the whole loaf each friend has, divide: $\frac{1}{2} \div 4$.

Method 1: Use a model.

❶ Show $\frac{1}{2}$.

❷ Divide $\frac{1}{2}$ into 4 equal parts.

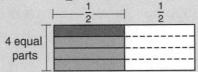

Each part is $\frac{1}{8}$. $\frac{1}{2} \div 4 = \frac{1}{8}$

Method 2: Use inverse operations.

❶ Write a division sentence.

$$\frac{1}{2} \div 4 = n$$

❷ Multiply to undo the division.

$$\frac{1}{2} = 4 \times n$$

.**Think**..............
4 times what number equals $\frac{1}{2}$?
....

$$4 \times \frac{1}{8} = \frac{1}{2}$$
So, $n = \frac{1}{8}$.

Each friend has $\frac{1}{8}$ loaf of bread.

Practice

Use a model or inverse operations.

1. Corva has $\frac{1}{3}$ pound of seeds. She divides it evenly among 5 pots. What part of a pound does she use in each pot?

$\frac{1}{3}$	$\frac{1}{3}$	$\frac{1}{3}$
5 equal parts

$\frac{1}{3} \div 5 =$ _____

2. Brad has 5 pounds of seeds. He wants to put them in bags that each contain $\frac{1}{3}$ pound. How many bags can he fill?

$\frac{1}{3}$	$\frac{1}{3}$	$\frac{1}{3}$	$\frac{1}{3}$	$\frac{1}{3}$
$\frac{1}{3}$	$\frac{1}{3}$	$\frac{1}{3}$	$\frac{1}{3}$	$\frac{1}{3}$
$\frac{1}{3}$	$\frac{1}{3}$	$\frac{1}{3}$	$\frac{1}{3}$	$\frac{1}{3}$

$5 \div \frac{1}{3} =$ _____

Discuss and Write

3. Create one story problem for $5 \div \frac{1}{6}$ and another for $\frac{1}{6} \div 5$.

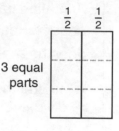
Problem Solving

Solve. Use a strategy that works best for you. Show your work.

4. A farmer has 4 acres of land to sell. He divides each acre into $\frac{1}{4}$-acre lots. How many lots can he sell?

$\frac{1}{4}$	$\frac{1}{4}$	$\frac{1}{4}$	$\frac{1}{4}$
$\frac{1}{4}$	$\frac{1}{4}$	$\frac{1}{4}$	$\frac{1}{4}$
$\frac{1}{4}$	$\frac{1}{4}$	$\frac{1}{4}$	$\frac{1}{4}$
$\frac{1}{4}$	$\frac{1}{4}$	$\frac{1}{4}$	$\frac{1}{4}$

_____

5. Mrs. Pierce has $\frac{1}{2}$ gallon of milk. She wants it to last for 3 days. If she uses the same amount each day, how much can she use each day?

3 equal parts

| $\frac{1}{2}$ | $\frac{1}{2}$ |

_____

6. Steve bikes one mile in $\frac{1}{6}$ hour. If he bikes for 2 hours, how far will he travel?

_____

7. Dillon has $\frac{1}{5}$ of a book left to read. He has 4 days to finish it. What fraction of the book must he read each day?

_____

8. A bag of flour contains 20 cups. If you scoop out $\frac{1}{4}$ cup at a time, how many $\frac{1}{4}$-cups will you scoop?

_____

9. Ruby has a garden that is $\frac{1}{8}$ of an acre. If she divides it into 3 equal sections, what is the size of each section?

_____

10. Rosa can play her favorite song 4 times in $\frac{1}{2}$ hour. Mariela can play her favorite song 3 times in $\frac{1}{3}$ hour. Whose favorite song is longer? Explain.

_____

11. Donny has a 10 pound bag of dog food. If he feeds his dog $\frac{1}{3}$ pound each day, will he have enough to feed his dog for 4 weeks?

_____

12. Write a problem that can be solved using $\frac{1}{3} \div 8$.

_____

13. Write a problem that can be solved using $8 \div \frac{1}{3}$.

_____

Critical Thinking

14. $3 \div \frac{1}{5} = n$

Will the quotient be greater than or less than the dividend? Explain your reasoning. Divide to check.

C For additional Practice, go to page 248 in this Workbook.
C Then go to Lesson 6-10B, pages 201–202 in this Workbook.

Name _____

Objective: To solve word problems involving fractions by using visual models and equations

The fifth graders have 3 yards of fabric to make flags. They need $\frac{1}{4}$ yard for each flag. How many flags can they make?

▶ To find how many flags can be made, you can use a model or an equation.

Method 1: Use a model.

❶ Draw 3 rectangles to represent 3 yards. Divide each rectangle into fourths.

| $\frac{1}{4}$ | $\frac{1}{4}$ | $\frac{1}{4}$ | $\frac{1}{4}$ | | $\frac{1}{4}$ | $\frac{1}{4}$ | $\frac{1}{4}$ | $\frac{1}{4}$ | | $\frac{1}{4}$ | $\frac{1}{4}$ | $\frac{1}{4}$ | $\frac{1}{4}$ |

❷ Count the number of $\frac{1}{4}$ yards.

❸ There are twelve $\frac{1}{4}$ yards in the model.

Method 2: Use an equation.

❶ Describe the situation in words. The number of flags is equal to 3 yards divided by $\frac{1}{4}$ yard.

❷ Write an equation. $f = 3 \div \frac{1}{4}$

❸ Solve. $f = 3 \times \frac{4}{1}$
    $= 12$

So, the students can make 12 flags from 3 yards of fabric.

Practice

Solve. Use a model or an equation.

1. Keiko has $\frac{7}{8}$ yard striped ribbon and $\frac{3}{4}$ yard dotted ribbon. Does she have more striped or dotted ribbon? How much more?

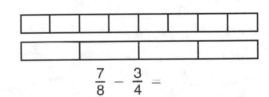

$$\frac{7}{8} - \frac{3}{4} =$$

_____

2. Mrs. Parsons has $\frac{1}{2}$ loaf of zucchini bread. She divides it evenly among 3 friends. What part of the whole loaf does each friend receive?

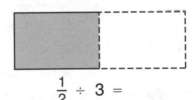

$$\frac{1}{2} \div 3 =$$

_____

3. Every day Al plays the trumpet for $\frac{2}{3}$ hour. How many hours does he play in 6 days?

$h = \frac{2}{3} \times$

$h =$

_____

Discuss and Write

4. When do you find it useful to use a model to solve a word problem? When do you use an equation only?

Problem Solving

Solve. Use a strategy that works best for you. Show your work.

5. Nia hikes at a rate of $3\frac{1}{3}$ miles per hour. She starts on a 10-mile hike at 8 A.M. Will she be done by 11:30 A.M.?

_____

6. Alexa can jump $8\frac{3}{4}$ feet. Gabriela can jump $\frac{2}{3}$ foot farther. How far can Gabriela jump?

_____

7. Every morning Lucas runs $1\frac{7}{10}$ miles. How far does he run in 5 days?

_____

8. Riley runs 4 laps around the track, a total of $2\frac{1}{2}$ miles. How long is one lap?

_____

9. Karen's time in the 100-meter dash improves. It drops from $14\frac{1}{2}$ seconds to $12\frac{3}{5}$ seconds. How much does it drop?

_____

10. Four boys run a relay race. Their individual times in seconds are $12\frac{1}{2}$, $15\frac{1}{3}$, $14\frac{3}{4}$, and $13\frac{2}{3}$. What is their total time?

_____

11. Lila's goal for the high jump is $4\frac{1}{4}$ feet. So far her best jump has been $3\frac{7}{8}$ feet. How much higher must she jump to reach her goal?

_____

12. Each member of a track team has a water bottle that holds $\frac{2}{3}$ pint. How many times can the coach fill a water bottle using a jug containing 16 pints of water?

_____

13. Neveah makes 1 loaf of bread with $1\frac{2}{3}$ cups white flour and $1\frac{1}{4}$ cups whole wheat flour. If she bakes 3 loaves, how much flour will she use in all?

_____

14. In one town, $\frac{1}{3}$ of all 5th graders play a sport. One fourth of those who are in sports are on a track team. What fraction of 5th graders participate in track?

_____

Explain Your Reasoning

15. Roger says that the product in multiplication is always greater than either factor. He also says that the quotient in division is always less than the dividend. Rosa says this is not true for fractions less than 1. Is Rosa right? Explain.

For additional Practice, go to page 249 in this Workbook. Then go to Lesson 6-11, pages 218–219 in the Student Book.

Objective: To use concrete models, drawings, and properties of operations to add decimals

▶ Add 0.46 + 0.2 + 0.09. $\boxed{0.2 = 0.20}$

You know that $\frac{46}{100} + \frac{20}{100} + \frac{9}{100} = \frac{n}{100}$.
So, the sum of 0.46 + 0.2 + 0.09 will be in the hundredths.

To find the sum, model each addend using base ten blocks.

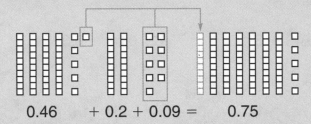

  0.46   + 0.2 + 0.09 =   0.75

▶ Add 0.28 + 4.5 + 0.81 + 0.09.
You can use properties of operations to find shortcuts when adding more than two numbers.

❶ Use the Associative Property. Look for two
digits with the same place value that make a 10.

$$0.28 + 4.5 + \overset{\lceil 0.10 \rceil}{(0.81 + 0.09)}$$
$$0.28 + 4.5 + \quad 0.90$$

❷ Use place value to write the addends in vertical format.
Line up the decimal points to correctly line up the
addends. Use zero as a place holder.

❸ Start with the hundredths. Add from right to left.
Regroup as needed.

```
  1
  0.28
  4.50  ◄— 4.5 = 4.50
+ 0.90
  5.68
```

So, 0.28 + 4.5 + 0.81 + 0.09 = 5.68.

Practice
Find the sum.

1. 1.3 + 0.12 + 2 _____

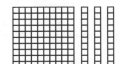

2. 0.45 + 0.05 + 0.6 _____

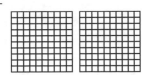

Discuss and Write

3. Why is it important to pay attention to the place value of the digits
before you add whether using models or properties of addition?

Practice

Find the sum.

4. 0.43 + 0.1

_____

5. 0.38 + 0.2 + 0.35

_____

6. 0.8 + 1.6 + 0.66

_____

7. 52.75 + 35.45

_____

8. 4.1 + 0.02 + 9.62

_____

9. 5.53 + 3.08 + 23.1

_____

10. 7.99 + 15.01 + 0.4

_____

11. 5.3 + 9.13 + 3

_____

12. 0.08 + 0.8 + 8

_____

13.
```
   0.53
   0.8
 + 0.62
```

14.
```
   25.3
   0.09
 + 4.61
```

15.
```
   0.88
   4.9
 + 0.02
```

16.
```
   8.1
   7
 + 5.6
```

17.
```
   5.53
   8.1
   0.64
 + 1.93
```

18.
```
   24.57
   3.91
   0.06
 + 13.2
```

19.
```
   8.04
   0.8
   6.6
 + 5.56
```

20.
```
   2.01
   6
   3.48
 + 3.2
```

Problem Solving

Solve. Use a strategy that works best for you. Show your work.

21. The choir director wants a program that will last about 12 minutes. What combination of songs is closest to 12 minutes?

Spring Melody: 4.8 minutes
Kite Song: 3.9 minutes
Marching Frogs: 4.4 minutes
Monkey Business: 3.8 minutes

22. A jeweler has a spool with 5.5 meters of wire. She uses 1.65 meters for a necklace and 0.25 meters for a pair of earrings. She also makes a bracelet. She then has 3.2 meters left. How much wire does the jeweler use for the bracelet?

_____   _____

What's the Error?

23. Jessie said that 0.72 + 0.5 = 0.77, but Alex said the total should be 1.22. Which answer is correct? What error did the person make to get the wrong answer?

C For additional Practice, go to page 250 in this Workbook.
C Then go to Lesson 8-2B, pages 205–206 in this Workbook.

Objective: To use place value and properties of addition to add decimals

▶ Add $0.3 + 0.8 + 0.7$.

Use properties of addition.	
Use the Commutative Property to change the order.	$0.3 + 0.7 + 0.8$
Use the Associative Property to make a "ten".	$(0.3 + 0.7) + 0.8$
Simplify inside the parentheses.	$1.0 + 0.8$
Add to simplify.	1.8

$0.3 + 0.8 + 0.7 = 1.8$

▶ Add $0.72 + 0.48$.

Use place value and properties of addition.	
Use place value to write in expanded form.	$0.70 + 0.02 + 0.40 + 0.08$
Use the Commutative Property to change the order.	$0.70 + 0.40 + 0.02 + 0.08$
Use the Associative Property to group by place value.	$(0.70 + 0.40) + (0.02 + 0.08)$
Simplify inside the parentheses.	$1.10 + 0.10$
Add to simplify.	1.20

$0.72 + 0.48 = 1.20$

▶ Find the sum $1.59 + 2.93$. Add by place value to find partial sums.

$$\begin{array}{r} 1.59 \\ + 2.93 \\ \hline \end{array}$$

Add the ones.	3.00
Add the tenths.	1.40
Add the hundredths.	0.12
Add the ones, tenths, and hundredths.	4.52

$1.59 + 2.93 = 4.52$

Practice

Find each sum using the given method.

1. Use properties of addition.

$0.4 + 0.9 + 0.6$

_____ + _____ + 0.9

_____

2. Use place value and properties of addition.

$0.54 + 0.52$

_____

3. Add by place value.

$$\begin{array}{r} 0.84 \\ + 0.67 \\ \hline \end{array}$$

Discuss and Write

4. When adding decimals, how do you decide which method to use?

Practice

Find each sum. Explain the method you use.

5. $0.92 + 0.16$ _____

6. $0.3 + 0.86$ _____

7. $0.04 + 0.68$ _____

8. $0.3 + 0.9 + 0.1$ _____

9. $0.49 + 0.84 + 0.51$ _____

10. $0.4 + 0.8 + 0.6$ _____

11. $0.27 + 0.56 + 0.8$ _____

12. $0.15 + 0.43 + 0.25$ _____

13. $0.33 + 0.3 + 0.03$ _____

14.
$$\begin{array}{r} 0.54 \\ + 0.59 \\ \hline \end{array}$$

15.
$$\begin{array}{r} 0.79 \\ + 0.3 \\ \hline \end{array}$$

16.
$$\begin{array}{r} 0.2 \\ + 0.09 \\ \hline \end{array}$$

17.
$$\begin{array}{r} 0.49 \\ + 0.51 \\ \hline \end{array}$$

18.
$$\begin{array}{r} 0.5 \\ 0.9 \\ + 0.1 \\ \hline \end{array}$$

19.
$$\begin{array}{r} 0.38 \\ 0.23 \\ + 0.37 \\ \hline \end{array}$$

20.
$$\begin{array}{r} 0.8 \\ 0.4 \\ + 0.2 \\ \hline \end{array}$$

21.
$$\begin{array}{r} 0.35 \\ 0.7 \\ + 0.25 \\ \hline \end{array}$$

Problem Solving

Solve. Use a strategy that works best for you. Show your work.

22. Eva walks 0.8 kilometer to her friend's house. Together they walk 0.4 kilometer to the park and 0.6 kilometer back to Eva's house. How far does Eva walk in all?

23. Juan walks 0.4 kilometer to his friend's house. Together they walk 0.6 kilometer to the park and 0.7 kilometer back to Juan's house. How far did Juan's friend walk in all?

24. Mrs. Daney has 3 pitchers of beverages containing the amounts shown. How many liters of juice does she have?

Apple juice: 0.95 liter
Orange juice: 0.75 liter
Milk: 0.85 liter

25. The label on a box says it has a mass of 1.5 kilograms of popcorn. It contains 0.4 kilogram of cheese popcorn and 0.4 kilogram of caramel corn. The rest is plain popcorn. How many kilograms of plain popcorn does it contain?

Explain Your Reasoning

26. How does adding by place value make addition simpler?

For additional Practice, go to page 251 in this Workbook.
Then go to Lesson 8-3, pages 272–273 in the Student Book.

Name _____

Objective: To use strategies to subtract decimals

▶ Subtract $0.32 - 0.18$.

You know that $\frac{32}{100} - \frac{18}{100} = \frac{n}{100}$.

So, the difference of $\frac{32}{100} - \frac{18}{100}$ will be in the hundredths.

To find the difference, model using base ten blocks.

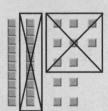

Show 0.32 as 3 tenths 2 hundredths. There are not enough hundredths to take away 8 hundredths.	Regroup 1 tenth as 10 hundredths. Then take away 1 tenth 8 hundredths.	The difference is 1 tenth 4 hundredths.

$0.32 - 0.18 = 0.14$

▶ Subtract $0.82 - 0.37$.
To find the difference, you can count on from 0.37 to 0.82 by adding.

Add to count on to the next tenth. $0.37 + 0.03 = 0.40$
Add to count on the tenth in 0.82. $0.40 + 0.40 = 0.80$
Add to count on to 0.82. $0.80 + 0.02 = 0.82$
Find the total that you counted on. 0.45

$0.82 - 0.37 = 0.45$

Practice

Subtract. Use a model or count on.

1. $0.75 - 0.26$

_____

2. $9.1 - 5.7$

$5.7 +$ _____ $=$ _____

$6.0 +$ _____ $=$ _____

$9.0 +$ _____ $=$ _____

_____

Discuss and Write

3. How does understanding place value help you use strategies to subtract?

Name _____

Practice

Subtract. Show your work.

4. 0.42 − 0.19

_____

5. 0.34 − 0.15

_____

6. 0.53 − 0.47

_____

7. 0.88 − 0.31

_____

8. 0.71 − 0.56

_____

9. 0.83 − 0.54

_____

10. 0.47 − 0.29

_____

11. 0.62 − 0.24

_____

12. 0.25 − 0.19

_____

13.   0.14
      − 0.06

14.   0.32
      − 0.13

15.   0.91
      − 0.22

16.   0.4
      − 0.18

17.   5.1
      − 2.39

18.   7.91
      − 5.43

19.   2.05
      − 1.09

20.   4.89
      − 1.97

Problem Solving

Solve. Use a strategy that works best for you. Show your work.

21. Pete has a glass with 0.75 liter of milk. He spills some so he only drinks 0.67 liter. How much milk does Pete spill?

_____

22. Lola completes 3.1 kilometers of a 5-kilometer race before she stops for water. How much farther does Lola have to go to complete the race?

_____

23. Eli's baby sister will need a new car seat once she weighs 40 pounds. She weighs 23.5 pounds now. Eli weighs 82.8 pounds. How much more than his sister does Eli weigh? How much weight does Eli's sister need to gain to get a new car seat?

_____

24. During the school year, Prima grows from 1.41 to 1.45 meters. Ellen grows from 1.29 to 1.36 meters. Who grows the most? How much more did she grow?

_____

What's the Error?

25. Baxter subtracted 0.7 − 0.53 and got 0.23 as his answer. Find the error Baxter made and give the correct answer.

C For additional Practice, go to page 252 in this Workbook.
C Then go to Lesson 8-6, pages 278–279 in the Student Book.

Name _____

Objective: To use drawings of models and properties of operations to multiply decimals

Jeremy pours 0.25 liter of lemonade into each of 3 glasses. How much lemonade does he pour in all?

Think
You want to find 3 groups of 0.25 liter.

▶ To find the answer, you can multiply 3 × 0.25.

● Use <u>base ten blocks</u> to model the multiplication as repeated addition.

	Add the tenths.	Add the hundredths. Regroup as needed.	Add the two sums.

   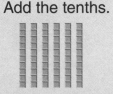   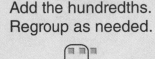

3×0.25	$\underline{0.20 + 0.20 + 0.20}$	$\underline{0.05 + 0.05 + 0.05}$	$0.60 + 0.15 = 0.75$
$0.25 + 0.25 + 0.25$	0.60	0.15	$3 \times 0.25 = 0.75$

● Use drawings to model the multiplication using the <u>Distributive Property</u>.

	Use the Distributive Property.	Find the tenths. Find the hundredths.	Add the tenths and the hundredths.
Break apart 0.25.			

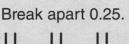
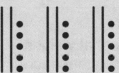

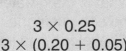

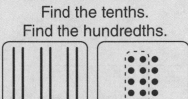

6 tenths   15 hundredths

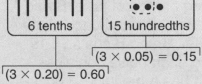

$(3 \times 0.05) = 0.15$

$(3 \times 0.20) = 0.60$

3×0.25	$3 \times (0.20 + 0.05)$		$0.60 + 0.15 = 0.75$
$3 \times (0.20 + 0.05)$	$(3 \times 0.20) + (3 \times 0.05)$		$3 \times 0.25 = 0.75$

So, Jeremy pours 0.75 liter of lemonade.

▶ Use fractions to check.

$$3 \times 0.25 \stackrel{?}{=} 0.75$$
$$3 \times \frac{25}{100} = \frac{75}{100}$$
$$= 0.75$$

Practice

Use base ten blocks or drawings to find each product.

1. $4 \times 0.32 =$ _____

2. $3 \times 1.15 =$ _____

Discuss and Write

3. How does using a model to multiply decimals help you understand what happens in the multiplication?

Name _____

Practice

Use base ten blocks or drawings to find each product.

4. 4 × 0.16

_____

5. 3 × 0.89

_____

6. 8 × 0.16

_____

7. 9 × 0.42

_____

8. 5 × 1.27

_____

9. 2 × 4.46

_____

10. 6 × 1.51

_____

11. 3 × 2.93

_____

12.   0.82
        ×   2
       _____

13.   0.77
        ×   4
       _____

14.   1.5
        ×   4
       _____

15.   3.1
        ×   5
       _____

Problem Solving

Solve. Use a strategy that works best for you. Show your work.

16. Bekkah is training for a race. She runs 1.25 miles every day for 4 days, then takes one day off. How far will she have run after 16 days?

_____

17. Bryan bakes 3 loaves of bread. Each measures 0.65 meters long. Without calculating, decide whether the total length of the bread is more or less than 1.5 meters. How did you decide?

_____

18. Lee is comparing brands of juice. Brand A costs $4.95 for 3 bottles and each bottle contains 0.95 liter. Brand B costs $5.19 for 5 bottles and each bottle contains 0.55 liter. Which has more juice: 3 bottles of Brand A or 5 bottles of Brand B?

_____

19. Mia has an envelope that weighs 0.15 ounce and photos that each weigh 0.16 ounce. What is the greatest number of photos she can put in the envelope so that the envelope and its contents weigh less than 1 ounce? What is the total weight?

_____

Explain Your Reasoning

20. The drawing shows finding the product of 4 and 0.15. Explain what happens in each step.

Step 1: _____

Step 2: _____

Step 3: _____

Step 4: _____

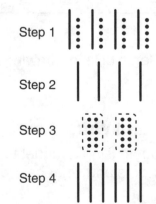

C For additional Practice, go to page 253 in this Workbook.
C Then go to Lesson 9-3, pages 298–299 in the Student Book.

Name _____

Objective: To use an array model to multiply decimals by decimals

Multiply 0.4 × 0.8.

You need to find 0.4 of a group of 0.8.

You know that $\frac{1}{10} \times \frac{1}{10} = \frac{1}{100}$ and $\frac{1}{10} = 0.1$

So, 0.1 × 0.1 = 0.01.

The product of 0.4 and 0.8 will be in the hundredths.

.........Think.........
Find $\frac{4}{10}$ of a group of $\frac{8}{10}$.

▶ To find the product, model each factor on one 10 × 10 grid which shows hundredths.

❶ Shade 8 of the columns to show 0.8. Shade 4 of the rows to show 0.4.

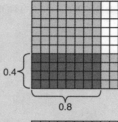

❷ The 32 squares where the shading overlaps shows the product, 0.4 × 0.8.

So, 0.4 × 0.8 = 0.32.

Check: $\frac{4}{10} \times \frac{8}{10} = \frac{32}{100}$

$\frac{32}{100} = 0.32$

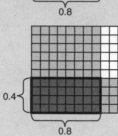

Practice

Multiply. Use each 10 × 10 grid to model each product.

1. 0.7 × 0.3

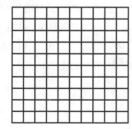

_____

2. 0.5 × 0.8

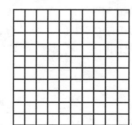

_____

3. 0.6 × 0.6

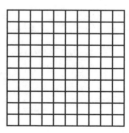

_____

Discuss and Write

4. What do you notice about the relationship between the factors and the product when multiplying two decimals less than 1?

Practice

Multiply. Use each 10 × 10 grid to model each product.

5. 0.3×0.9

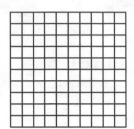

_____

6. 0.7×0.6

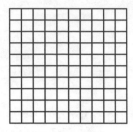

_____

7. 0.9×0.4

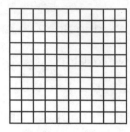

_____

Multiply. Use a separate sheet of paper to model each product.

8. 0.8
       $\times 0.9$

9. 0.4
       $\times 0.7$

10. 0.3
        $\times 0.6$

11. 0.4
        $\times 0.6$

12. 0.2
        $\times 0.2$

13. 0.9
        $\times 0.7$

14. 0.5
        $\times 0.3$

15. 0.7
        $\times 0.5$

Problem Solving

Solve. Use a strategy that works best for you. Show your work.

16. An artist designs a rectangular logo that is 0.8 meter by 0.3 meter. She reduces it so that the sides are 0.2 times as large. What are the new dimensions?

_____

17. An average cat has a body that is about 0.5 meter long. The average tail is about 0.6 times as long as the body. What is the length of the tail of an average cat?

_____

18. A recipe for fruit cobbler calls for 0.3 kilogram of apples and 0.8 kilogram of pears. A chef wants to make 0.8 times as much. How many kilograms of fruit will he use in all?

_____

19. Emmett has a 1-kilogram bag of potatoes. He composted 0.2 kilogram of the potatoes because they were soft. The amount he cooked was 0.7 of what was left. How many kilograms did Emmett cook?

_____

Test Preparation

20. When Jake multiplied 0.7 times another number, his answer was 0.49.

  a. Explain how to find the other factor.

  b. What numbers did Jake multiply?

C For additional Practice, go to page 254 in this Workbook.
C Then go to Lesson 9-4, pages 300–301 in the Student Book.

Model Dividing a Decimal by a Whole Number
Chapter 9, Lesson 6A

Objective: To use models to divide decimals by whole numbers

Macie bought 1.75 pounds of salmon. She cuts it into 5 equal parts before she cooks it. How much does each part weigh?

▶ Use models to divide 1.75 by 5.

1 Model 1.75 with base-ten blocks. Then make a drawing to record the modeling.

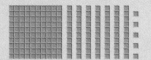 

2 There are not enough ones to divide into 5 equal groups. Regroup. Divide the tenths into 5 equal parts.

 Regroup 1 as 10 tenths and make 5 equal parts.

3 Divide the remaining 2 tenths 5 hundredths into 5 equal groups. Regroup.

 Regroup 0.2 as 20 hundredths and make 5 equal parts.

4 Add the tenths and the hundredths to make 5 equal groups.

 0.30 + 0.05 = 0.35

1.75 ÷ 5 = 0.35

Each part of the salmon weighs 0.35 pounds.

Practice
Divide. Model with base-ten blocks and then record each division with drawings.

1. 0.78 ÷ 6 _____

2. 2.56 ÷ 4 _____

Discuss and Write
3. When using models to divide, how do you know when to regroup?

Name _____

Practice

Use models to divide.

4. 0.87 ÷ 3 _____   **5.** 5.76 ÷ 8 _____   **6.** 2.85 ÷ 5 _____   **7.** 0.84 ÷ 7 _____

8. 5.67 ÷ 9 _____   **9.** 3.56 ÷ 4 _____   **10.** 0.18 ÷ 6 _____   **11.** 1.45 ÷ 5 _____

12. 6.42 ÷ 3 _____   **13.** 0.72 ÷ 8 _____   **14.** 0.48 ÷ 4 _____   **15.** 3.84 ÷ 6 _____

Problem Solving

Solve. Use a strategy that works best for you. Show your work.

16. Lucia pours 1.44 L of milk into 3 glasses so that each has the same amount. How much milk is in each glass?

17. Eight students are painting a mural that is 5.36 m long. First they divide the mural so that each student paints an equal part. What length does each student paint?

18. Jared weighs 5 bagels and lists the results in ounces.

3.75, 4, 4.25, 4.25, 3.5

What is the average weight?

19. A real estate agent has 4 lots of land to sell. The sizes in acres for 3 of them are 0.47, 0.36, and 0.32. The average lot size is 0.35 acre. What is the size of the fourth lot?

Test Preparation

20. Joe uses a different strategy to divide decimals. He just divides as if both numbers were whole numbers. Then he estimates the quotient to decide where to place the decimal point. Use Joe's strategy to divide 2.94 ÷ 6.

a. Tell what you will do first. What is the result of that step?

b. How will you estimate the quotient? What is your estimate?

c. What is 2.94 ÷ 6?

For additional Practice, go to page 255 in this Workbook.
Then go to Lesson 9-7, pages 306–307 in the Student Book.

Objective: To model dividing a decimal by a decimal

What is the quotient of $0.42 \div 0.06$?

▶ To find the quotient, use a model.

❶ Model 0.42.

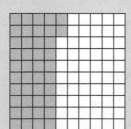

❷ Identify 0.06 or *6 hundredths*.

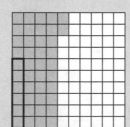

❸ Count the number of *6 hundredths* in 0.42.

There are 7 groups of 6 hundredths in 42 hundredths.
So, $0.42 \div 0.06 = 7$.

What is the quotient of $4.8 \div 1.2$?

❶ Model *4 and 8 tenths*.

❷ Count the number of *1 and 2 tenths* in 4.8.

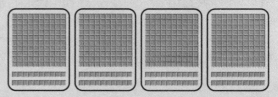

There are 4 groups of 1 and 2 tenths in 4 and 8 tenths.
So, $4.8 \div 1.2 = 4$.

Practice

Use a model to find each quotient.

1. $0.64 \div 0.08$ _____

2. $0.36 \div 0.04$ _____

3. $5.1 \div 1.7$ _____

4. $7.2 \div 1.2$ _____

Discuss and Write

5. When you use a model to find a quotient, why is it important to make the groups all of equal sizes?

Practice

Write the division problem shown by each model.
Explain how you know.

6.

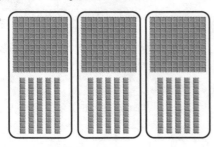

_____

7.

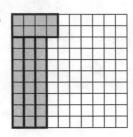

_____

Use a model to find each quotient.

8. $0.65 \div 0.13$ _____

9. $4 \div 0.5$ _____

10. $3.6 \div 0.9$ _____

11. $0.88 \div 0.11$ _____

12. $0.96 \div 0.08$ _____

13. $6.3 \div 0.9$ _____

Problem Solving

Solve. Use a strategy that works best for you. Show your work.

14. A box can hold 10.5 kg of books. You want to fill it with books that measure 0.7 kg each. What is the greatest number of books that you can put in the box?

15. A bag contains several wrapped granola bars. The label says that the bag of granola weighs 8.2 ounces and each separate granola bar weighs 2.1 ounces. Explain why this is not possible.

16. Sarah has a recipe that makes 8 oatmeal muffins with 0.2 kg of batter. How many muffins can she make with 1.1 kg of batter? Explain.

17. Mr. Spencer is making 8 liters of punch. He uses 0.45 liters of fruit juice for each liter of punch. Mr. Spencer has 5 liters of fruit juice. How much fruit juice will he have left? Explain.

Test Preparation

18. Jerry made this drawing to model $1.2 \div 0.06$.

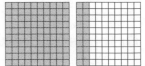

   a. What mistake did he make in his drawing? How do you know?

   b. How can you change the model to show $1.2 \div 0.06$? What is the correct answer?

C For additional Practice, go to page 256 in this Workbook.
C Then go to Lesson 9-8B, pages 217–218 in this Workbook.

Objective: To use place value to divide two decimals

Joe builds a tower that is 0.63 meter tall. Manuel builds a tower that is 0.3 meter tall. How many times as tall is Joe's tower as Manuel's?

▶ To solve the problem, divide 0.63 by 0.3. To divide by a decimal, it is sometimes helpful to rewrite the division so that the division is a whole number.

Think about place value. If you move the decimal point the same number of places in both the divisor and the dividend, the quotient will remain the same.

> To change 0.3 to a whole number divisor, multiply by 10. Then multiply the dividend 0.63 by 10.

❶ Move the decimal point in the *divisor* to form a whole-number divisor. Then move the decimal point in the *dividend* to the right the *same number* of places.

$$0.3 \overline{)0.63}$$

❷ Place the decimal point in the quotient and then divide.

$$0.63 \div 0.3 = 6.3 \div 3$$

$$
\begin{array}{r}
2.1 \\
3{\overline{)6.3}} \\
-6 \\
\hline
0\ 3 \\
-3 \\
\hline
0
\end{array}
$$

So, Joe's tower is 2.1 times as tall as Manuel's tower.

Practice

Move the decimal point in the divisor and the dividend.
Then find the quotient.

1. $0.54 \div 0.3$

$$0.3 \overline{)0.54}$$

2. $1.44 \div 0.6$

$$0.6 \overline{)1.44}$$

3. $7.28 \div 0.07$

$$0.07 \overline{)7.28}$$

Discuss and Write

4. How does moving both decimal points the same number of places relate to multiplying the divisor and dividend by 10, 100, and 1000?

Name _____

Practice
Find the quotient.

5. $0.27 \div 0.3$

6. $2.7 \div 0.3$

7. $0.27 \div 0.03$

8. $0.68 \div 0.4$

9. $8.73 \div 0.9$

10. $0.96 \div 0.08$

11. $1.96 \div 0.4$

12. $0.84 \div 0.03$

13. $2.94 \div 0.07$

14. $0.8\overline{)1.28}$

15. $0.7\overline{)0.49}$

16. $0.04\overline{)0.52}$

17. $0.3\overline{)6.51}$

18. $1.1\overline{)4.84}$

19. $0.05\overline{)2.95}$

20. $0.25\overline{)5.75}$

21. $0.2\overline{)27.8}$

Problem Solving
Solve. Use a strategy that works best for you. Show your work.

22. Enrique has 25.2 pounds of pecans. He wants to fill bags with 0.7 pound in each bag. How many bags can he fill?

23. Lydia bought a bag containing 10.4 kilograms of dog food. Her dog eats 0.4 kilogram each day. How many days will the bag of food last?

24. When a number is divided by 0.5, the quotient is a whole number. When the same number is multiplied by 0.5, the product is 1.25. What is the quotient when the number is divided by 0.5? Explain.

25. Ike needs to hang 20 pictures for an art show. He uses 0.6 meter of wire to hang each picture. He has 13.5 meters of wire. Does he have enough wire? Explain.

Critical Thinking
26. $1.85 \div 0.5$ $18.5 \div 0.5$ $1.85 \div 0.05$ $18.5 \div 0.05$
Look at the divisions shown above. How can you find which two have the same quotient without actually dividing?

For additional Practice, go to page 257 in this Workbook.
Then go to Lesson 9-9, pages 310–311 in the Student Book.

Name _____

Objective: To classify two-dimensional figures into categories based on properties

► The name of a quadrilateral often refers to its sides and angles. The sides and angles of a quadrilateral are attributes you can use to identify the best name for classifying the quadrilateral.

What is the best name to use to classify this quadrilateral?

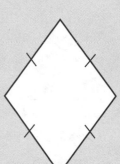

❶ Each pair of opposite sides is congruent. It is a parallelogram.

❷ It is a parallelogram with four congruent sides, so it is a rhombus.

So, the best name for this quadrilateral is rhombus.

► Some quadrilaterals have *more than one name* because they have the same attributes as other quadrilaterals.

What is another way to describe the rhombus?

❶ Both pairs of opposite sides are parallel.

❷ Both pairs of opposite sides are congruent.

So, the rhombus can also be classified as a parallelogram, because its opposite sides are parallel and congruent.

Practice

For each quadrilateral, answer the questions and write the best name to use to classify it. Then write any other possible names.

1. How many pairs of parallel sides? _____
All congruent sides? _____
All right angles? _____

_____

2. How many pairs of parallel sides? _____
All congruent sides? _____
All right angles? _____

_____

Write what you know about each quadrilateral.

3. square

_____

4. parallelogram

_____

Discuss and Write

5. Explain how a square shares attributes with other kinds of quadrilaterals.

Name _____

Practice

For each quadrilateral, first write the best name to use to classify it.
Then write any other possible names.

6.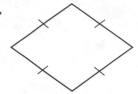

_____

7.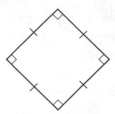

_____

8.

_____

9.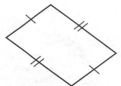

_____

10.

_____

11.

_____

Problem Solving

Solve. Use a strategy that works best for you. Show your work.

12. Carmen drew a quadrilateral and one of
its diagonals. The diagonal divided it into
2 congruent isosceles obtuse triangles.
What type of quadrilateral did she draw?

13. Amy says a figure is a rhombus. Derek
says the same figure is a rectangle. Could
they both be right? Explain.

_____

_____

Test Preparation

14. Mrs. Mayfield asked her students to draw
a quadrilateral with two 70° angles and
two 110° angles. Dave and Bessie made
these drawings.

 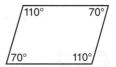

Dave's Drawing   **Bessie's Drawing**

  A. Do both drawings follow the directions?
  How are they different?
  B. How should the directions change to make
  all drawings like Dave's?
  C. How should the directions change to make
  all drawings like Bessie's?

C For additional Practice, go to page 258 in this Workbook.
Then go to Lesson 10-7, pages 336–337 in the Student Book.

Objective: To find the area of a rectangle with fractional dimensions

A note card is $3\frac{1}{2}$ in. long and $2\frac{1}{2}$ in. wide. What is its area?

▶ To find the area of a rectangle, you can use a model or a formula.

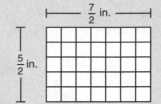

<u>Method 1</u>: Use a model.
You can cover the surface with unit squares. First, show each side length of the rectangle as an improper fraction. The LCD of the side lengths of the rectangle is 2. So, the side length of each unit square measures $\frac{1}{2}$ in. The area of each unit square is $\frac{1}{4}$ in².

Thirty-five unit squares cover the rectangle.

So, the total area is $\frac{35}{4}$ in.²

$\frac{35}{4}$ in.² = $8\frac{3}{4}$ in.²

<u>Method 2</u>: Use a formula.

$A = \ell \times w$

$A = 3\frac{1}{2}$ in. $\times 2\frac{1}{2}$ in.

  $= \frac{7}{2}$ in. $\times \frac{5}{2}$ in.

  $= \frac{35}{4}$ in.²

  $= 8\frac{3}{4}$ in.²

Remember:
Area = length × width
$A = \ell \times w$

So, the note card has an area of $8\frac{3}{4}$ in.²

Practice

Find the area of the rectangle.

1. $1\frac{1}{2}$ in. *by* $1\frac{1}{4}$ in.

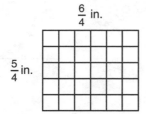

$\frac{6}{4}$ in.

$\frac{5}{4}$ in.

Each ☐ measures $\frac{1}{4}$ in. $\times \frac{1}{4}$ in.
The area of a ☐ is $\frac{1}{16}$ in.²

$\frac{}{16}$ in.² = _____ in.²

2. $3\frac{2}{3}$ ft *by* $1\frac{1}{4}$ ft

$3\frac{2}{3} \times 1\frac{1}{4} = \frac{}{3} \times \frac{}{4}$

$= \frac{}{12}$

$= $ _____ ft²

Discuss and Write

3. How is finding the area of a rectangle with mixed number dimensions different from finding the area of one with whole number dimensions?

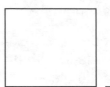
Practice

Find the area of each rectangle. Simplify your answer if needed.

4. $1\frac{3}{4}$ in. *by* $\frac{3}{8}$ in.

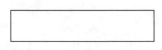

_____

5. $1\frac{1}{3}$ yd *by* $1\frac{1}{6}$ yd

_____

6. $2\frac{1}{4}$ ft *by* $1\frac{5}{6}$ ft

_____

7. $2\frac{1}{2}$ in. *by* $2\frac{1}{3}$ in.

_____

8. $2\frac{2}{3}$ yd *by* $1\frac{3}{4}$ yd

_____

9. $2\frac{1}{2}$ in. *by* $\frac{7}{8}$ in.

_____

10. $5\frac{1}{4}$ yd *by* $1\frac{1}{3}$ yd

_____

11. 10 mi *by* $7\frac{1}{2}$ mi

_____

Problem Solving

Solve. Use a strategy that works best for you. Show your work.

12. Lou painted both the front and back of a tile that was $1\frac{3}{4}$ inches wide and $1\frac{5}{8}$ inches high. What total area did he paint?

_____

13. Twila made three small flags. Each was $\frac{7}{8}$ in. *by* $1\frac{1}{2}$ in. What is the total area of all three flags?

_____

14. A patio is $6\frac{1}{4}$ yards *by* $5\frac{1}{2}$ yards. It has a hot tub in the middle that is $2\frac{1}{4}$ yards *by* $2\frac{1}{2}$ yards. If you tile the patio only, what is the area to be tiled?

_____

15. A wall is $8\frac{1}{3}$ feet *by* $7\frac{1}{2}$ feet. It has a window that is $4\frac{1}{2}$ feet *by* $2\frac{2}{3}$ feet. If you paint the wall, what is the area that will be painted?

_____

Explain Your Reasoning

16. Bridget designed a poster that is $2\frac{1}{4}$ ft *by* $1\frac{1}{2}$ ft. Mel designed one that is $1\frac{1}{4}$ ft *by* $2\frac{1}{2}$ ft. Bridget says they will have the same area because both posters had dimensions with 1, 2, $\frac{1}{4}$, and $\frac{1}{2}$ ft. Mel says the areas will be different. Explain who is correct.

C For additional Practice, go to page 259 in this Workbook.
C Then go to Lesson 12-6, pages 392–393 in the Student Book.

Name _____

Objective: To use formulas to find the volume of a right rectangular prism

▶ Two formulas can be used to find the volume of a right rectangular prism.

Both formulas will give the same result. You can use the Associative Property to show that the two formulas are equivalent.

Volume Formulas

Volume = *length* × *width* × *height*

$V = \ell \times w \times h$

Volume = *Base area* × *height*

$V = B \times h$

$V = \ell \times w \times h$

$V = (\ell \times w) \times h$ Use the Associative Property to group $\ell \times w$.

$V = \quad B \quad \times h$ Replace $(\ell \times w)$ with B, because $\ell \times w$ is the area of the base or bottom face of the prism.

$\ell \times w \times h$ and $B \times h$ both equal V. $\ell \times w \times h = B \times h$.

The dimensions are 12 in. by 5 in. by 3 in. What is the volume of this prism?

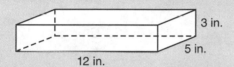

3 in.
5 in.
12 in.

❶ Use the formula $V = \ell \times w \times h$.

❷ Substitute the dimensions of the prism in the formula and simplify.

$V = 12 \times 5 \times 3$
$V = 180$

The volume of the prism is 180 in.³

The same rectangular prism is 3 in. high. The area of its base is 60 in.² What is its volume?

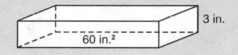

3 in.
60 in.²

❶ Use the formula: $V = B \times h$.

❷ Substitute the dimensions of the prism in the formula and simplify.

$V = 60 \times 3$
$V = 180$

The volume of the prism is 180 in.³

Practice

Use the formula to find the volume of the rectangular prism.

1. $V = \ell \times w \times h$

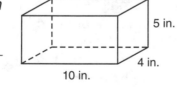

_____

5 in.
4 in.
10 in.

2. $V = B \times h$

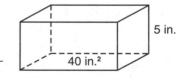

_____

5 in.
40 in.²

Discuss and Write

3. The dimensions in inches of two boxes are whole numbers greater than 1. One box is 5 in. long, 3 in. wide, and 4 in. high. The other box is 4 in. high and the area of its base is 15 in.² What do you know about these boxes?

Name _____

Practice

Find the volume of each rectangular prism.

4.

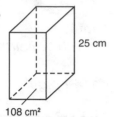

25 cm

108 cm²

_____

5.

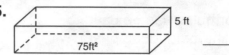

5 ft

75ft²

_____

6.

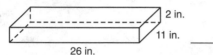

2 in.

11 in.

26 in.

_____

7.

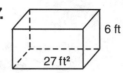

6 ft

27 ft²

_____

8. $B = 48$ cm², $h = 9$ cm

9. $B = 39$ ft², $h = 15$ ft

10. $\ell = 9$ in., $w = 13$ in., $h = 3$ in.

_____   _____   _____

11. $B = 36$ m², $h = 4$ m

12. $\ell = 48$ cm, $w = 35$ cm, $h = 16$ cm

13. $B = 64$ ft², $h = 7$ ft

_____   _____   _____

Problem Solving

Solve. Use a strategy that works best for you. Show your work.

14. A rectangular aquarium is 20 in. long and 10 in. wide. Its volume is 2400 in.³ What is its height?

_____

15. The area of the base of a storage locker is 168 ft². Its volume is 1344 ft³. How tall is the storage locker?

_____

16. A blue box has a base of 35 in.² and a height of 5 in. A red box has a base of 70 in.² and a height of 10 in. How many times greater is the volume of the red box than the volume of the blue one?

_____

17. A small tissue box has a base of 20 in.² and a height of 4 in. A large tissue box has a base of 40 in². Its volume is 3 times greater than the small box. What is the height of the large box?

_____

Explain Your Reasoning

18. The volume of a rectangular prism is 120 cm³. Its base is 24 cm² and the height is 5 cm. Can you conclude that the base is 4 cm *by* 6 cm? Explain.

For additional Practice, go to page 260 in this Workbook.
Then go to Lesson 12-11B, pages 225–226 in this Workbook.

Objective: To find volume by separating solid figures into known shapes

When finding the volume of a solid figure, sometimes it can be helpful to separate the figure into simpler known shapes. Then you can add the volumes of the simpler shapes to find the total volume of the figure.

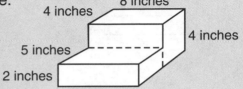

Find the volume of the solid figure shown to the right by separating it into smaller known shapes.

▶ Separate the solid figure into two separate prisms.

❶ Find the volume of the larger prism.

$V = \ell \times w \times h$
$V = 8 \times 4 \times 4 = 128$

❷ Find the volume of the smaller prism.

$V = \ell \times w \times h$
$V = 8 \times 5 \times 2 = 80$

❸ Add the volumes together.

$128 + 80 = 208$

So, the volume of the solid figure is 208 in.^{3}

Brett designed a building shaped like the model shown. Both floors will be 10 ft tall. The area of the first floor will be 1600 ft^2. The area of the second floor will be 400 ft^2. What will be the volume of the entire building?

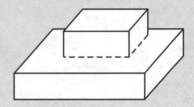

❶ Find the volume of the first floor.

$V = B \times h$
$V = 1600 \times 10 = 16,000$

❷ Find the volume of the second floor.

$V = B \times h$
$V = 400 \times 10 = 4000$

❸ Add the volumes together.

$16,000 + 4000 = 20,000$

So, the volume of the entire building is 20,000 ft^3.

Practice

Find the volume of the figure.

1.

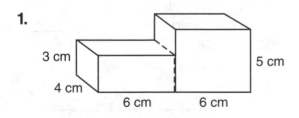

Find the volume of the left prism.

$V = $ _____ $\times$ _____ $\times$ _____ $=$ _____

Find the volume of the right prism.

$V = $ _____ $\times$ _____ $\times$ _____ $=$ _____

The total volume is

_____ $+$ _____ $=$ _____ cm^3.

Discuss and Write

2. Draw two ways to separate this figure into two smaller known shapes to find its volume. Does it matter which way you separate the figure? Explain.

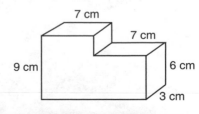

Practice

Separate the figure into two simpler known shapes. Then find the total volume.

3.

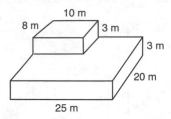

Top _____

Bottom _____

Total _____

4.

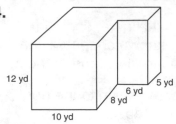

Left _____

Right _____

Total _____

5.

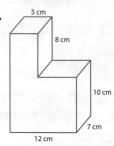

Top _____

Bottom _____

Total _____

6.

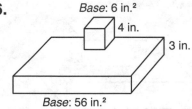

_____

7.

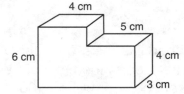

_____

8.

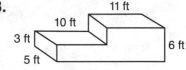

_____

Problem Solving

Solve. Use a strategy that works best for you. Show your work.

9. Eric wants to fill the planter shown with soil. How many cubic feet of soil does he need?

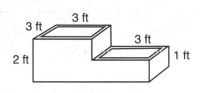

10. Curt wants to use exactly 350 cubes that are 1 in.³ to build the structure shown. How tall should he build the taller part?

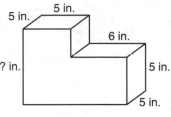

Explain Your Reasoning

11. Explain how to find the total volume two ways. What is the total volume?

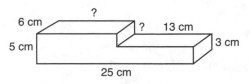

For additional Practice, go to page 261 in this Workbook.
Then go to Lesson 12-12, pages 404–405 in the Student Book.

Name _____

Objective: To make and use line plots to display data and solve problems

The table shows the lengths of several pencils. What is the difference between the median and the mode of the data? What fraction of the pencils is longer than $6\frac{1}{4}$ in.?

Lengths of Pencils (inches)

$6\frac{1}{2}$	$5\frac{5}{8}$	6	$5\frac{1}{2}$	$6\frac{1}{2}$
$6\frac{1}{4}$	$6\frac{3}{8}$	$6\frac{1}{4}$	$6\frac{1}{4}$	$5\frac{7}{8}$
$5\frac{5}{8}$	$5\frac{7}{8}$	$6\frac{1}{4}$	$5\frac{7}{8}$	$5\frac{5}{8}$

▶ You can use a line plot to organize and examine data.

Make a line plot. Use intervals of eighths.

Lengths of Pencils

```
                                          X
                                          X
          X              X                X
          X              X                X              X
 X        X              X       X        X       X      X
 ←——┼─────┼──────┼──────┼───────┼────────┼───────┼──────┼——→
   5½     5⅝     5¾     5⅞      6       6⅛      6¼     6⅜     6½
                              Inches
```

Use the line plot to find the median and the mode.
The median is 6 and the mode is $6\frac{1}{4}$.
Subtract to find the difference between them.

$6\frac{1}{4} - 6 = \frac{1}{4}$

So, the difference between the median and the mode is $\frac{1}{4}$ in.

To find the number of pencils in all and the number longer than $6\frac{1}{4}$ in., count Xs on the line plot.

There are 15 pencils and 3 are longer than $6\frac{1}{4}$ in. $\frac{3}{15} = \frac{1}{5}$

So, $\frac{1}{5}$ of the pencils are longer than $6\frac{1}{4}$ in.

> **Remember:**
> The **median** is the middle number in an ordered set of numbers.
>
> The **mode** is the number that occurs most frequently.

Practice

Make a line plot for the data.

1.

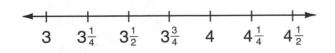

Time to Run One Lap (minutes)

$3\frac{1}{2}$	$3\frac{3}{4}$	3	$4\frac{1}{2}$
$4\frac{1}{4}$	$3\frac{3}{4}$	$3\frac{1}{4}$	$3\frac{1}{2}$
$3\frac{3}{4}$	$3\frac{1}{2}$	$3\frac{1}{2}$	$3\frac{1}{2}$
$3\frac{1}{2}$	$3\frac{1}{4}$	$4\frac{1}{4}$	$3\frac{3}{4}$

Discuss and Write

2. How do you decide on the range and the intervals to use on a line plot?

Practice

The data shows the amount of fruits and vegetables eaten by several people. Make a line plot for the data. Then answer the questions.

Fruits and Vegetables Eaten in One Day (cups)

$3\frac{1}{3}$	3	$2\frac{2}{3}$	$2\frac{1}{3}$	4
$2\frac{1}{3}$	$3\frac{1}{3}$	$1\frac{1}{3}$	$2\frac{2}{3}$	4
3	$1\frac{2}{3}$	4	$1\frac{1}{3}$	$1\frac{2}{3}$
$2\frac{1}{3}$	$1\frac{1}{3}$	$1\frac{1}{3}$	2	$2\frac{1}{3}$

3. What are the two modes? What is the difference between them?

_____

4. How many people ate fewer than 2 cups of fruits and vegetables?

_____

5. What fraction of people ate more than 3 cups of fruits and vegetables?

_____

6. What is the range of the data set?

_____

7. How many people are represented in the data set?

_____

8. If the cups of fruit and vegetables were distributed evenly, how much would each person get?

_____

Problem Solving

Use the line plots to answer the questions.

Height of Plants in Soil A

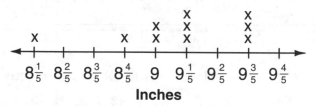

Inches

Height of Plants in Soil B

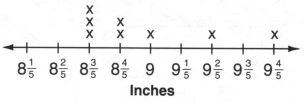

Inches

9. Without actually finding the mean, in which type of soil did the plants have the greatest average height? Explain.

10. If you want to grow tall plants, would you choose Soil A or Soil B? Explain.

_____

_____

What's the Error?

11. Shawn says that the median of the data on the line plot is $3\frac{3}{4}$ minutes. Explain his mistake.

Lengths of Songs

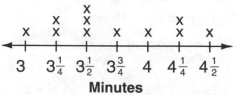

Minutes

For additional Practice, go to page 262 in this Workbook. Then go to Lesson 12-13, pages 406–407 in the Student Book.

Name _____

Objective: To use the coordinate plane to solve real-world problems

Using the coordinate plane to model situations can help you visualize situations to solve problems.

Toby's house is located at (0, 0). He walks 4 blocks east and 5 blocks north to the library at (4, 5). Then Toby walks 1 block west and 2 blocks north to Ray's house at (3, 7). He walks home by going 3 blocks west and 7 blocks south. How much shorter is Toby's route home from Ray's house than his route to Ray's house?

▶ You can use a coordinate plane to compare.

  1 Graph the locations.

  2 Count the distance Toby walks to Ray's house. 12 blocks

  3 Count the distance Toby walks home. 10 blocks

  4 Subtract to find the difference. $12 - 10 = 2$

So, the route Toby takes home is 2 blocks shorter.

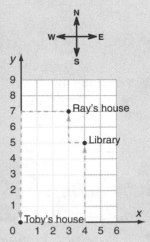

The coordinate plane to the right shows the number of laps and the time in minutes it takes five students to run them. What do the coordinates (3, 8) mean?

▶ Use the coordinate plane to find what the point at (3, 8) means.

  1 3 is the x-coordinate, the number of laps run.

  2 8 is the y-coordinate, the running time in minutes.

So, (3, 8) means a student runs 3 laps in 8 minutes.

Students' Track Times

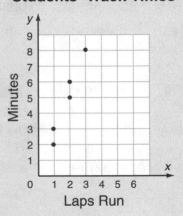

Practice

Use the coordinate plane for exercises 1 and 2.

1. Graph the point for Kay's house at (6, 3).

2. Zoe, Emma, and Kay walk from their houses to the park. Which two walk the same distance? How far do they walk?

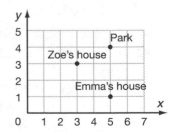

_____

Discuss and Write

3. How can you know what the x- and y-coordinates of a point represent in a given situation? How can using a coordinate plane help you to explain?

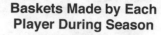

Practice

Use the coordinate plane for exercises 4–6.

4. What do the points (8, 9) and (4, 0) mean?

_____

5. Graph the points (6, 7) and (7, 6).

6. What is the difference in the meaning of (6, 7) and (7, 6)?

_____

Baskets Made by Each Player During Season

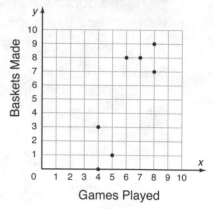

Problem Solving

Solve. Use the coordinate plane above.

7. Two points on the coordinate plane have 8 as the *x*-coordinate, but they have different *y*-coordinates. Explain why.

_____

8. Suppose a player plays in 10 games. About how many baskets would you expect the player to make? Explain.

_____

9. If each basket counts as 2 points, how would you change the label on the *y*-axis and the title to show the number of points each player scored? Cross out and replace the label and the title.

10. If each basket counts as 2 points, and you made a graph showing the points each player scored, how would the *x*- and *y*-coordinates change? Find the number of points each player scored and plot the new set of points.

_____

Test Preparation

11. Noralyn went on a 6-hour hike. At the end of each hour, she graphed the distance she traveled.
  a. How long did it take Noralyn to hike 7 miles?
  b. What might have happened between the third and fourth hours?
  c. Did Noralyn's speed increase or decrease as the hike progressed? Explain.

Noralyn's Hike

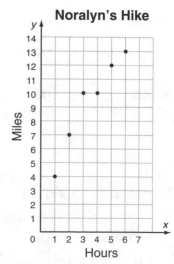

For additional Practice, go to page 263 in this Workbook.
Then go to Lesson 14-13B, pages 231–232 in this Workbook.

Name _____

Objective: To write and use sequence rules

Marcos counted the number of guppies in his aquarium each week. He recorded the results in the table below. What rule describes the sequence?
Predict the number of guppies Marcos will have in Week 6.

> Numbers in a pattern are called a **sequence**. A **term** is one of the numbers in a sequence.

Week	1	2	3	4	5
Guppies	2	4	8	16	32

▶ To find the rule described by the sequence, look at the number of guppies to see how it changes weekly.

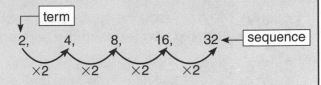

Notice, Marcos started with 2 guppies. The number then doubles each week. So, the rule is: Begin with 2. Multiply by 2 to find the next term.

Use the rule to predict the number of guppies in Week 6.

So, Marcos will have 64 guppies in Week 6.

Nina's grandfather gave her $50. Every week she spent $8. How much money did she have left at the end of 5 weeks?

▶ To find how much money Nina has at the end of 5 weeks, write a sequence to show the amount of money Nina has each week.

Week	0	1	2	3	4	5
Money	$50	$42	$34	$26	$18	$10

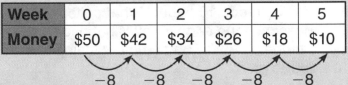

Begin the sequence with $50. Show a constant change of a decrease of $8 each week.

So, at the end of 5 weeks Nina will have $10.

Practice

Use the rule to write the next three terms.

1. Rule: Begin with 45; add 5.

45, 50, 55, ...

Identify the sequence rule.

2. 5, 20, 80, 320, 1280, ...

_____

Discuss and Write

3. Look at the sequence rules used in exercises 1 and 2. What two types of information are given in each? Why are both important?

Practice

Use the rule to write the next three terms in the sequence.

4. Rule: Begin with 1; multiply by 7

1, 7, 49, 343, … _____

5. Rule: Begin with 25; add 2.5

25, 27.5, 30, 32.5, … _____

6. Rule: Begin with 2; add $\frac{1}{4}$

2, $2\frac{1}{4}$, $2\frac{1}{2}$, $2\frac{3}{4}$, … _____

7. Rule: Begin with 210; subtract 7

210, 203, 196, 189, … _____

Describe the rule used to create each sequence.
Then find the next two terms in the sequence.

8. 3, 6, 12, 24, …

_____

9. 60, 54, 48, 42, …

_____

10. 4.8, 2.4, 1.2, 0.6, …

_____

11. $\frac{1}{10}$, $\frac{2}{10}$, $\frac{3}{10}$, $\frac{4}{10}$, …

_____

Problem Solving

Solve. Use a strategy that works best for you. Show your work.

12. Andre's book begins on page 2. Every day he reads 10 pages. What pattern rule describes the sequence? What page number is Andre on at the beginning of the fourth day?

_____

13. Mr. Garcia pays Sherman $6.00 the first time he mows his lawn. Each time Sherman mows his lawn again, Mr. Garcia increases his pay $0.75. After how many times is Sherman's pay double the first amount?

_____

14. Pamela has a 20-ounce box of kitten food. Every day her kitten eats 3 ounces of food. How much food is left at the end of 10 days? Explain how you know.

_____

15. A fire truck holds 500 gallons of water. If the firefighters use water at the rate of 40 gallons a minute, how much water is left after 6 minutes of use?

_____

Test Preparation

16. A term is missing from this sequence.   90, ?, 78, 72, 66, 60

   a. Identify the constant change in the sequence.
   b. What is the sequence rule?
   c. Use the rule to find the twelfth term in the sequence.
       Explain how you found your answer.

For additional Practice, go to page 264 in this Workbook.
Then go to Lesson 14-13C, pages 233–234 in this Workbook.

Objective: To identify the relationships between corresponding terms in two sequences

For every $1 donated by the Caring School to the homeless shelter, the Happy Store will donate $2. How are the two different donations related?

▶ To understand the relation, make two number patterns, or sequences, using a table. The table should show possible $1 donations that can be made by the school, and possible $2 donations that can be made by the store. Then graph the values in the table to explain the relation.

❶ Make a table.

Homeless Shelter Donations

Caring School	$0	$1	$2	$3	$4	$5	$6	← Add 1
Happy Store	$0	$2	$4	$6	$8	$10	$12	← Add 2

❷ Use the corresponding terms of the sequences to write a list of ordered pairs. Use the *Add-1* term as the *x*-coordinate and the *Add-2* term as the *y*-coordinate.
(0, 0), (1, 2), (2, 4), (3, 6), (4, 8), (5, 10), (6, 12)

❸ Graph the ordered pairs. Connect the points of the sequence to show a line that represents the relation between the donations.

▶ Look at the points on the line. The *y*-coordinate is always 2 times the *x*-coordinate.

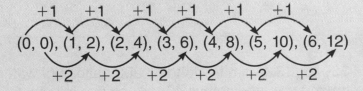

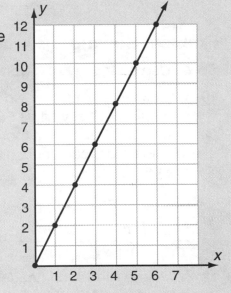

Practice

1. Identify the rules for each sequence. What will be the 6th term in both sequences?

Sequence 1	3	3	3	3	3
Sequence 2	2	4	8	16	32

_____

2. Write ordered pairs (*x, y*) using the corresponding terms of the sequence.

_____

3. On grid paper, plot the points and connect them to show a line.

4. How do the two sequences compare? _____

Discuss and Write

5. Using the example above, how much would the Happy Store donate if the Caring School donates $3.50? Explain.

Practice

6. Identify the rules for each sequence. What will be the 7th term in both sequences?

Sequence 1	5	10	15	20	25
Sequence 2	1	4	7	10	13

_____

7. Write ordered pairs (x, y) using the corresponding terms of the sequence.

8. On grid paper, plot the points and connect them to show a line.

_____

9. How do the two sequences compare?

_____

Problem Solving

Solve. Use a strategy that works best for you. Show your work.

10. Casey and Pat start down a trail at the same time. Casey hikes 5 kilometers each hour. Pat rides a mountain bike 12 kilometers each hour. How far apart are they after 3 hours?

_____

11. Kate cares for her neighbors' cats. Mr. Moya pays her $10 the first time, and increases her pay $10 each time. Mrs. Wilson pays her $1 the first time, and doubles the amount each time. How do the rates of pay compare after 4 jobs? After 8 jobs?

_____

12. Mike and Alex each needed to save $30 to buy a game. Mike had $10 to start with and saved $3 each month. Alex had no money to start with but saved $5 a month. Which boy saved $30 first? How much longer did it take the other boy?

_____

13. A fire truck holds 200 gallons of water and sprays 40 gallons per minute. A smaller truck holds 125 gallons and sprays 20 gallons per minute. If they started at the same time, how many gallons are left in the smaller truck when the other runs out of water?

_____

Critical Thinking

14. Assume you know that the hundredth term of Sequence 1 is 496, how can you predict the hundredth term of Sequence 2?

Sequence 1	1	6	11		
Sequence 2	4	9	14		

_____

C For additional Practice, go to page 265 in this Workbook.
C Then go to Lesson 14-14, pages 466–467 in the Student Book.

Practice for Additional CCSS Lessons

Powers of Ten

Name _____

- Write $(3 \times 10^3) + (6 \times 10^2) + (1 \times 10^1) + (8 \times 1)$ in standard form.

  $(3 \times 10^3) + (6 \times 10^2) + (1 \times 10^1) + (8 \times 1)$

  $(3 \times 1000) + (6 \times 100) + (1 \times 10) + (8 \times 1)$

  $\quad 3000 \quad + \quad 600 \quad + \quad 10 \quad + 8 \qquad = 3618$

  So, $(3 \times 10^3) + (6 \times 10^2) + (1 \times 10^1) + (8 \times 1) = 3618$.

- Write 14,609 in expanded form using powers of 10.

  $14{,}609 = 10{,}000 + 4000 + 600 + 9$

  $\qquad\quad = (1 \times 10{,}000) + (4 \times 1000) + (6 \times 100) + (9 \times 1)$

  $\qquad\quad = (1 \times 10^4) \quad + (4 \times 10^3) \quad + (6 \times 10^2) \quad + (9 \times 1)$

  So, $14{,}609 = (1 \times 10^4) + (4 \times 10^3) + (6 \times 10^2) + (9 \times 1)$.

Write each number in standard form.

1. $(6 \times 10^4) + (1 \times 10^3) + (2 \times 10^2) + (5 \times 1)$

   _____

2. $(8 \times 10^5) + (2 \times 10^3) + (9 \times 10^2) + (6 \times 1)$

   _____

3. $(2 \times 10^3) + (5 \times 10^2) + (7 \times 10^1) + (3 \times 1)$

   _____

4. $(3 \times 10^6) + (5 \times 10^3) + (6 \times 10^2)$

   _____

5. $(7 \times 10^4) + (1 \times 10^3) + (8 \times 10^1)$

   _____

6. $(9 \times 10^5) + (3 \times 10^3) + (4 \times 10^2) + (3 \times 1)$

   _____

Write each number in expanded form using powers of 10.

7. 3608

   _____

8. 415,087

   _____

9. 12,863

   _____

10. 701,400

    _____

Problem Solving

11. The Moon is about (2×10^5) miles from Earth. Could the Moon be 2,389,000 miles from Earth? Explain.

    _____

12. The population of Prairie Town is 8462 people. The population of Sunville is just over (9×10^2) people. Which place has the larger population? Explain.

    _____

Use with Lesson 1-3A, pages 175–176 in this Workbook.
Then go to Lesson 1-4, pages 36–37 in the Student Book.

Decimals and Expanded Form

Name _____

<table>
<tr><td>

Write 0.538 in expanded form using fractions for the decimal part.

$0.538 = 0.5 \quad + \quad 0.03 \quad + 0.008$

$\quad\quad = (5 \times \frac{1}{10}) + (3 \times \frac{1}{100}) + (8 \times \frac{1}{1000})$

So, $0.538 = (5 \times \frac{1}{10}) + (3 \times \frac{1}{100}) + (8 \times \frac{1}{1000})$.

</td><td>

Write $(6 \times 1) + (4 \times \frac{1}{10}) + (9 \times \frac{1}{1000})$ as a decimal in standard form.

$(6 \times 1) + (4 \times \frac{1}{10}) + (9 \times \frac{1}{1000})$

$\quad 6 \quad + \quad 0.4 \quad + \quad 0.009 = 6.409$

So, the decimal form is 6.409.

</td></tr>
</table>

Write in expanded form.

1. 0.631

2. 1.207

_____

_____

3. 5.562

4. 6.983

_____

_____

Write in decimal form.

5. $(2 \times 1) + (6 \times \frac{1}{10}) + (9 \times \frac{1}{1000})$ _____

6. $(5 \times 1) + (2 \times \frac{1}{10}) + (1 \times \frac{1}{100}) + (6 \times \frac{1}{1000})$ _____

7. $(3 \times 1) + (8 \times \frac{1}{100}) + (2 \times \frac{1}{1000})$ _____

8. $(1 \times 1) + (4 \times \frac{1}{10}) + (6 \times \frac{1}{100}) + (3 \times \frac{1}{1000})$ _____

Problem Solving

9. In the number 2023, how does the value of the digit in the tens place compare to the value of the digit in the thousands place?

_____

10. In the number 1808, how does the value of the digit in the hundreds place compare to the value of the digit in the ones place?

_____

C Use with Lesson 1-4A, pages 177–178 in this Workbook.
C Then go to Lesson 1-5, pages 38–39 in the Student Book.

237

Use Arrays to Divide

Name _____

Find the quotient 128 ÷ 16.

Use an array.	Use an area model.

Use an array.

- Make rows of 16 to model 128.

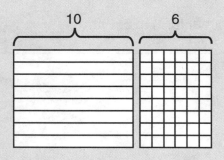

10   6

- Count the rows.

So, 128 ÷ 16 = 8.

Use an area model.

- Write the dividend and divisor. Multiply and subtract. Estimate: 120 ÷ 20 = 6.

Estimate →

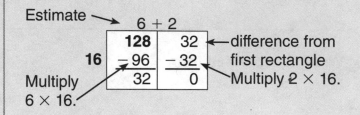

6 + 2

16

128	32
− 96	− 32
32	0

← difference from first rectangle

Multiply 2 × 16.

Multiply 6 × 16.

- Add to find the quotient.

6 + 2 = 8

So, 128 ÷ 16 = 8.

Use an array or area model to find the quotient.

1. 450 ÷ 15 = _____

2. 476 ÷ 28 = _____

3. 468 ÷ 18 = _____

4. 528 ÷ 11 = _____

5. 864 ÷ 36 = _____

6. 208 ÷ 13 = _____

7. 551 ÷ 29 = _____

8. 770 ÷ 35 = _____

9. 432 ÷ 16 = _____

10. 252 ÷ 18 = _____

11. 525 ÷ 21 = _____

12. 364 ÷ 28 = _____

13. 1620 ÷ 36 = _____

14. 2132 ÷ 26 = _____

15. 1752 ÷ 12 = _____

Problem Solving

16. Mariah makes picture frames for a craft fair. It takes 7 days to make the picture frames. Mariah places 12 stars on each frame. She has 360 stars. How many picture frames can Mariah make?

17. A pet food store has 840 cans of cat food that sell for $0.69 each. The cans are in 56 packages. How many cans are in each package?

_____

_____

Use with Lesson 3-9A, pages 179–180 in this Workbook.
Then go to Lesson 3-10, pages 114–115 in the Student Book.

Use Strategies to Divide

Name _____

Solve for *n*: 361 ÷ 19 = *n*

Method 1: Use Multiplication

$$n \times 19 = 361$$

- Estimate.

$$n \times 18 = 360$$
$$20 \times 18 = 360$$

So, *n* is about 20.

- Multiply. Use the estimate.

$$20 \times 19 = 380$$

380 > 361. Try a factor < 20.

$$19 \times 19 = 361$$

So, 361 ÷ 19 = 19.

Method 2: Break Apart the Dividend

- Multiply and subtract.

$$10 \times 19 = 190 \longleftarrow \text{Not enough}$$
$$20 \times 19 = 380 \longleftarrow \text{Too much}$$

- Use an area model.

```
            10   +    9
        ┌────────┬────────┐
   19   │  361   │  171   │
        │ -190   │ -171   │
        ├────────┼────────┤
        │  171   │   0    │
        └────────┴────────┘
```

- Check   361 = 19 × (10 + 9)

$$361 = 19 \times 19$$

Find the quotient. Use a strategy.

1. 2664 ÷ 74 = _____

2. 1472 ÷ 46 = _____

3. 2257 ÷ 61 = _____

4. 1456 ÷ 28 = _____

5. 1020 ÷ 15 = _____

6. 2822 ÷ 34 = _____

7. 4818 ÷ 66 = _____

8. 2128 ÷ 38 = _____

9. 1690 ÷ 26 = _____

10. 5037 : 73 = _____

11. 2064 ÷ 43 = _____

12. 4824 ÷ 72 = _____

13. 1643 ÷ 31 = _____

14. 3990 ÷ 38 = _____

15. 1767 ÷ 93 = _____

Problem Solving

16. A printing company prints 432 newspapers. The newspapers are wrapped in bundles of 12. How many bundles of newspapers are wrapped?

17. A museum gives tours to groups of 14. Today, 602 visitors tour the museum. How many groups tour the museum?

C Use with Lesson 3-10A, pages 181–182 in this Workbook.
C Then go to Lesson 3-11, pages 116–117 in the Student Book.

239

Variables and Expressions

A library receives 3 boxes of books. Each box has 4 hard cover books and 5 soft cover books. The library gives away 7 of the books. How many books does the library have left?

- Write an expression. Use grouping symbols.

$$[3 \times (4 + 5)] - 7$$

- Evaluate the expression.

$$[3 \times (4 + 5)] - 7$$

$$[3 \times 9] - 7$$

$$27 \quad - 7 = 20$$

So, the library has 20 books left.

Simplify each expression.

1. $3 \times [(5 + 6) - 4]$

_____

2. $[9 - (18 \div 6)] + (15 \div 5)$

_____

3. $[(2 \times 8) \div (3 + 1)] + 6$

_____

4. $5 + [(40 - 10) \div (7 - 2)]$

_____

5. $[48 \div (2 \times 6)] \times 6$

_____

6. $[(3 \times 4) + (3 \times 7)] \div 11$

_____

Write an expression for each situation. Do not simplify.

7. Marla has 2 pennies, 5 dimes, and 4 nickels. How much money does she have in all?

_____

8. Vince has 4 boxes of crayons. Each box has 3 red crayons, 4 blue crayons, and 2 green crayons. If his friend gives him 5 more crayons, how many crayons will he have?

_____

Compare the two expressions without evaluating. Explain.

9. $5 + (6 \times 2)$ and (6×2)

_____

10. $8 \times (7 + 3)$ and $(3 + 7) \times 8$

_____

11. $(9 - 4) \times 5$ and $(9 - 4) \div 5$

_____

12. $(1 + 8) \div 3$ and $(1 + 8)$

_____

240

Use with Lesson 3-14A, pages 183–184 in this Workbook.
Then go to Lesson 3-15, pages 124–125 in the Student Book.

Add Fractions with Unlike Denominators

Name _____

Add: $\frac{1}{8} + \frac{3}{4}$

- Model the problem under the strip for 1 whole.

- Rename the fractions with a common denominator and find the total.

1

$\frac{1}{8}$	$\frac{1}{4}$	$\frac{1}{4}$	$\frac{1}{4}$

$\frac{1}{8}$	$\frac{1}{8}$	$\frac{1}{8}$	$\frac{1}{8}$	$\frac{1}{8}$	$\frac{1}{8}$	$\frac{1}{8}$

$\frac{1}{8} + \frac{6}{8} = \frac{7}{8}$

Add. Write the answer in simplest form.

1. $\frac{2}{12} + \frac{1}{3} =$ _____

2. $\frac{1}{4} + \frac{1}{2} =$ _____

3. $\frac{1}{2} + \frac{2}{5} =$ _____

4. $\frac{1}{6} + \frac{3}{4} =$ _____

5. $\frac{1}{3} + \frac{1}{6} =$ _____

6. $\frac{1}{2} + \frac{3}{8} =$ _____

7. $\frac{1}{10} + \frac{2}{5} =$ _____

8. $\frac{2}{3} + \frac{1}{9} =$ _____

9. $\frac{3}{12} + \frac{1}{6} =$ _____

10. $\frac{1}{8} + \frac{1}{6} =$ _____

11. $\frac{1}{8} + \frac{3}{4} =$ _____

12. $\frac{1}{5} + \frac{1}{4} =$ _____

13. $\frac{7}{10} + \frac{2}{5} =$ _____

14. $\frac{3}{5} + \frac{1}{2} =$ _____

15. $\frac{4}{9} + \frac{2}{3} =$ _____

Problem Solving

16. Mary added $\frac{1}{2}$ cup blue sand, $\frac{2}{5}$ cup red sand, and $\frac{3}{10}$ cup white sand to a vase for an art project. If the vase can hold 2 cups of sand, how much more sand can she add?

17. Ned rode his bicycle $\frac{1}{4}$ mile from his home to the park. He rode another $\frac{3}{8}$ mile at the park. Then he rode back home from the park. Did he ride at least 1 mile? Explain.

_____

_____

Use with Lesson 5-1A, pages 185–186 in this Workbook.
Then go to Lesson 5-2, pages 166–167 in the Student Book.

241

Subtract Fractions with Unlike Denominators

Name _____

Subtract: $\frac{2}{3} - \frac{1}{4}$

- Model the problem under a strip for 1 whole.

1

$\frac{1}{3}$	$\frac{1}{3}$

$\frac{1}{4}$	?

- Rename the fractions with a common denominator.

$\frac{1}{12}$	$\frac{1}{12}$	$\frac{1}{12}$	$\frac{1}{12}$	$\frac{1}{12}$	$\frac{1}{12}$	$\frac{1}{12}$	$\frac{1}{12}$

$\frac{1}{12}$	$\frac{1}{12}$	$\frac{1}{12}$	?

$\frac{1}{12}$	$\frac{1}{12}$	$\frac{1}{12}$	$\frac{1}{12}$	$\frac{1}{12}$

- Find the difference.

$$\frac{2}{3} - \frac{1}{4} = \frac{5}{12}$$

Subtract. Write the answer in simplest form.

1. $\frac{9}{10} - \frac{2}{5} =$ _____

2. $\frac{5}{6} - \frac{1}{2} =$ _____

3. $\frac{4}{5} - \frac{1}{2} =$ _____

4. $\frac{7}{12} - \frac{1}{4} =$ _____

5. $\frac{1}{2} - \frac{2}{8} =$ _____

6. $\frac{5}{8} - \frac{1}{4} =$ _____

7. $\frac{3}{4} - \frac{1}{3} =$ _____

8. $\frac{11}{12} - \frac{1}{3} =$ _____

9. $\frac{9}{10} - \frac{4}{5} =$ _____

10. $\frac{7}{9} - \frac{2}{3} =$ _____

11. $\frac{7}{8} - \frac{1}{4} =$ _____

12. $\frac{5}{6} - \frac{1}{4} =$ _____

13. $\quad \frac{3}{4}$
   $- \frac{2}{3}$

14. $\quad \frac{11}{12}$
   $- \frac{1}{3}$

15. $\quad \frac{8}{9}$
   $- \frac{2}{3}$

Problem Solving

16. Ian bought $\frac{3}{4}$ yard of wire. He used $\frac{1}{6}$ yard for his science project. How much does he have left?

_____

17. Lilly's plant grew $\frac{11}{12}$ foot last week. Sean's plant grew $\frac{2}{3}$ foot. Whose plant grew more?

_____

How much more? _____

Use with Lesson 5-6A, pages 187–188 in this Workbook.
Then go to Lesson 5-7, pages 176–177 in the Student Book.

Subtract Fractions and Whole Numbers from Mixed Numbers

Name _____

Subtract: $4\frac{1}{2} - 2$

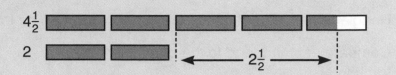

• Model $4\frac{1}{2}$ and 2.

• Compare the models.

So, $4\frac{1}{2} - 2 = 2\frac{1}{2}$.

Subtract. Use models to help.

1. $\frac{5}{6} - \frac{1}{3} =$ _____

2. $\frac{7}{12} - \frac{1}{4} =$ _____

3. $\frac{7}{8} - \frac{1}{4} =$ _____

4. $\frac{5}{8} - \frac{1}{4} =$ _____

5. $3\frac{1}{8} - 2 =$ _____

6. $3\frac{3}{4} - 2 =$ _____

7. $4\frac{1}{5} - 2 =$ _____

8. $3\frac{2}{3} - 3 =$ _____

Problem Solving

9. One of Fran's dogs is $2\frac{5}{8}$ feet tall and the other is 2 feet tall. How much taller is one dog than the other?

10. Tim is weighing rocks in his collection. Together, three rocks weigh $4\frac{1}{4}$ pounds. He removes one rock that weighs 2 pounds. How much do the remaining rocks weigh?

_____

_____

Use with Lesson 5-8A, pages 189–190 in this Workbook.
Then go to Lesson 5-9, pages 180–181 in the Student Book.

243

Use Benchmark Fractions

Name _____

Reggie adds $\frac{2}{3} + \frac{1}{5}$. He finds the sum $\frac{7}{15}$. How can he tell if his answer is reasonable?

Compare each addend to the benchmark fraction $\frac{1}{2}$.

$\frac{2}{3} > \frac{1}{2}$ and $\frac{1}{5} < \frac{1}{2}$ $\frac{2}{3} + \frac{1}{5}$ is about 1.

The sum $\frac{7}{15}$ is about $\frac{1}{2}$, so his answer is not reasonable.

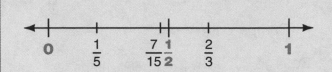

Decide whether the answer is reasonable.

1. $\frac{7}{9} + \frac{2}{3} = \frac{1}{3}$ _____

2. $\frac{5}{6} - \frac{1}{4} = \frac{7}{12}$ _____

3. $\frac{5}{8} - \frac{1}{4} = \frac{3}{8}$ _____

4. $\frac{3}{4} - \frac{1}{6} = \frac{1}{12}$ _____

5. $\frac{1}{5} + \frac{1}{2} = \frac{3}{10}$ _____

6. $\frac{11}{12} - \frac{1}{3} = \frac{9}{10}$ _____

7. $\frac{1}{2} + \frac{2}{8} = \frac{3}{4}$ _____

8. $\frac{7}{8} - \frac{1}{4} = \frac{5}{8}$ _____

9. $\frac{7}{12} + \frac{1}{4} = \frac{2}{8}$ _____

Give a reasonable estimate.

10. $\frac{1}{3} + \frac{2}{5}$

11. $\frac{7}{8} - \frac{1}{2}$

12. $\frac{3}{4} + \frac{1}{8}$

13. $\frac{3}{4} - \frac{1}{6}$

_____   _____   _____   _____

Problem Solving

14. Lena needs 1 pound of fertilizer. She has $\frac{2}{3}$ pound in one bag and $\frac{3}{4}$ pound in another bag. How can she estimate to see if she has enough?

15. A farmer is planting corn seeds on an acre of land. He plants seeds on $\frac{2}{5}$ acre. Does he have more than half left? How do you know?

_____   _____

244

C Use with Lesson 5-9A, pages 191–192 in this Workbook.
C Then go to Lesson 5-10, pages 182–183 in the Student Book.

Use Properties to Multiply Fractions and Whole Numbers

Name _____

What is $\frac{2}{3} \times 6$?

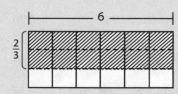

$\frac{2}{3} \times 6 = \frac{12}{3}$

So, $\frac{2}{3} \times 6$ is the same as multiplying 2×6 and dividing by 3.

What is $\frac{2}{3} \times \frac{3}{4}$?

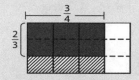

$\frac{2}{3} \times \frac{3}{4} = \frac{6}{12}$

So, $\frac{2}{3} \times \frac{3}{4}$ is the same as multiplying 2×3 and dividing by 3×4.

Use a model to multiply.

1. $\frac{2}{5} \times \frac{3}{4} =$ _____

2. $\frac{7}{8} \times 4 =$ _____

3. $\frac{5}{6} \times \frac{1}{2} =$ _____

4. $\frac{3}{4} \times 8 =$ _____

5. $\frac{1}{3} \times \frac{2}{6} =$ _____

6. $\frac{4}{9} \times 5 =$ _____

7. $\frac{5}{9} \times \frac{3}{4} =$ _____

8. $\frac{2}{3} \times \frac{4}{7} =$ _____

9. $\frac{2}{3} \times \frac{4}{6} =$ _____

10. $\frac{2}{3} \times 7 =$ _____

11. $\frac{3}{4} \times \frac{7}{8} =$ _____

12. $\frac{5}{6} \times 3 =$ _____

Problem Solving

13. Mr. Tucker has 6 pounds of clay. He gives $\frac{3}{4}$ of it to the class for a project. How many pounds does he use?

14. Blake has $\frac{5}{6}$ of a bag of potting soil. He uses $\frac{2}{3}$ of the potting soil on his plants. How much of a full bag does he use?

_____

_____

C Use with Lesson 6-2A, pages 193–194 in this Workbook.
C Then go to Lesson 6-2B, pages 195–196 in this Workbook.

245

Scaling Fractions

Name _____

Multiply $\frac{2}{3} \times \frac{4}{4}$	Multiply $\frac{2}{3} \times \frac{3}{4}$	Multiply $\frac{2}{3} \times \frac{5}{4}$
When one factor is *equal to* 1, use the Identity Property of Multiplication.	When both factors are *less than* 1, the product is *less than* either factor.	When one factor is *greater than* 1, the product is *greater than* the other factor.
$\frac{4}{4} = 1$ $\frac{2}{3} \times 1 = \frac{2}{3}$	$\frac{2}{3} < 1$ and $\frac{3}{4} < 1$	$\frac{5}{4} = 5 \times \frac{1}{4}$, so $\frac{5}{4} > 1$.
So, the product of $\frac{2}{3} \times \frac{4}{4} = \frac{2}{3}$.	So, the product of $\frac{2}{3} \times \frac{3}{4} < \frac{2}{3}$.	So, the product of $\frac{2}{3} \times \frac{5}{4} > \frac{2}{3}$.

Decide if each product will be less than, equal to, or greater than the first factor.

1. $\frac{7}{8} \times \frac{3}{5}$

_____

2. $\frac{4}{5} \times \frac{6}{5}$

_____

3. $\frac{2}{1} \times \frac{4}{3}$

_____

4. $\frac{2}{10} \times \frac{7}{8}$

_____

5. $\frac{2}{6} \times \frac{9}{8}$

_____

6. $\frac{3}{4} \times \frac{2}{2}$

_____

7. $\frac{5}{3} \times \frac{5}{6}$

_____

8. $\frac{1}{2} \times \frac{6}{6}$

_____

9. $\frac{4}{5} \times \frac{3}{7}$

_____

10. $\frac{2}{3} \times \frac{5}{5}$

_____

11. $\frac{4}{1} \times \frac{5}{2}$

_____

12. $\frac{5}{6} \times \frac{4}{9}$

_____

Write a fraction that makes a true statement.

13. $\frac{4}{5} \times$ _____ $< \frac{4}{5}$ 14. $\frac{7}{3} \times$ _____ $> \frac{7}{3}$ 15. $\frac{1}{8} \times$ _____ $= \frac{1}{8}$ 16. $\frac{3}{4} \times$ _____ $> \frac{3}{4}$

17. $\frac{3}{2} \times$ _____ $= \frac{3}{2}$ 18. $\frac{3}{3} \times$ _____ $< \frac{3}{3}$ 19. $\frac{5}{7} \times$ _____ $> \frac{5}{7}$ 20. $\frac{1}{1} \times$ _____ $= \frac{1}{1}$

Problem Solving

21. It takes Enrique $\frac{3}{5}$ hour to clean his room. It takes his sister $\frac{2}{3}$ times as long as Enrique to clean her room. Who takes longer to clean? How do you know?

22. Loren runs $\frac{3}{4}$ mile during track practice. Her friend Kate runs $\frac{5}{4}$ times the distance Loren runs. Who runs the longer distance? How do you know?

_____

_____

Use with Lesson 6-2B, pages 195–196 in this Workbook.
Then go to Lesson 6-3, pages 202–203 in the Student Book.

Interpret the Remainder

Name _____

Problem Solving

1. Leo is packing books in a box. He has 25 books. He can fit 8 books in each box. How many boxes can he fill?

2. Ryan has 13 ft of wood. He needs one 3 ft piece of wood for each birdhouse he makes. How many birdhouses can Ryan make?

_____

3. Four friends find 11 seashells. They want to share them equally. How many seashells does each friend get?

4. Tara is putting photos in an album. She has 29 photos and she can fit 6 photos on each page. How many pages does she need to fit all of the photos?

_____

5. Bryan has 33 rocks in his collection. He can fit 5 rocks in each display box. How many display boxes does he need for his rock collection?

6. Mrs. Harrison made 55 candles. She packs them in cases of 8. How many cases can she fill with the candles?

_____

7. Kelly plans to decorate each table with 13 balloons. There are 40 tables. The balloons come 24 to a package. How many packages does Kelly need?

8. Mr. Brady needs 96 tiles to complete his tile floor. The tiles are sold in packages of 26. How many packages should Mr. Brady buy?

_____

Use with Lesson 6-7A, pages 197–198 in this Workbook.
Then go to Lesson 6-8, pages 212–213 in the Student Book.

247

Division with a Unit Fraction

Alex sews gift bags using $\frac{1}{3}$ yard of fabric for each bag. How many bags can Alex make with 6 yards of fabric?

Find $6 \div \frac{1}{3}$. Use a model.

- Show 6 ones.

- Divide each one into thirds.

1/3	1/3	1/3
1/3	1/3	1/3
1/3	1/3	1/3

1/3	1/3	1/3
1/3	1/3	1/3
1/3	1/3	1/3

Alex can make 18 bags. $6 \div \frac{1}{3} = 18$

Kay has 1 acre of land. She prepares $\frac{1}{3}$ acre for planting. If she has 6 days to prepare the land, what fraction of the acre must she prepare each day?

Find $\frac{1}{3} \div 6$. Use inverse operations.

- Write a division sentence.

  $\frac{1}{3} \div 6 = n$

- Multiply to undo the division.

  $\frac{1}{3} = 6 \times n$

  $6 \times \frac{1}{18} = \frac{1}{3}$ So, $n = \frac{1}{18}$.

Kay must prepare $\frac{1}{18}$ of the acre each day.

Problem Solving

1. Camden has $\frac{1}{4}$ yard of rope. If he divides it into 3 equal pieces, how long will each piece be?

   _____

2. Theresa has $\frac{1}{3}$ of her project left to finish. She has 2 days to finish it. What fraction of the project must she complete each day?

   _____

3. A bag of sand contains 18 cups. Meg scoops out $\frac{1}{3}$ cup at a time. How many $\frac{1}{3}$ cups will she scoop?

   _____

4. Thomas has a pitcher with 2 gallons of water. He pours $\frac{1}{5}$ gallon of water onto each of the shrubs in his backyard. Does he have enough to water 8 shrubs?

   _____

5. Three friends share $\frac{1}{2}$ foot of ribbon. How much ribbon does each friend get?

   _____

6. A scientist has 16 pounds of soil for an experiment. She needs $\frac{1}{2}$ pound for each sample. How many samples can she make?

   _____

Use with Lesson 6-10A, pages 199–200 in this Workbook.
Then go to Lesson 6-10B, pages 201–202 in this Workbook.

Word Problems Involving Fractions

Name _____

Mr. Pete has 2 gallons of paint. He needs $\frac{1}{3}$ gallon to paint
one park bench. How many benches can he paint?

Method 1: Use a model.

- Draw 2 rectangles.
  Divide each rectangle into thirds.

$\frac{1}{3}$	$\frac{1}{3}$	$\frac{1}{3}$	$\frac{1}{3}$	$\frac{1}{3}$	$\frac{1}{3}$

- Count the number of $\frac{1}{3}$ gallons.
- There are six $\frac{1}{3}$ gallons.

Method 2: Use an equation.

- Describe in words.
  The number of benches is equal to
  2 gallons divided by $\frac{1}{3}$ gallon.
- Write an equation.

  $b = 2 \div \frac{1}{3}$

  $b = 2 \times \frac{3}{1}$

  $\quad = 6$

So, Mr. Pete can paint 6 benches.

Problem Solving

1. Jennie's pumpkin weighs $3\frac{1}{2}$ pounds. Samantha's pumpkin is $\frac{1}{3}$ pound heavier. How much does Samantha's pumpkin weigh?

   _____

2. A frog jumps $2\frac{1}{4}$ feet in its first jump. It jumps twice as far in its second jump. How far does the frog jump in its second jump?

   _____

3. Alex has $\frac{3}{4}$ pound of black clay and $\frac{5}{6}$ pound of white clay. Does he have more black clay or white clay? How much more?

   _____

4. Ben makes a chain that is $1\frac{1}{3}$ yards long. He wants to break it up into 4 equal sections. How long will each section be?

   _____

5. Marissa plays the piano for $\frac{1}{2}$ hour every day. How many hours does she play in 5 days?

   _____

6. It takes Gerry $\frac{2}{3}$ hour to do her math homework and $\frac{2}{5}$ hour to do her reading homework. How long does it take her in all?

   _____

Use with Lesson 6-10B, pages 201–202 in this Workbook.
Then go to Lesson 6-11, pages 218–219 in the Student Book.

249

Use Models to Add Decimals

Add 0.32 + 0.4 + 0.05.

- Use base ten blocks.

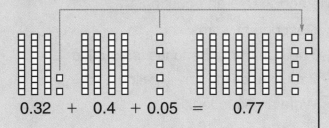

0.32 + 0.4 + 0.05 = 0.77

So, 0.32 + 0.4 + 0.05 = 0.77.

Add 0.16 + 5.3 + 0.42 + 0.08.

- Use the Associative Property.

$$0.16 + 5.3 + (\overbrace{0.42 + 0.08}^{0.10})$$

0.16 + 5.3 +   0.50

- Write the addends in vertical format and add.

```
  0.16
  5.30
+ 0.50
------
  5.96
```

So, 0.16 + 5.3 + 0.42 + 0.08 = 5.96.

Find the sum.

1. 0.29 + 0.5

_____

2. 0.45 + 0.3 + 0.61

_____

3. 0.5 + 2.8 + 0.33

_____

4. 37.12 + 40.84

_____

5. 6.2 + 0.09 + 7.13

_____

6. 9.21 + 1.5 + 0.6

_____

7. 41.56 + 29.32

_____

8. 2.9 + 7.14 + 3

_____

9. 0.04 + 0.4 + 4

_____

10.
```
  0.24
  0.9
+ 0.56
```

11.
```
  18.2
  0.03
+ 5.27
```

12.
```
  0.96
  3.8
+ 0.01
```

13.
```
  6.89
  3.4
+ 0.25
```

14.
```
  32.15
  6.89
+ 0.04
```

15.
```
  16.12
  0.8
+ 3.08
```

16.
```
  7.06
  0.3
+ 4.9
```

17.
```
  8.09
  1.3
+ 0.02
```

Problem Solving

18. It rained 2.3 inches on Monday. It rained 1.8 inches on Tuesday. It rained a total of 4.8 inches on Monday, Tuesday, and Wednesday. How much did it rain on Wednesday?

_____

Use with Lesson 8-2A, pages 203–204 in this Workbook.
Then go to Lesson 8-2B, pages 205–206 in this Workbook.

Mental Math: Add Decimals

Name _____

Add 0.2 + 0.5 + 0.8.	Add 0.44 + 0.26.	Add 2.47 + 1.82.
Use properties of addition.	Use place value and properties of addition.	Add by place value to find partial sums.
0.2 + 0.8 + 0.5	0.40 + 0.04 + 0.20 + 0.06	2.47
(0.2 + 0.8) + 0.5	0.40 + 0.20 + 0.04 + 0.06	+ 1.82
1.0 + 0.5	(0.40 + 0.20) + (0.04 + 0.06)	3.00
1.5	0.60 + 0.10	1.20
	0.70	0.09
		4.29
0.2 + 0.5 + 0.8 = 1.5	0.44 + 0.26 = 0.70	2.47 + 1.82 = 4.29

Find each sum. Explain the method you use.

1. 0.78 + 0.1

_____

2. 0.4 + 0.54

_____

3. 0.09 + 0.26

_____

4. 0.5 + 0.3 + 0.2

_____

5. 0.36 + 0.72 + 0.55

_____

6. 0.7 + 0.3 + 0.4

_____

7. 0.41 + 0.68 + 0.5

_____

8. 0.55 + 0.5 + 0.05

_____

9. 0.2 + 0.08 + 0.25

_____

10. 0.36 + 0.32 + 0.2

_____

11. 0.17 + 0.39 + 0.4

_____

12. 0.63 + 0.14 + 0.57

_____

13. 　　0.51
　　+ 0.46

14. 　　0.37
　　+ 0.5

15. 　　0.13
　　+ 0.26

16. 　　0.52
　　+ 0.69

17. 　　1.34
　　+ 2.54

18. 　　2.51
　　+ 3.73

19. 　　3.72
　　+ 1.09

20. 　　1.48
　　+ 2.15

21. 　　0.6
　　　0.7
　　+ 0.9

22. 　　0.22
　　　0.38
　　+ 0.51

23. 　　0.3
　　　0.2
　　+ 0.1

24. 　　0.63
　　　0.2
　　+ 0.34

Use with Lesson 8-2B, pages 205–206 in this Workbook.
Then go to Lesson 8-3, pages 272–273 in the Student Book.

251

Use Models to Subtract Decimals

Name _____

Subtract 0.25 − 0.12.

Model 0.25 as 2 tenths 5 hundredths.	Take away 1 tenth 2 hundredths.	The difference is 1 tenth 3 hundredths.

So, 0.25 − 0.12 = 0.13.

Subtract. Show your work.

1. 0.84 − 0.45

_____

2. 0.56 − 0.23

_____

3. 0.84 − 0.58

_____

4. 0.65 − 0.17

_____

5. 0.76 − 0.49

_____

6. 0.24 − 0.13

_____

7. 0.46 − 0.31

_____

8. 0.93 − 0.55

_____

9. 0.42 − 0.20

_____

10.   0.19
        − 0.05
        _____

11.   0.39
        − 0.16
        _____

12.   0.84
        − 0.37
        _____

13.   0.65
        − 0.38
        _____

14.   6.4
        − 3.18
        _____

15.   6.14
        − 4.28
        _____

16.   3.01
        − 1.08
        _____

17.   7.62
        − 4.83
        _____

Problem Solving

18. Kara and Megan enter the skating competition. Kara skates to the finish line in 2.55 minutes. Megan skates to the same finish line in 1.46 minutes. Who arrives at the finish line first? How much earlier?

_____

Use with Lesson 8-5A, pages 207–208 in this Workbook.
Then go to Lesson 8-6, pages 278–279 in the Student Book.

Multiply Decimals

Name _____

Multiply: 3 × 0.14

- Use base ten blocks to model the multiplication as repeated addition.

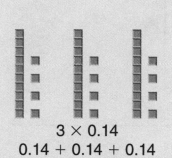

Add the tenths.

Add the hundredths.
Regroup

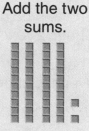

Add the two sums.

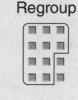

3 × 0.14
0.14 + 0.14 + 0.14

0.10 + 0.10 + 0.10
0.30

0.04 + 0.04 + 0.04
0.12

0.30 + 0.12 = 0.42
3 × 0.14 = 0.42

- Use drawings to model the multiplication using the Distributive Property.

Break apart 0.14.

Use the Distributive Property.

Find the tenths.
Find the hundredths.

Add.

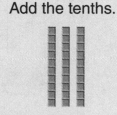
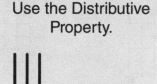
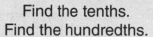
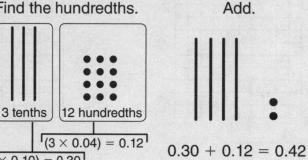

3 × 0.14
3 × (0.10 + 0.04)

3 × (0.10 + 0.04)
(3 × 0.10) + (3 × 0.04)

3 tenths   12 hundredths
(3 × 0.04) = 0.12
(3 × 0.10) = 0.30

0.30 + 0.12 = 0.42
3 × 0.14 = 0.42

Use base ten blocks or drawings to find each product.

1. 3 × 0.28 _____

2. 8 × 0.15 _____

3. 9 × 0.53 _____

4. 2 × 0.47 _____

5. 6 × 1.05 _____

6. 4 × 1.27 _____

7. 2 × 3.21 _____

8. 3 × 1.68 _____

9.   0.74
  ×   3

10.   0.63
  ×   2

11.   1.2
  ×   6

12.   3.4
  ×   3

Problem Solving

13. A bamboo plant grows 1.6 centimeters each day. How much does it grow in 4 days?

_____

Use with Lesson 9-2A, pages 209–210 in this Workbook.
Then go to Lesson 9-3, pages 298–299 in the Student Book.

253

Model Multiplying Two Decimals

Name _____

Multiply 0.2 × 0.6.

- Model each factor on a 10 × 10 grid.

- Shade 6 *columns* to show 0.6.
  Shade 2 *rows* to show 0.2.

- The 12 squares where the shading overlaps show the product.

So, 0.2 × 0.6 = 0.12.

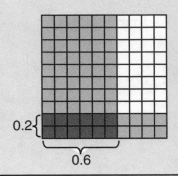

Multiply. Use each 10 × 10 grid to model each product.

1. 0.4 × 0.7

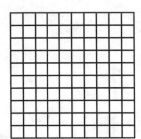

_____

2. 0.3 × 0.8

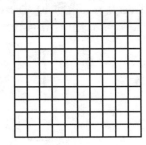

_____

3. 0.6 × 0.5

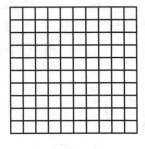

_____

Multiply. Use a separate sheet of paper to model each product.

4.   0.2
   × 0.6

5.   0.5
   × 0.9

6.   0.3
   × 0.4

7.   0.9
   × 0.6

8.   0.4
   × 0.4

9.   0.7
   × 0.2

10.   0.8
   × 0.6

11.   0.7
   × 0.8

Problem Solving

12. The length of a box is 0.8 ft. The width is 0.2 times the length. What is the width of the box? _____

13. Beth cuts a piece of ribbon that is 0.4 of a yard. She cuts another piece that is 0.5 times the length of the first piece. What is the length of the second piece of ribbon? _____

€ Use with Lesson 9-3A, pages 211–212 in this Workbook.
€ Then go to Lesson 9-4, pages 300–301 in the Student Book.

Model Dividing a Decimal by a Whole Number

Name _____

Divide 1.44 ÷ 8.

- Model with base ten blocks.

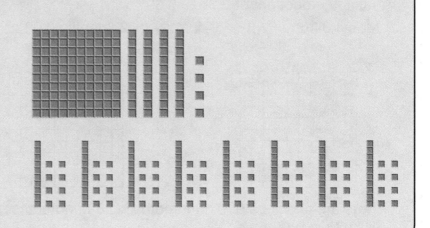

- Divide into 8 equal groups.

  Regroup as needed.

  Add the tenths and the hundredths.

So, 1.44 ÷ 8 = 0.18.

Use models to divide.

1. 0.96 ÷ 4 _____   **2.** 4.65 ÷ 5 _____   **3.** 2.49 ÷ 3 _____   **4.** 3.24 ÷ 6 _____

5. 0.36 ÷ 9 _____   **6.** 0.54 ÷ 9 _____   **7.** 1.85 ÷ 5 _____   **8.** 3.69 ÷ 9 _____

9. 0.81 ÷ 3 _____   **10.** 6.78 ÷ 6 _____   **11.** 5.20 ÷ 8 _____   **12.** 1.32 ÷ 6 _____

13. 2.56 ÷ 8 _____   **14.** 0.28 ÷ 7 _____   **15.** 3.92 ÷ 4 _____   **16.** 1.38 ÷ 3 _____

Problem Solving

17. Drake distributes 2.60 L of liquid soap equally between 4 dispensers. How much soap is in each dispenser?

18. A scientist measures the temperature of several liquids and lists the results in degrees Celsius.

2.56, 3.02, 2.7
What is the average temperature?

_____   _____

Model Dividing a Decimal by a Decimal

Name _____

What is the quotient of $0.36 \div 0.09$?

1. Model 0.36.

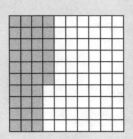

2. Identify 0.09 or *9 hundredths*.

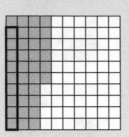

3. Count the number of *9 hundredths* in 0.36.

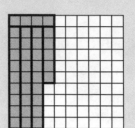

There are 4 groups of 9 hundredths in 36 hundredths.
So, $0.36 \div 0.09 = 4$.

Use a model to find each quotient.

1. $0.84 \div 0.12 =$ _____

2. $0.48 \div 0.06 =$ _____

3. $0.54 \div 0.09 =$ _____

4. $0.60 \div 0.15 =$ _____

5. $0.91 \div 0.13 =$ _____

6. $0.42 \div 0.14 =$ _____

7. $3.6 \div 1.2 =$ _____

8. $7.5 \div 1.5 =$ _____

9. $6.4 \div 1.6 =$ _____

10. $9.9 \div 1.1 =$ _____

11. $9.6 \div 1.2 =$ _____

12. $5.6 \div 0.8 =$ _____

13. $8 \div 0.4 =$ _____

14. $0.45 \div 0.05 =$ _____

15. $4.2 \div 0.7 =$ _____

Problem Solving

16. A bag has 11.2 kg of birdseed. You want to pour 0.4 kg of seeds into each bird feeder. How many bird feeders can you fill? _____

Use with Lesson 9-8A, pages 215–216 in this Workbook.
Then go to Lesson 9-8B, pages 217–218 in the Student Book.

Divide Decimals

Name _____

Divide 0.72 ÷ 0.4.

- Move the decimal point in the *divisor* to form a whole-number divisor. Then move the decimal point in the *dividend* the same *number of places.*

- Place the decimal point in the quotient and then divide.

So, 0.72 ÷ 0.4 = 1.8.

$$0.4\overline{)0.72}$$

```
  1.8
4)7.2
 -4
  3 2
 -3 2
    0
```

Find the quotient.

1. 0.32 ÷ 0.4 = _____

2. 3.2 ÷ 0.4 = _____

3. 0.32 ÷ 0.04 = _____

4. 0.72 ÷ 0.8 = _____

5. 0.81 ÷ 0.9 = _____

6. 0.56 ÷ 0.7 = _____

7. 1.44 ÷ 0.4 = _____

8. 5.85 ÷ 0.9 = _____

9. 2.58 ÷ 0.6 = _____

10.
$$0.3\overline{)0.72}$$

11.
$$0.06\overline{)0.54}$$

12.
$$0.3\overline{)4.26}$$

13.
$$1.2\overline{)2.76}$$

14.
$$0.05\overline{)1.85}$$

15.
$$0.7\overline{)0.63}$$

 Problem Solving

16. Amanda has 22.4 meters of wallpaper trim. She wants to cut it into 0.8-meter sections. How many sections can she cut? _____

17. Darren currently runs 1.5 miles a day. How many days will it take Darren to run a total of 22.5 miles if he runs 1.5 miles each day? _____

C Use with Lesson 9-8B, pages 217–218 in this Workbook.
Then go to Lesson 9-9, pages 310–311 in the Student Book.

257

Classify Quadrilaterals

Name _____

Classify the quadrilateral.

- Each pair of opposite sides is congruent. It is a parallelogram.

- It is a parallelogram with four congruent sides, so it is a rhombus.

- It has four right angles, so it is a square.

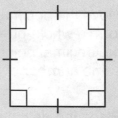

For each quadrilateral, first write the best name to use to classify it. Then write any other possible names.

1.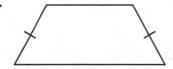

_____

2.

_____

3.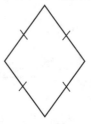

_____

4.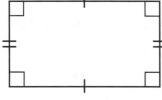

_____

5.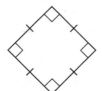

_____

6.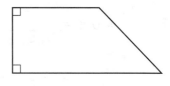

_____

Problem Solving

7. The windows on a building are all parallelograms, rectangles, and squares. What do they all have in common?

_____

8. Paula draws a trapezoid for an art project. What characteristics must her drawing have?

_____

9. Juan draws a quadrilateral that is not a rhombus, a rectangle, or a parallelogram. What type of quadrilateral might it be?

_____

10. Mia draws a quadrilateral that is a rhombus, a rectangle, and a parallelogram. What is another name for the quadrilateral?

_____

Ⓒ Use with Lesson 10-6A, pages 219–220 in this Workbook.
Then go to Lesson 10-7, pages 336–337 in the Student Book.

Find Areas of Rectangles and Squares

Name _____

A patio is $2\frac{1}{2}$ yd long and $1\frac{1}{4}$ yd wide. What is its area?

Method 1: Use a model.

each ☐ $= \frac{1}{16}$ yd²

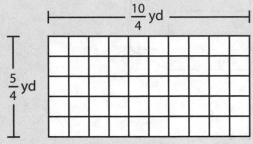

The total area is $\frac{50}{16}$ yd².

$\frac{50}{16}$ yd² $= 3\frac{1}{8}$ yd²

So, the patio has an area of $3\frac{1}{8}$ yd².

Method 2: Use a formula.

$A = \ell \times w$

$A = 2\frac{1}{2}$ yd $\times 1\frac{1}{4}$ yd

$\quad = \frac{5}{2}$ yd $\times \frac{5}{4}$ yd

$\quad = \frac{25}{8}$ yd²

$\quad = 3\frac{1}{8}$ yd²

Find the area of each rectangle. Simplify your answer if needed.

1. $3\frac{1}{2}$ in. by $1\frac{1}{3}$ in.

2. $1\frac{2}{3}$ mi by $1\frac{1}{2}$ mi

3. $5\frac{1}{3}$ yd by $1\frac{1}{4}$ yd

_____

_____

_____

4. $2\frac{2}{3}$ ft by $1\frac{1}{4}$ ft

5. $2\frac{3}{4}$ in. by $1\frac{1}{3}$ in.

6. $3\frac{3}{4}$ mi by 10 mi

_____

_____

_____

7. $2\frac{3}{4}$ yd by $\frac{5}{6}$ yd

8. $3\frac{1}{4}$ ft by $2\frac{1}{3}$ ft

9. $1\frac{1}{6}$ ft by $1\frac{1}{4}$ ft

_____

_____

_____

Problem Solving

10. Jean drew on a canvas that was $3\frac{1}{3}$ inches wide and $6\frac{1}{2}$ inches tall. What total area did she draw on?

11. A room is $5\frac{1}{4}$ yards by $4\frac{1}{2}$ yards. It has a square floor in the center that is 1 yard on each side. The rest of the room is covered by carpet. What area is covered by carpet?

_____

_____

Use with Lesson 12-5A, pages 221–222 in this Workbook.
Then go to Lesson 12-6, pages 392–393 in the Student Book.

259

Find Volume

Name _____

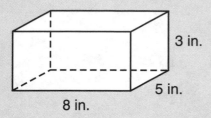
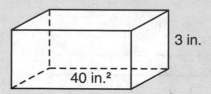
Find the volume of each rectangular prism.

1. $B = 12$ ft^2, $h = 6$ ft

2. $\ell = 5$ cm, $w = 10$ cm, $h = 12$ cm

3. $B = 25$ m^2, $h = 5$ m

_____

4. $\ell = 12$ in., $w = 15$ in., $h = 22$ in.

5. $\ell = 9$ ft, $w = 6$ ft, $h = 8$ ft

6. $B = 10$ ft^2, $h = 15$ ft

_____

7. $B = 42$ cm^2, $h = 5$ cm

8. $B = 28$ in.^{2}, $h = 12$ in.

9. $\ell = 7$ m, $w = 12$ m, $h = 3$ m

_____

Problem Solving

10. A rectangular toy bin is 36 in. long and 20 in. wide. Its volume is 7200 in.^{3} What is its height?

11. Jane's container has a base of 72 cm^2 and a height of 2 cm. Martin's container has a base of 108 cm^2 and a height of 4 cm. How many times greater is the volume of Martin's container than the volume of Jane's container?

_____

Use with Lesson 12-11A, pages 223–224 in this Workbook.
Then go to Lesson 12-11B, pages 225–226 in this Workbook.

Separate Solid Figures

Name _____

Find the volume of the solid figure.

- Separate the solid figure into separate prisms.

1. Find the volume of the larger prism.

   $V = \ell \times w \times h$

   $V = 14 \times 3 \times 7 = 294$

2. Find the volume of the smaller prism.

   $V = \ell \times w \times h$

   $V = 6 \times 3 \times 3 = 54$

3. Add the volumes.

   $294 + 54 = 348$

So, the volume of the solid figure is 348 cm³.

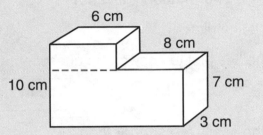

Separate the figure into two simpler known shapes. Then find the total volume.

1.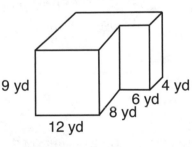

Left _____

Right _____

Total _____

2.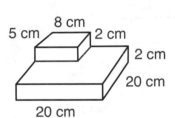

Top _____

Bottom _____

Total _____

3.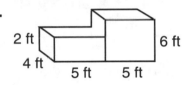

Left _____

Right _____

Total _____

4.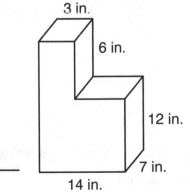

_____

5.

3 in.

6 in.

12 in.

7 in.

14 in.

_____

6.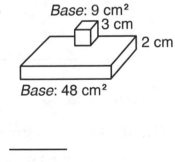

Base: 9 cm²

3 cm

2 cm

Base: 48 cm²

_____

Problem Solving

7. Mr. Reimer designed a platform for the school play. He is going to make it out of cubes that measure 1 ft³. How many cubes does he need to build the platform?

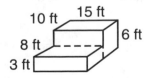

10 ft   15 ft

8 ft   6 ft

3 ft

_____

☞ Use with Lesson 12-11B, pages 225–226 in this Workbook.

☞ Then go to Lesson 12-12, pages 404–405 in the Student Book.

261

Line Plots

The table shows the lengths of several snails. What is the mode of the data? What fraction of the snails is shorter than $\frac{6}{8}$ inches?

- Make a line plot.

- Use the line plot to answer the questions.

The mode is $\frac{5}{8}$ inches.

$\frac{9}{14}$ of the snails are shorter than $\frac{6}{8}$ inches.

Lengths of Snails (inches)

$\frac{2}{8}$	$\frac{4}{8}$	$\frac{5}{8}$	$\frac{7}{8}$	$\frac{5}{8}$	$\frac{4}{8}$	$\frac{5}{8}$
$\frac{4}{8}$	$\frac{5}{8}$	$\frac{6}{8}$	$\frac{6}{8}$	$\frac{6}{8}$	$\frac{5}{8}$	$\frac{6}{8}$

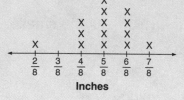

Lengths of Snails

Inches

A local gasoline station asks customers how much gas remained in their gas tanks. The data shows their responses.

1. Make a line plot of the data.

Customers' Remaining Gas (as part of a tank)

$\frac{1}{8}$	$\frac{3}{8}$	$\frac{4}{8}$	$\frac{7}{8}$	$\frac{4}{8}$	$\frac{3}{8}$
$\frac{3}{8}$	$\frac{4}{8}$	$\frac{2}{8}$	$\frac{4}{8}$	$\frac{6}{8}$	$\frac{4}{8}$

Customers' Remaining Gas

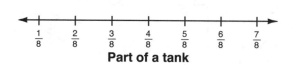

Part of a tank

2. How many customers are represented in the data set?

_____

3. What is the range of the data set?

_____

4. What is the mode of the data?

_____

5. How many customers said that they had more than $\frac{3}{8}$ tank of gas?

_____

6. What fraction of the customers said that they had either $\frac{1}{8}$ or $\frac{2}{8}$ tank of gas?

_____

7. What fraction of the customers said that they had more than $\frac{5}{8}$ tank of gas?

_____

Problem Solving

Use the line plots to answer the question.

8. If you want a larger puppy, would you choose puppies from Puppy Litter A or Puppy Litter B? Explain.

_____

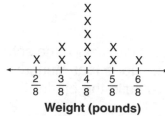

Birth Weights of Puppies Puppy Litter A

Weight (pounds)

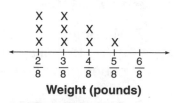

Birth Weights of Puppies Puppy Litter B

Weight (pounds)

Use with Lesson 12-12A, pages 227–228 in this Workbook.
Then go to Lesson 12-13, pages 406–407 in the Student Book.

Use Coordinate Graphs

Name _____

The coordinate plane to the right shows the distance a train travels and the time in minutes it takes to travel.

What do the coordinates (3, 6) mean?

• 3 is the *x*-coordinate, the time in minutes.

• 6 is the *y*-coordinate, the distance in miles.

So, (3, 6) means that the train traveled 3 miles in 6 minutes.

Train Travel

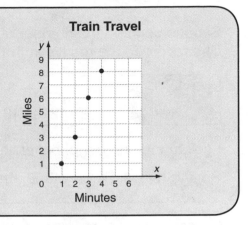

Use the coordinate plane for exercises 1–4.

1. What do the points (2, 0) and (4, 1) mean?

_____.

2. Graph the points (3, 2) and (2, 3).

3. What is the difference in the meaning of (3, 2) and (2, 3)?

_____

4. What was the greatest number of points scored and how many rings were tossed for that score?

_____

Ring Toss Game at School Carnival

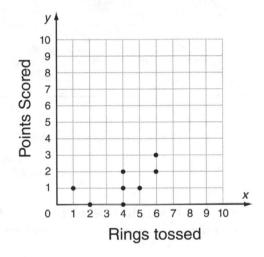

Problem Solving

Solve. Use the coordinate plane above.

5. Three points on the coordinate plane have 1 as the *y*-coordinate, but they have different *x*-coordinates. Explain why.

6. Players score points by tossing their rings into different sections of a target. How would the graph change if the number of points in each section were doubled?

_____   _____

☞ Use with Lesson 14-13A, pages 229–230 in this Workbook.
☞ Then go to Lesson 14-13B, pages 231–232 in this Workbook.

263

Sequences

Name _____

Simone counted the number of butterflies in her garden each week.
She recorded the results in the table below. What rule describes the sequence?

Week	1	2	3	4	5
Butterflies	6	12	18	24	30

Look at the number of butterflies.

So, the rule is: Begin with 6, then add 6 to find the next term.

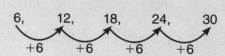

Use the rule to write the next three terms in the sequence.

1. Rule: Begin with 80; subtract 6

   80, 74, 68, 62, … _____

2. Rule: Begin with 704; divide by 2

   704, 352, 176, 88, … _____

3. Rule: Begin with 1; multiply by 3

   1, 3, 9, 27, … _____

4. Rule: Begin with 10; add 1.5

   10, 11.5, 13, 14.5, … _____

5. Rule: Begin with 1; add $\frac{1}{2}$

   1, $1\frac{1}{2}$, 2, $2\frac{1}{2}$, … _____

6. Rule: Begin with $\frac{1}{5}$, add $\frac{1}{5}$

   $\frac{1}{5}$, $\frac{2}{5}$, $\frac{3}{5}$, $\frac{4}{5}$, … _____

Describe the rule used to create each sequence.
Then find the next three terms in the sequence.

7. 42, 38, 34, 30, …

_____

8. 5.3, 5.9, 6.5, 7.1, …

_____

9. 2, 4, 8, 16, …

_____

10. 25, 24.8, 24.6, 24.4, …

_____

Problem Solving

11. One thousand pounds of recycled paper are needed for
a product. If a machine in a factory produces 30 pounds
of recycled paper every minute, how many more pounds
of recycled paper are needed after 8 minutes?

_____

Use with Lesson 14-13B, pages 231–232 in this Workbook.
Then go to Lesson 14-13C, pages 233–234 in this Workbook.

Compare Sequences

Name _____

For each swimmer that goes to Practice Squad A, three swimmers go to Practice Squad B. How are the practice squads related?

- Make a table. Write a list of ordered pairs.

Swimmers on Practice Squads

Squad A	0	1	2	3	4	← Add 1
Squad B	0	3	6	9	12	← Add 3

Ordered pairs:

(0, 0), (1, 3), (2, 6), (3, 9), (4, 12)

- Graph the ordered pairs. Connect the points.

- Look at the points on the line. Compare the relation between the Practice Squads.

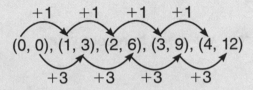

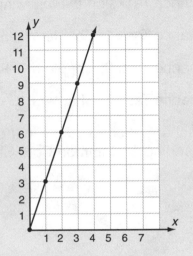

The y-coordinate is always 3 times the x-coordinate. So, for every swimmer at Practice Squad A there are 3 times the swimmers at Practice Squad B.

---

1. Identify the rules for each sequence. What will be the 9th term in both sequences?

Sequence 1	2	4	6	8	10
Sequence 2	1	5	9	13	17

_____

2. Write ordered pairs (x, y) using the corresponding terms of the sequence.

3. On grid paper, plot the points and connect them to show a line.

_____

4. How do the two sequences compare?

_____

Problem Solving

5. Tina and Lisa start reading at the same time. Tina reads 12 pages each hour. Lisa reads 18 pages each hour. How many pages apart are they after four hours?

_____

Ⓒ Use with Lesson 14-3C, pages 233–234 in this Workbook.
Ⓒ Then go to Lesson 14-14, pages 466–467 in the Student Book.

Dear Student,

Pages 268–282 of this workbook have Performance Tasks that let you show your understanding of the Common Core math taught in *Progress in Mathematics.*

Each performance task has five parts. The content of each part meets the Common Core State Standards (CCSS) for *Progress in Mathematics* lessons. The goal of each performance task is for you to apply critical thinking skills and various problem-solving strategies to the math content learned in the chapters. The Performance Tasks are useful tools for evaluating your understanding of Grade 5 math and the Common Core State Standards. You will find the Performance Tasks on the following pages.

Performance Task 1: Chapters 1–5   pages 268–272

Performance Task 2: Chapters 6–9   pages 273–277

Performance Task 3: Chapters 10–14   pages 278–282

Your teacher will use a rubric in the Teacher's Edition of this workbook to record your understanding of Common Core State Standards.

Performance Task Contents

CPerformance Task 1
Summer Vacation: Year 2995

1 Yolanda and her family are voyaging to the edge of the Milky Way for summer vacation. But she still has to do her summer math project! To start the assignment, Yolanda records the distance the spaceship traveled since breakfast.

> 7,837,927,457 miles

A. Write the value of each 7. If Yolanda starts with the 7 in the ones place, how could she get numbers equal to the values of the other 7s?

B. HANK, the family robot, printed some decimals for Yolanda.

Write each in standard form. Then order them from greatest to least.

> six hundred eighty-three thousandths
>
> $(7 \times \frac{1}{10}) + (8 \times \frac{1}{100})$
>
> $(6 \times \frac{1}{10}) + (1 \times \frac{1}{100}) + (8 \times \frac{1}{1000})$
>
> seven hundred eight thousandths

C. HANK gives Yolanda another task. He asks her to round each decimal in problem **B** above to the nearest tenth.

Performance Task 1
A Handy Helper

Name _____

2 Yolanda's brother George also has to keep up with his summer math project. When George sits down with HANK, the robot prints some incomplete multiplication sentences.

A. Help George complete the multiplication sentences below. Then describe the pattern. Write the next multiplication sentence in the pattern.

30 × 20 = _____

3_____ × 20 = 6,000

3,000 × 20 = _____

3_____ × 20 = 600,000

Yolanda and George's home on Earth has a greenhouse with 68 tomato plants. Last week HANK told the greenhouse computer to give each tomato plant 284 mL of water. This week HANK told the greenhouse computer to give each tomato plant 307 mL of water.

B. How much water did the tomato plants get in all?

C. Next week each tomato plant will need 20 mL more than half the water it got this week. Write an expression for the direction HANK might give to the greenhouse computer.

Name _____

3 A member of the space ship crew checks the supply of fruit snacks. He notices that there are 15,481 fruit snacks left in the holding bin of the ship. Unfortunately, he also sees that space mice have munched on 1,128 of the snacks. There are 47 people on the spaceship. Each person gets one fruit snack each day.

A. How long can the voyage continue before the space ship runs out of fruit snacks?

Here are some strategies you can use.
- Draw an array.
- Draw an area model.
- Multiply to divide.
- Break apart the dividend.

Twice a day, each of the 47 people on the spaceship takes a vitamin capsule. They also take a mineral capsule at breakfast, lunch, and dinner, however 12 people do not take these mineral capsules.

B. Write an expression for the total number of capsules taken each day. Evaluate your expression.

4 George is working on his miniature magnetic train. The rocket locomotive is $\frac{7}{8}$ inch long. George attaches a meteor car that is $\frac{2}{3}$ inch long. Then he attaches a Martian cattle car that is $\frac{5}{6}$ inch long.

A. How long is the magnetic train now? Write your answer in simplest form.

Yolanda is making a model of a galaxy worm. The worm's head is $2\frac{1}{2}$ meters long. She decides that is too long, so she cuts $\frac{3}{4}$ meter off. Then Yolanda attaches the worm's tail, which is $3\frac{3}{5}$ meters long.

B. How long is the galaxy worm? Write your answer in simplest form.

5 The fuel tank on Yolanda's space suit was $\frac{9}{10}$ full. She went on a space walk before lunch and used $\frac{3}{4}$ tank of fuel. At lunch, Yolanda's dad asks how much fuel she had left in her tank. Yolanda thinks a moment before replying, "The tank must be $\frac{3}{5}$ full now."

A. Is Yolanda's answer reasonable? Explain.

George's space scooter has $4\frac{1}{8}$ liters of fuel in its tank. He adds $2\frac{1}{2}$ liters of fuel and takes the scooter for a ride around the spaceship. During the ride, the scooter uses $1\frac{1}{4}$ liters of fuel.

B. How much fuel is left in the tank?

1 Vincent is a waiter at his family's pizzeria, The Golden Crust. This restaurant is known for its large vegetarian-style rectangular pizzas. It is no surprise that many patrons take home some of their leftover pizza.

A. The Dozzo family has $\frac{4}{5}$ of the asparagus pizza left over from their dinner. Mr. Dozzo wants to take home $\frac{3}{4}$ of it. Will Vincent give him less than $\frac{4}{5}$ pizza, more than $\frac{4}{5}$ pizza, or $\frac{4}{5}$ pizza? Explain.

B. Mr. Benvenuto loves the broccoli pizza. There are $1\frac{1}{2}$ broccoli pizzas left from his family's dinner. Mr. Benvenuto tells Vincent he only wants $\frac{2}{3}$ of the broccoli pizzas to take home. How much pizza will Vincent give him?

- Draw a diagram.
- Write a multiplication sentence.

CPerformance Task 2
The Pizza Take Out Counter

Name _____

2 Vincent's cousin Terry also works at The Golden
Crust. She is usually assigned to the take out counter.
Today, one third of the Mediterranean pizza is left.
Five coworkers want to buy the remaining Mediterranean
pizza. They ask Terry to cut the pizza so they can share
it equally.

A. How much pizza will each coworker receive?
- Draw an diagram.
- Write a division sentence.
- Check your answer by multiplying.

B. Ms. Tucci orders 4 artichoke pizzas for her birthday party.
She asks Terry to cut them into $\frac{1}{3}$ pizzas. How many thirds
will Ms. Tucci take home?

Name _____

3 Vincent gets three packages of fresh mozzarella from the refrigerator. The first package weighs 0.84 pound. The second package weighs 1.37 pounds. The third package lost its label. Vincent weighs the three packages together and finds the total weight is 4.3 pounds.

A. How much does the third package of mozzarella weigh?

Here are some strategies you can use.
- Use ones flats, tenths rods, and hundredths cubes.
- Draw models.
- Use properties of addition.
- Use place value.

Terry is making three pizzas with ricotta cheese. She starts with 2.14 pounds of ricotta. She puts 0.45 pound of ricotta on a large pizza. She puts 0.28 pound of ricotta on a medium pizza. And she puts 0.14 pound of ricotta on a small pizza.

B. Estimate how much ricotta Terry put on the three pizzas. Calculate how much ricotta Terry has left.

C Performance Task 2

A More Important Ingredient

4 Vincent made dough and cut it into 6 pieces to make
6 pizzas. Each piece of dough weighed 0.54 pounds.
His dad looked at the scale and said, "That's too light.
Each pizza dough should weigh 0.9 pound."

A. How much more dough does Vincent need to make?

Here are some strategies you can use.
- Use tenths rods and hundredths cubes.
- Draw models.
- Use place value.

Terry is making pizza dough for two small pizzas. The first dough
weighs 0.7 pound. The second dough weighs 0.8 times as much as
the first dough.

B. How much does the second dough weigh?

- Use an array.

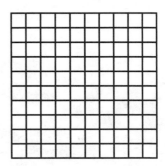

Name _____

5 The Golden Crust received a delivery of 212.5 pounds of flour. Terry needs to separate the flour into equal amounts to store it in the basement. Her uncle tells her she can separate the flour into 10, 100, or 1,000 bags.

A. Complete the table below. How much will each bag weigh if Terry puts the flour into 10 bags? 100 bags? 1,000 bags? Describe the pattern in the table.

Total Flour (lb)	÷10	÷100	÷1,000

This morning, The Golden Crust received a delivery of 6.86 pounds of mushrooms. The pizza chef said, "That isn't enough mushrooms!" So he called the mushroom distributor and ordered more. In the afternoon, another 30.5 pounds of mushrooms arrived. The chef asks Vincent to separate the mushrooms into 8 equal piles.

B. How much will each pile weigh?

Performance Task 3
Sorento Signs, Inc.

Name _____

1 Teresa works for Sorento Signs, a family-owned company that makes all kinds of signage for schools, cities, and businesses.

A. Help Teresa classify the signs below by completing the table and writing the names of the polygons. Then write the letter of each sign in **one** category. Be careful—some signs fit in more than one category!

B   E   F   A   D   C

Polygon	Sides	Angles	Sign
_____	4 sides		_____
_____	just 1 pair of parallel sides		_____
_____	2 pairs of parallel, congruent sides		
_____	2 pairs of parallel, congruent sides	4 right angles	_____
_____	2 pairs of parallel sides; all 4 sides congruent		_____
_____	2 pairs of parallel sides; all 4 sides congruent	4 right angles	_____

B. How else could sign D be classified?

_____

C. How else could be sign E be classified?

_____

D. How else could sign F be classified?

_____

C Performance Task 3
Painting Signs

Name _____

2 Fred is a sign painter at Sorento Signs. Today he has
to paint 3 red signs. The first sign will take 7 pints of
paint. The second sign will take 4 quarts of paint. The
third sign will take 6 cups of paint. Once Fred knows
what paint color, or colors, all the signs will be, he
goes to the storage warehouse to get the paint. In this
situation, he only needs the color red.

A. Determine whether Fred should get a 1-gallon can,
a 2-gallon can, or a 3-gallon can of red paint from
the warehouse.

> **Think**
> 2 cups = 1 pint
> 2 pints = 1 quart
> 4 quarts = 1 gallon

Fred climbs 2.3 meters up a ladder to paint a sign. Then he moves
down the ladder 500 millimeters to do some more painting. Finally
he climbs 75 centimeters back up the ladder to finish the painting.

B. How many meters off the ground is Fred when he finishes the
painting of this sign?

> **Think**
> 1 m = 1,000 mm
> 1 m = 100 cm

CPerformance Task 3
The Area of Signs

Name _____

3 Teresa is making a rectangular sign for a health club. The sign will be $\frac{1}{4}$ yard wide and $\frac{4}{5}$ yard long.

A. Fred tells Teresa he has enough paint to cover $\frac{1}{8}$ square yard of the health club's sign. Will Fred need more paint to complete the painting of this sign? Explain.

Here are some strategies you can use.
- Draw a diagram.
- Use the formula for area.

> **Think**
> $A = \ell \times w$

Sorento Signs got an additional order from the health club for two more signs. The first sign will be a rectangle that measures $12\frac{1}{2}$ feet long and $4\frac{2}{5}$ feet wide. The second sign will be a square with sides that measure $7\frac{1}{2}$ feet.

B. How many square feet will Fred need to paint in all?

Unique Designs

Name _____

4 Teresa is making a sign for a pet store that specializes in fish. The sign is a clear rectangular prism that looks like an aquarium. The sign has a length of 9 feet, a width of 4 feet, and a height of 6 feet. The sign will be filled with blue foam to look like water.

A. What is the volume of the sign?

Here are some strategies you can use.
- Draw a diagram and count the unit cubes.
- Use a formula for volume.

> **Think**
> $V = \ell \times w \times h$
> $V = B \times h$

A box store orders a sign that will look like three stacked boxes. The bottom box will measure 8 feet long, 6 feet wide, and 4 feet tall. The middle box will measure 5 feet long, 4 feet wide, and 3 feet tall. The top box will measure 3 feet long, 2 feet wide, and 2 feet tall.

B. What is the total volume of the sign?

CPerformance Task 3
The Mystery Sign

Name _____

5 Fred is painting a billboard in the city. But his directions are mysterious—he doesn't know what words he will paint! He is given seven sets of ordered pairs, one for each letter on the billboard. For each set, he must locate the points on the billboard. Then he must connect the points to form the letter.

A. Help Fred paint the billboard. The key is to connect the points of each letter in order. So, each time you locate a new point, connect it to the last point. What kind of company ordered the billboard?

Letter	Point 1	Point 2	Point 3	Point 4	Point 5	Point 6	Point 7	Point 8
1	(1, 7)	(1, 11)	(3, 11)	(3, 9)	(1, 9)	(3, 9)	(3, 7)	(1, 7)
2	(5, 11)	(5, 7)	(7, 7)	(7, 11)				
3	(9, 11)	(10, 9)	(11, 11)	(10, 9)	(10, 7)			
4	(1, 1)	(1, 5)	(3, 1)	(3, 5)				
5	(5, 5)	(5, 1)	(7, 1)	(7, 5)				
6	(9, 5)	(11, 5)	(10, 5)	(10, 1)				
7	(15, 5)	(13, 5)	(13, 3)	(15, 3)	(15, 1)	(13, 1)		

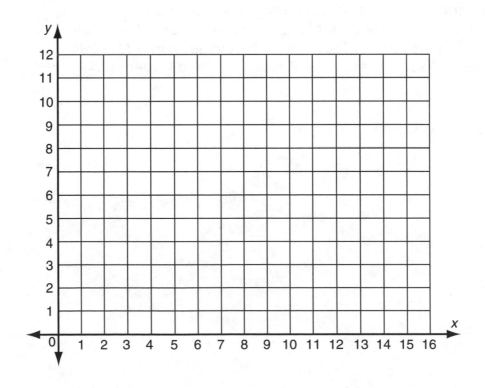